Handbook of project management procedures

Handbook of project management procedures

Albert Hamilton

Thomas Telford

Published by Thomas Telford Publishing, Thomas Telford Ltd, 1 Heron Quay, London E14 4JD.
URL: http://www.thomastelford.com

Distributors for Thomas Telford books are
USA: ASCE Press, 1801 Alexander Bell Drive, Reston, VA 20191–4400, USA
Japan: Maruzen Co. Ltd, Book Department, 3–10 Nihonbashi 2-chome, Chuo-ku, Tokyo 103
Australia: DA Books and Journals, 648 Whitehorse Road, Mitcham 3132, Victoria

First published 2004

Also available from Thomas Telford Books
Managing projects for success: a trilogy. A. Hamilton. ISBN 0 7277 2941 1
Managing innovation in construction. M. Jones and M. Saad. ISBN 0 7277 3002 9
Managing construction supply chains. A. Cox and P. Ireland. ISBN 0 7277 3001 0

A catalogue record for this book is available from the British Library
ISBN: 0 7277 3258 7

Printed and bound in Great Britain by MPG Books, Bodmin

Contents

Preface

It is often found that project managers, and those other stakeholders involved in some aspect of project planning, execution and control, have to 'make it up' as they go along. In the absence of any company or corporate governance relating to the management of projects, project stakeholders may have to rely on inspiration and, more often than not, good old common sense. Most people should agree that these natural instincts are necessary, but they are not enough.

A search of available published guidance on 'what he or she should do and how' is ostensibly not available, as the published work on project management is either very academic, and of little use to the practitioner, or is very general, and therefore is probably only of passing interest. It is with this view of project management publications and those many thousands of people who work with projects, who deserve meaningful support at a tactical level, that I decided to create a handbook of what I perceived as best-practice procedures. Within this Handbook the procedures and their associated policies and processes are based on methods that I and other colleagues have applied in our quest to manage capital projects more effectively.

The development and production of the *Handbook of Project Management Procedures* is both a response to my findings of working within the project management industry over the past 35 years and my wish to spread to a much wider audience a rational approach to managing projects.

A comment that can be levelled at creating such a 'how to do it' publication is one of concern that the author has a view on how projects are to be managed but that it is but one view. A fundamental wish of mine is therefore to create a 'virtual think tank' of practitioners in which those who invest in and use the Handbook can share their experiences with fellow users — perhaps the users could be viewed as an alumni of Handbook holders. This alumni would have the opportunity to prepare modifications to existing procedures, draft new procedures that the Handbook does not contain, propose any change that would lead to a greater understanding of project management and/or improve the outcome of using any procedure. I am of the view that the virtual think tank concept is an important way of maximising knowledge and skills transfer, and ensuring continuing currency of the Handbook.

Each Handbook holder can decide at any time whether they wish to be included within the alumni; those who do should register at the book's dedicated web site www.pmhandbook.com in the section titled Handbook alumni. Through registering to become part of the virtual think-tank, the individual will be in direct contact with the author via email from the web site. This means that the individual can relate in-use experiences to the author and can obtain advice about regular planned revisions to the Handbook. Individual feedback of interesting experiences will be shared with the global alumni through the planned use of email newsletters. Contributions from the alumni will be a vital means of improving project management procedures for everyone.

The Handbook has been developed in four parts.

- Part 1: Introduction and general information
- Part 2: Projects — three integrated structures
- Part 3: Project management procedures
- Part 4: Route maps — from conception to completion.

Part 1 contains the index for the Handbook, recommendations on how to use the Handbook, a glossary of terms that have been used, a list of acronyms found in the Handbook, and a reference list of institutional publications that were consulted during the drafting of the Handbook.

Part 2 debates the three structures that are an integral aspect of any project: the corporate structure, the project team structure and the work breakdown structure that reflects the work scope of the project.

Discussion in Part 2 centres on organisation structures used in handling project-related work. It explains the case for establishing a Project Support Office (PSO) when the conditions are right for such an intervention. Discussion includes the strategies and tactics of a PSO, the project office working environment, and other matters that pertain to the working organisation that has to deliver projects successfully.

Part 3 is the principal section of the Handbook and contains the procedures that, if used, provide a uniformity of approach to the project-related organisation. The procedures are grouped into 10 knowledge areas and are presented alphabetically, starting with communications management and ending with value management. Each procedure is numbered for ease of reference and each procedure is presented using the same format.

The format for each procedure includes:

- a policy that is a potential 'best practice' statement
- the anticipated outcome(s) of the procedure
- the process to achieve the outcome (often supported with a flow diagram)
- standard forms that may be used by the practitioner
- exhibits showing certain techniques or aspects of a procedure to simplify the understanding.

Part 4 contains a series of diagrams that show a life cycle for a capital works project and flow diagrams for each life cycle stage that give guidance on which procedures could be used in what stage.

The flow diagrams show the stages of a capital works project and the likely procedures that could be used at any stage and the possible sequence of application; but the latter are not to be interpreted prescriptively.

In drafting the Handbook I have tried to think globally but continually remind myself that no one nation, and no one institution, has the sole ownership of project management. Although I have structured Part 3 basically, but not exactly, in accordance with the knowledge areas of the PMI (Project Management Institute) in the USA, the procedures have been drafted as if the practitioner were managing a project in Europe. I have also tried to be sympathetic to the requirements of the Handbook's sponsors and their members, namely the ICE and the APM in the UK, by cross-referring the procedures to the APM's body of knowledge.

Reference documents that have been used (see listing in Part 1) would therefore be those that apply principally to the institutional and working environment within the UK and to some extent Europe. However, I believe that project management stakeholders within other jurisdictions, such as Canada, the Far East, the southern hemisphere continents, etc., should find that this Handbook is equally applicable to them. Although there are differences between the various geographical institutions and associations dealing with the project management industry, however I am of the view that there is much, much more that is common than separates these bodies.

As a Handbook holder I welcome you and invite you to participate in the virtual think tank, to be part of the user network of project management stakeholders and to share your experiences. In the first instance please go to this publication's web site at www.pmhandbook.com and register under the section Handbook alumni, as detailed in Part 1. I look forward to receiving your communication.

Albert Hamilton
March 2004

Part 1

Introduction and general information

The Handbook and how to use it

Registration of holders

As a holder of this Handbook, registering to join the alumni is simple. Open the dedicated web site www.pmhandbook.com and register your details in the section titled Handbook alumni. To register, the following information is required:

- your name
- your position/job title
- your company name
- your email address
- your postal address.

Once registered, the individual can then email the author directly with comments and experiences of using this Handbook or other relevant procedures they have used, and receive information on any planned future revisions of the Handbook based on feedback from the alumni.

Handbook format

Part 1 of the Handbook is general and provides an introduction on how to use the Handbook. This part also contains a glossary of terms, a list of acronyms and a list of references that were used in checking for consistency with the Handbook content.

   Part 2 is an important section because, although brief, it deals with three topics that together are essential for creating the structure for any project. The three structures are

- a performing organisation
- a project organisation

- the 'scope of work' structure of a project.

An important element of the organisation structure that is dealt with in this part is the establishment of a PSO (project support office) within the corporate organisation, which has responsibility for the better governance of the project management process.

Part 3 is the core of the Handbook. It contains information on the philosophy and approach used in creating the content of the Handbook. Part 3 contains guidance but more importantly it contains processes that can help in creating corporate working standards and working procedures in managing projects.

The Handbook procedures, contained within Part 3, are presented using a common format. Each procedure is initiated with a policy statement, in other words what the procedure is intended to address and how the procedure can satisfy management's requirements. This is followed by a description of the outcome or outcomes that the procedure is expected to deliver. The stepped process to be used in achieving the outcome follows this. In many cases the process is further enhanced by a flow diagram, which shows the sequence, the stakeholders and the role of each stakeholder. Standard forms are then presented that provide templates for information capture, stakeholder circulation, and the procedure approval/sign-off process. In some cases exhibits are also included that are intended to help the user to understand the process and the standard forms.

Part 4 contains a number of useful diagrams; namely, a capital works life cycle and various procedure flow diagrams for each of the eight stages of the capital works project. When consulting Parts 1, 2 and 3 it is probably worth referring to any appropriate, or all of the, route maps in Part 4.

The Handbook as a set of guidelines

The Handbook should be of interest to the wider organisation engaged in undertaking project work. It should also be of significant assistance to individuals engaged in managing a range of projects or a one-off project. The Handbook has been created to help users determine the strategy, working standards, staff training, daily support and project auditing that together are needed to reform working practices used in managing capital projects, producing products or providing services.

The Handbook procedures may be used as they appear in the Handbook, but that is not the intention. The primary intention is for the Handbook to be referred to and procedures adopted or developed to suit the specific requirements of the performing organisation and the project under consideration.

The Handbook should provide guidance and inspiration for the members of a project team to develop a project manual designed specifically to manage their project (reference procedure CN-004 in Part 3). One of the first actions of a project manager should be to create a project manual and to start developing it from as early in a project's life as possible. Each project manual therefore contains management procedures that are specifically tailored for the project under consideration.

Each stage in a project is likely to require modification of the manual's content, the addition of new procedures and/or the deletion of certain procedures that were used in the last stage. The Handbook provides guidance on what are likely to be the most appropriate procedures to use at each stage of a project's life cycle.

Glossary of terms

The following terms have been used in drafting the *Handbook of Project Management Procedures* and are issued for information and use by the Handbook holder. Each term is linked to a brief explanatory note. Words appearing in italics in the 'explanation' column are words that are in the list of terms. For a fuller listing of project management terms and definitions other publications should be referred to.[4,9]

AC   Actual cost. The progressive out-turn cost of a project that is related to the *planned value* of a project (also referred to as BCWS) and its *earned value* (also referred to as BCWP). The actual cost is also known as the ACWP (the actual cost of work performed).

activity   An element of *stakeholder* work being part of a project's work breakdown structure (*WBS*) of a project carried out during the development life cycle of a project. A subactivity is called a *task*.

audit   An independent assessment of a project's records and a project team's (owner/*SP*/contractor) performance. Usually carried out by two specialists from a PSO over a ± 2-day period. Normally undertaken at least once within each *stage* of a project's *life cycle*.

baseline   The original approved *cost budget* shown as a time-related cash flow (see *CBS*). Otherwise known as the planned value or BCWS.

bidder   To secure the services of an *SP* or a contractor each entity that plans to submit, or has been invited to submit, an offer is referred to as a bidder.

brainstorming   A creative *activity* used in a *workshop* environment to structure ideas that can be used to develop a project's *RFP*, analyse value, assess risks, etc.

budget at completion   The total amount of money that has been estimated to be required to cover a project's total cost, including the *SP*'s work, the construction cost and the project team costs. It normally excludes *contingency reserve*, which should be separately identified.

CA   The Contracting Authority which, unless otherwise stated, is the *performing organisation* for a project. Also referred to as the owner and by *external entities* in the UK as the client.

CBS   Cost breakdown structure. This is the breakdown of any *cost budget* showing the distribution of *activity* and *task* costs against their *time schedule*. The CBS provides a framework which links cost components to organisational *stakeholders*, the *OBS* and *WBS* activities.

change order   This follows the initiation of a change report, which is triggered by a planned change (variation) to any aspect of a project, if approved a change order is issued. *Change orders* are used proactively and are the only official sanctioning of variations to a project.

charter   This relates to both *study charters* and *project charters*. Contains, *inter alia*, the roles and authorities of a project *sponsor* and *project manager*. When signed it becomes an important project document for the delegation of senior management's function.

code of accounts   A numbering system that is used to uniquely identify each *task* within a *WBS*, which is then used in project *activity* tracking and *control*.

contingency reserve   The amount of money and time identified as additional to a project's *baseline* budget and time schedule that is linked to an acceptable probability of 'not to be exceeded'.

control   The process of comparing actual performance with planned performance of any project *activity* or all activities (a project) and determining variances.

corrective action   Project decisions taken to bring future performance in line with the plan.

cost budgets   These are achieved by applying an appropriate *estimate* of resources to the *WBS* activities and *tasks*. A project normally has a developing cost budget that progresses from order of magnitude, study, approval and tender, through to a definitive budget that is used for contract *control* and performance. When appropriate the budget is an amalgam of separately identified domestic and foreign components.

critical path   The in-series activities which create the longest chain in the total network of sequenced *activities* and hence determine the *duration* of a project.

deliverable   Any document or verifiable outcome at the end of each *stage* of a project, including the final product of a project. See *gateway*.

duration   The number of work periods (hours, days, months, etc.) required to complete a project or any part (*activity* or *task*) thereof.

earned value   The value, based on the initial *estimate* of each *activity's* budget, of the work completed or partially completed at any date when a project's performance, or any work package's performance, is measured. Also known as the BCWP (budgeted cost of work performed).

estimate   The means of assessing the resources, *duration* and budget cost of any *activity* or *task*.

external entity   Any project *stakeholder* that is contracted by a *performing organisation* to carry out a service or undertake works.

fast tracking   Compressing a project's overall time schedule by overlapping packages of work.

forecast   A current evaluation of the future completion of a project or any part thereof. Can relate to time forecasting and/or cost forecasting.

gateway   The end of each *stage* in a project's *life cycle*. The event of a project passing through a gate or gateway is subject to satisfactorily meeting criteria established at the beginning of that *stage*.

life cycle   Unless otherwise specified, this means a project's eight development *stages* from beginning to end, namely: concept (CT), feasibility (FS), outline design (D1), statutory and legal (SL), detailed design (D2), procurement (PR), construction (CN) and commissioning (CO). It would not normally include operation and decommissioning, which would traditionally be included as part of facilities management.

life cycle cost   Abbreviated to LCC. Uses future cash flows to evaluate options or alternatives. LCC includes the initial budget, maintenance budget, replacement budget and operating budget over the operating life of the item under consideration. Usually discounted to a net present value or cost.

milestone   A significant event in a project usually linked to the completion of a *deliverable*, or to the achievement/hand-over of something important.

mini-risk   A qualitative assessment of a project's risks such that potential risk events are classified as, for example, high, medium or low in order that a response can be specified for each risk class. Mini-risk requires assessments of probability and consequence to determine risk class.

network diagram   A diagram that shows the sequence of undertaking the work *activities* and *tasks* that are the *WBS* or a part thereof. The network (also referred to as logic) diagram does not show times nor is it calendar related.

OBS   Organisational breakdown structure. This structure relates to the primary project team and other *stakeholders* that are secondary and tertiary resources providing support, input or are impacted by a project.

owner   Also referred to as owner organisation (see *performing organisation*). The organisation that initiates a project to satisfy a need.

performing organisation   The organisation which undertakes a project and normally for whom the project *deliverables* are intended.

planned value   The cost of the work scheduled plus the budget of any authorised planned work assessed at any status update or date for measuring performance. Also known as the BCWS (budgeted cost of work scheduled).

prequalify   Used during the procurement process to reduce a long list of potentially interested entities to a preferred short list of *bidder*s.

PRID   Project requirements and information document. A document prepared at the end of the concept stage that becomes an input to the feasibility stage.

procurement management plan   The plan for procuring external services and products (*SP*s, contractors, vendors, etc.) against which all subsequent procurement actions are managed by a project team.

project   Any series of sequenced *activities* and *tasks* that, when integrated, effectively resourced and managed, achieves predetermined *deliverables*.

project charter   A signed document that formally recognises the authorisation to define (design) and implement (manufacture, develop, construct, etc.) a project. A most significant aspect of the *charter* is the authorised transfer of the day-to-day management of a project to the *project manager*.

project engineer   A team title reserved for an individual who performs the engineering function within a project team.

project manager   The individual named in a project *charter* having responsibility and authority for managing the named project.

project (study) manual   A developing document created for each project, using the standards specified in a corporate handbook, that sets out the 'what, how, when, how long and how much' of a project's management. At concept and feasibility *stages* the document is referred to as a study manual.

RAM   Responsibility assignment matrix. A document that relates the activities in the *WBS* to each project *stakeholder* and states, where it is applicable, the role of each individual.

ranking   The arranging of an array of results that places them in decreasing or increasing order according to an agreed method of measurement.

RFP   Request for proposal. A document assembled by a project team that leads to procuring a *service provider* to undertake some aspect of a project.

RFT   Request for tender. A document that is used to procure the services of an *external entity* to supply and/or implement the specified works. Also referred to as 'seek a tender', 'obtain a tender', etc.

risk management plan   The plan for undertaking the strategy and tactics relating to all aspects of managing a project's risk events.

risk response   The response decided on to address a risk event; it is normally selected from four options. The four options normally used for projects are avoid, transfer, mitigate and accept.

SP   Service provider; also generally referred to as consultant. The service provider is usually appointed as the preferred *bidder* after evaluation of all submitted *RFP*s.

sponsor   The individual appointed by executive management who has been discharged with the responsibility of identifying a *project* (*study*) *manager*, preparing a *project* (*study*) *charter*, arranging for the resources needed, and reporting continuously to management on the progress and performance of a project (study).

stage   A subpart of a project phase. Concept, feasibility, outline design, etc., are stages of a project.

stakeholders   Individuals within the performing and any other organisation who are directly involved in a project or who are impacted by a project.

study charter   A signed document that formally recognises the authorisation of the start of the concept *stage* (sometimes the feasibility *stage*) of a potential project. A most significant aspect of the *charter* is the transfer of the day-to-day running of the study to a *study manager*.

study manager   The individual named in the *study charter* having responsibility and authority for managing the named study.

task   A sub*activity* and the lowest level of work identified within a *WBS*.

team roles   The positions within a project team, including that of a *project manager*. Includes both internal (*performing organisation*) roles and *external entity* roles.

time schedule   A calendar-based diagram showing a project's *activities* and *tasks*. The time schedule is required to be the result of a network analysis such as a CPM, PERT or other acceptable method of sequencing and mathematically assessing *activities* and *tasks*.

training charter   A signed agreement between the training facilitator and each participant who has been identified for project management training. The *charter* sets out the responsibilities and undertakings of the facilitator and a participant.

variance   The measurable difference between what was planned and what has actually happened or been achieved.

VE   Value engineering. A process for creating increased functionality at the lowest *life cycle* cost.

VP   Value planning. Uses many of the techniques of *VE*, but at the concept and feasibility *stages* to ensure that the right option(s) is/are identified that satisfies the requirements.

WBS   Work breakdown structure. This is a decomposition of the scope of the study, design, procurement and implementation of a project. It identifies the assemblies, sub-assemblies, elements, activities and tasks.

workshop The primary method used in assembling project *stakeholders* for the range of important actions that confront project *stakeholders* during a project's *life cycle*.

List of acronyms

A list of acronyms that are used in this Handbook are presented below. There are other comprehensive lists of acronyms and specialist listings of acronyms used in project management which may be referred to.[4,9]

AC	actual cost (or ACWP)
ACWP	actual cost of work performed
ATE	actual time expended
BCWP	budgeted cost of work performed
BCWS	budgeted cost of work scheduled
CA	contracting authority
CBS	cost breakdown structure
CLT	central limit theorem
CN	construction stage
CO	commissioning stage
CPI	cost performance index
CPM	critical path method
CR	client's representative
CT	concept stage
CV	cost variance
DCF	discounted cash flow
EF	early finish
EIS	environmental impact statement
ETC	estimated time to completion
ES	early start
EV	earned value (or BCWP)
EVMS	earned value management system
FF	free float (between activities on the same chain)
FS	feasibility stage
FtoF	finish to finish
FS	feasibility stage
FtoS	finish to start
IRR	internal rate of return
KPI	key performance indicator
LCC	life cycle cost
LF	late finish
LS	late start
mu	monetary unit
NEW	New Engineering Contract

NPC	net present cost
NPV	net present value
OBS	organisation breakdown structure
ORP	overriding purpose
PC	prime contractor
PERT	programme and evaluation review technique
PFI	private finance initiative
PICT	project integrated core techniques
PIMS	project integrated management strategy
PPP	public–private partnership
PR	procurement stage
PRID	project requirements and information document
PSO	project support office
PV	planned value (or BCWS)
QMP	quality management plan
RAM	responsibility assignment matrix
RFP	request for proposal
RFT	request for tender
RMP	risk management plan
ROI	return on investment
RtoP	request to participate
SL	statutory and legal
SP	service provider
SPI	schedule performance index
SV	schedule variance
TF	total float (within an activity)
TS	(project) time schedule
VE	value engineering
VMP	value management plan
VP	value planning
WBS	work breakdown structure

References

1. Association of Project Management (2000) *Project Management Body of Knowledge*, 4th edn. London: Association of Project Management.
2. British Standards Institute (1997) *BS ISO 10006: Quality Management — Guidelines to Quality in Project Management*. London: British Standards Institute.
3. British Standards Institute (2000) *BS 6079-1: Project Management — Part 1: Guide to Project Management*. London: British Standards Institute.
4. British Standards Institute (2000) *BS 6079-2: Project Management — Part 2: Vocabulary*. London: British Standards Institute.
5. British Standards Institute (2000) *BS 6079-3: Project Management — Part 3: Guide to the Management of Business Related Project Risk*. London: British Standards Institute.
6. British Standards Institute (2000) *BS EN 12973: The European Standard for Value Management*. London: British Standards Institute.

7. HM Treasury (1996) *Guidance Note No. 54: Value Management*. London: Central Unit on Procurement.
8. Institute of Civil Engineers (1992) *Management Development in the Construction Industry*. London: Thomas Telford.
9. Project Management Institute (2000) *A Guide to the Project Management Body of Knowledge*. Pennsylvania: Project Management Institute.
10. Saunders R, Wheeler T (1991) *Handbook of Safety Management*. London: Pitman.

Part 2

Projects — three integrated structures

Recognising projects as organised undertakings

Why project management?

Modern project management surfaced in the second half of the 20th century (about 1958); this is when many of the tools that we use today in project management came into use. These tools include sophisticated methods of decision-making, such as activity planning, time scheduling, cost budgeting, forecasting and reporting. After the Second World War the concepts of logical sequencing of project activities in a graphical format, together with the use of what is known as the critical path methodology, led to a prioritising of how work was carried out.

Since about this time projects were becoming increasingly complex and hence costly; budget and time schedule overruns were common. The cost of borrowing money for capital works (buildings, equipment, etc.) and the interest on such borrowings was becoming a major element of the total cost of a project. Responding to the need to control costs, parallel efforts were used to develop better estimates and better means to control changes that through their introduction were impacting on the management of time and cost effects of projects.

This was also a period of dramatic change in the power of the computer and the introduction thereafter of the personal computer (PC). The PC was a timely tool that assisted enormously with the task of processing the data necessary for planning and monitoring the time and cost aspects of project work.

It is generally accepted that modern project management has been developing over the past 40–50 years, having started in the USA. Much insight can be gained by briefly looking at this development process. During the first 10 years (mid-1950s to mid-1960s) *project organisational structures* were experimented with and adopted. The next 10 years saw the period of formal adoption of the people side of projects, i.e. the *people characteristics* needed to better undertake and manage projects. In the 1980s organisations concentrated on improving the *procedures and techniques* to ensure that the people within the organisational structures functioned more effectively. Since the 1990s the project management industry has been in what is being referred to as the period of maturity.

A view of project management within Europe might indicate that reaching maturity is still some distance away. Project management in Europe is probably about 30–35 years old and some may question if the experiences of the USA have been fully appreciated. Many have yet to understand fully the general concept of project management, the effect of different organisational structures, the importance of people in teams and the range of procedures and techniques available to initiate or work on projects.

The use of project management has been increasing rapidly in recent years. New applications are being discovered each year; some of the more interesting applications are:

- mending interpersonal relationships
- diagnosing business conflicts
- analysing historical events
- managing a business
- developing a process.

As most people are constrained by the sort of project work that is found in their sector, this selection of applications may be somewhat surprising. Project management, as many people are beginning to appreciate, is very broad in its concept. It may be used in a wide variety of cases. Ideal situations for using the project management process exist when some, or all, of the following conditions are present:

Table 2.1 *Classification of projects by their source of ownership (i.e. by the performing organisation)*

Owner	Examples
Personal or family	Prepare for an important written examination Add a new extension to your house Rebuild a classic car
For your organisation	Install a new piece of equipment Prepare an annual report Relocate to new premises
By your organisation	Design and/or build a sports stadium Carry out a land survey of a piece of land Prepare documents to procure specialist equipment
By other organisation for building your organisation	Overhaul the elevators (lifts) within your office Provide tailor made training course Undertake a specialist feasibility study
By a government entity	Prepare a new national development plan Issue a new coin Decide on implementing some aspect of social/physical infrastructure

- a definable purpose
- requirement for multidisciplinary effort
- non-repetitive situations
- where there is uncertainty and hence risk
- the temporary nature of the required resources.

Distinguishing characteristics of projects

There are many ways to classify projects. One way is to introduce the terms 'hardware' and 'software'. Hardware projects are those projects that produce a final, physical result. Software projects are those that produce something, such as a report, but the product is not tangible. Returning to the imaginary project, the installation of a conservatory would be a hardware project because it provides a physical end result.

Projects can also be classified by their source of ownership, i.e. by who is the performing organisation; some examples are listed in Table 2.1. If a family is the owner of a project then the management process is likely to be very informal. If the owner is a government body then the process is likely to be very formal. If a company is the owner, or another organisation dealing with the company is the owner, then the process is likely to be formal but, in certain cases, may be informal.

Whether or not a project is carried out under contract to another organisation probably affects how formal the process should be. It is wise to introduce as much formality as possible, irrespective of category of owner and irrespective of contract. This pretence helps ensure that enough formality is introduced such that the project can be managed more successfully. For instance, a project that is undertaken for another organisation normally requires a contract with a clear, detailed statement of what is to be done, by when and for how much. Such a job specification is sometimes lacking at the initiation of many projects. In general, a project is undertaken by someone or by some organisation for someone else or for some other organisation. For whom a project is undertaken generally affects how it is undertaken.

Projects can also be classified on the basis of size and complexity. The English Channel tunnel rail link across Kent requires many years of effort and the expenditure of billions of pounds. Conversely, defining and implementing a house extension can be carried out in a matter of months for a cost that is likely to be in tens of thousands of pounds. Hence, size and complexity do not distinguish a project from any other activity. Projects are normally defined by degree of uncertainty and complexity.

Projects and their management

The demand by society for sophisticated products and effective infrastructure together with the advent of the computer has led to modern project management being seen as having three important ingredients. These ingredients are the:

- project organisational structure
- people roles within project teams
- project procedures and techniques.

The development of project management coincides with these ingredients.

Project organisational structures

There are several options available when choosing a project organisational structure. Each option has its own strengths and weaknesses; the type of structure chosen can significantly affect the success of a project.

Basically, the academic researcher advises that there are five alternative organisational structures found in the projects environment. These alternatives are functional, functional matrix, balanced matrix, project matrix and project team; these are quoted in order of increasing influence of a project manager relative to a functional or line manager.

The basic factors that are found to influence the selection of the best form of project management organisational structure include:

- project size and value
- project complexity

- project length of time
- experience with project management organisational structures
- philosophy and visibility of the owner
- project location
- available resources
- unique aspects of a project.

People roles within project teams

Today's project manager knows that having a strong discipline background and knowledge of project management procedures and techniques are not the complete answer to running a successful project. The astute project manager knows that his or her personal attributes and the ability to lead, motivate and integrate a project team are equally important factors.

A project management team must be skilled in the management of technical design, procurement, planning, scheduling and time/cost tracking and control, value management, risk analysis, etc. Project coordination with strong technical orientation is not project management. To be successful the multidisciplinary team needs to be led and managed by an individual with the clear responsibility and authority to achieve a project's objectives; this is a project manager's role.

Human resources (people) accomplish projects, but project resources needed include plant, equipment, money, etc., under the leadership of a project manager. Many of the required resources are only marginally under the effective control of a project manager. For instance, the bricks used to build the house in an imaginary project are made by a brick works, which is controlled by the brick manufacturing company's management, not a project manager.

A project manager must form the correct human resources into a team in order to take advantage of the needed physical resources. A project manager has to deal with the constraints and emotional problems inherent in people, while trying to accomplish a project owner's technical performance goals within the pre-set time schedule and cost budget. Managing people is often the most difficult aspect of managing a project.

A project manager's goal is to utilise organisational resources, which requires internal selling to people in his or her company, to achieve project objectives. However, a project manager may often be frustrated by the many other directions in which the organisation seems to be (and often is) moving. These multiple directions can arise because of the various parochial interests of different components of the organisation, or because of many projects being carried out simultaneously.

Failure to identify a project for what it really is usually leads to missed specification, late completion and/or a budget overrun or other effect. The solution is to recognise that there is a project — something must be done that can be defined as a project — and then to organise to complete a project in the best possible way. A further solution is to expend the needed effort in planning and organising everything as early in the life cycle of a project as possible.

Project procedures and techniques

Project management involves, for a relatively short period of time, the planning, organising, directing and controlling of resources that have been established to achieve the predetermined objectives and goals of a project. The requirements of a project's owner normally consist of meeting, in accordance with predefined values, the three project objectives of:

- performance (project scope and quality)
- overall project period and completion date
- project cost to completion.

It is the role of the leader of a project team, the project manager, to work closely with the owner to develop and refine the owner's requirements and eventually settle on their relative and absolute values.

Project management is therefore characterised by methods of restructuring management and adopting special management techniques. The purpose of project management is to obtain better planning, organising and control of the use of existing resources. Also, project management is often used because traditional management structures cannot respond to the rapidly changing environments found in the pre-investment activities, the design, the procurement and the execution of projects.

The three structures

Having identified a project and that it is likely to need all, or some, of the techniques of project management, it is important that the systemic nature of projects is fully appreciated. Irrespective of a project's type, size or complexity, there are three structures that together form a project's framework from which all other substructures, processes and resources are linked. These three structures, which are not mutually exclusive, are:

- the structure of the performing organisation and other stakeholder organisations
- the structure of a project team
- the structure of a project's scope of work, which is known as the work breakdown structure.

It is important that these three structures are adequately addressed when dealing with all but a very small project. The significance of each structure and the degree to which each structure is likely to impact on a project and determine the management of a project is discussed in the subsections that follow in this part of the Handbook.

The corporate organisation structure

Alternative forms of organisation

The management of projects is usually practised within one of three different organisational corporate structures. There are variants to these structures, but these three are the most commonly found. They are known as:

- the functional structure
- the project, or projectised, structure
- the matrix structure.

Functional organisation

The functional structure is the classic organisational structure with separate departments, or work groups, each having personnel with similar or clearly related disciplines or functions. An example of this structure within a Local Authority would probably reveal separate departments for technical, finance, housing, information technology, roads and streets, and so on.

Organisationally the functional structure practices what it does within a hierarchy, within discipline departments, and with bosses at the top and other personnel at the bottom. With the hierarchy comes bureaucracy and line of command. The functional structure is driven from the top down and the emphasis on 'verticality' can be seen in communications, responsibilities, authorities and in the role that the individual has as his or her perceived job or function. Projects undertaken by a functional organisation are not likely to have a separate division and are more than likely to be handled by the department whose function lies closest to a project's development sector. Difficulties arise when a project is multifunctional and crosses a number of department functions.

Usually functional management coordinates the various activities of the departments. A project authorised under this form of structure needs to be managed in the same way; if there is a formally designated project manager he or she is likely to be no more than a coordinator. Functional management under this arrangement, as is traditional, would be responsible for both projects and the operation of their department.

Within a functional structure it is often found that in defining and executing projects problems arise through a general confusion of individual priorities. Most people would tend to concentrate on departmental concerns and few become serious or take responsibility for project-type work.

The functional structure is likely to be the least disruptive of the available organisational options, particularly if a project is assigned to the functional department that would be most involved. The reason for this is that a project structure replicates the corporate structure and is in no way disruptive to the corporate structure. Many companies in the private sector and almost all the public sector use this structure when undertaking their projects. The characteristics of the functional structure are:

- division of personnel (labour) based on functional specialisation
- well-defined hierarchy of authority
- system of rules covering the rights and duties of personnel
- system of procedures dealing with the work situation
- interpersonal relations are impersonal
- promotion and selection for employment is based on technical competence.

Project organisation

Although less common, at the opposite end of the organisational structure spectrum is what is referred to as the project structure. With this option there is likely to be no departmental structure and the work is organised by project with an identified and assigned project manager. Functional departments, where they exist, would be for normal support functions covering such matters as finance, personnel, etc. The appointed project managers would be given fairly broad, but by no means absolute, authority over the conduct of project personnel. While this approach encourages effective project performance it can be disruptive to the conduct of non-project business in the departments. The normal close ongoing relationship to provide continuity in what the company does is likely to be lost when undertaking projects under this organisation structure.

A project structure consists of all those individuals assigned to produce a product or service for a project. They are sometimes referred to as a 'task force'. It is not usually considered to include those functional managers whose personnel have been assigned to a project. This project task force may be grouped together in one geographical location (grouped task force) or they may remain in their departments (dispersed task force).

Most project managers prefer their task force to be located in a single area. The primary reason for this is that a project manager can exercise a greater degree of control over the work. Improved communications, particularly in handling changes, is another very important reason to have all the team members together. There is also evidence that greater team spirit can be engendered with a grouped task force.

The quality of the work output is generally materially improved through the centralised efforts of the group task force. Improvements in communication, by having everyone working in close proximity, are the likely reason for this. A grouped task force also benefits those people who want to progress in their careers by assuming more responsibility for multidisciplinary efforts.

The main advantages of a project structure include the following:

- a project manager has full authority for a project and there is a complete workforce devoted to a project
- all members of a project team are directly responsible to a project manager, as there are no functional heads whose permission must be sought before making technological decisions
- the lines of communication are short, resulting in faster communications with fewer failures
- a project team with a strong and separate identity tends to develop a high level of commitment from its members
- a project structure is simple and flexible, and it is therefore easy to understand and to implement
- a project structure tends to support the systems approach.

The principal disadvantages of a project structure include the following:

- the company that takes on several projects, with each one using a project structure, can find a duplication of effort in every area
- removing technical control from the functional departments can cause problems in the high-technology areas
- policies and procedures can be subject to corner-cutting
- a strong 'we–they' can develop as team members form strong attachments to a project and each other.

Matrix organisation

In order to capture the advantages of each of the previous two options, a third option, called the matrix organisational structure, is often found as the adopted corporate structure. The matrix structure calls for adding a temporary parallel organisation with a short-term specific purpose (the reason for calling it 'matrix' is because the traditional vertical management structure now has overlain on it a horizontal management structure).

This temporary organisation draws on the resources of the permanent functional organisation (the departments) until its identified purpose, or goal, has been achieved and all the work has been completed. Here the departmental managers assume authority for certain aspects of a project, while a project manager exercises authority over other aspects. To avoid conflict these areas of authority need to be carefully defined.

There are variations of the matrix structure, which may be differentiated by the relative authority of the departmental manager and a project manager. In organisations where a project manager has more authority the matrix is defined as a strong (project) matrix. Where a project manager's authority is less than that of the functional manager the organisational structure is defined as a weak (functional) matrix. The weak matrix is one where there is, at best, project coordination and most, if not all, project personnel stay within their departments. Conversely, the strong matrix is one where a project manager formally exists and where most, if not all, project personnel have been assigned to a project and are working within a project team and are physically distant from their departments.

Some responsibilities are assigned to the functional managers and others to a project manager. Certain of the personnel, such as the leaders of each discipline on a project assignment, have a dual reporting relationship, responsible not only to their discipline supervisor but also to a project manager.

Definition of responsibility is important in the matrix structure. Typically a project manager controls:

- what is to be done (the scope)
- when it is to be done (the schedule)
- what resources are required (the skills, equipment and money budget).

The functional manager controls:

- who should do the work (the people)
- how the work is be carried out (the methods and procedures).

Functional management also has the responsibility for maintaining the technical position of the discipline and for administration and the professional development of personnel. There are, of course, many variants to the assignment of responsibilities.

The most important advantages of the matrix organisation are:

- project objectives and the responsibility for achieving them are made clear
- employee morale is high through visible achievement as a part of a project team, while obtaining continuity in career opportunities within the functional organisation
- efficient use of part-time specialists, on each of several projects, through integration into a team(s) with improved disciplinary coordination and communication.

A matrix structure creates problems, some of the more important ones being:

- the protocol of a matrix system is complicated; definition of responsibilities and authority must be made and followed
- conflicting priorities cause problems, especially when the available resources are tight (conflicts tend to be disruptive)
- discipline leaders may receive different instructions from their two supervisors (functional and project)
- management at all levels has difficulty in balancing the objectives of projects versus the considerations for the functional elements.

Project support office (PSO)

The organisation that is frequently and even continuously engaged in delivering projects needs to ensure that sufficient attention is given to capital expenditure projects at senior management level. Most organisations that handle projects are invariably engaged in operations of some sort or other. *Operations* refers to continuous effort in which the work is on going, has little or no uncertainty attached to it, and usually delivers a service or a product. For instance, public sector organisations are primarily involved in operations (e.g. the provision of various social services), but a significant amount of their effort is spent on project work (e.g. introducing a new bus network). Private sector companies are more varied, they can be purely project based, almost solely operations based or something in between.

To provide a project focus in organisations that handle project-based work but are engaged in operations requires senior management to realise that management balance at their level is required. A concentration on function-based department management is not likely to work when a department is engaged in a significant number of and/or medium to large projects or when projects span across the functional departments. It is recommended that the management of projects should be given a 'seat' at the top corporate level in order to provide proper balance between function-based and project-based work. The role at senior management level could be titled 'director of projects' and the incumbent's responsibilities would fall into five reform practice categories, namely:

- setting project management policy guidelines
- producing working project management processes
- providing in-house support to project teams
- auditing projects and project teams
- transferring project management skills to personnel.

For the organisation that has already established, or is working on creating, balance between its operations and project-based work then in consolidating that situation the focus should be on reaching project management maturity. Maturity is reached when:

- senior management provide equitable status for projects within the organisation
- organisational structures reflect what is needed to handle projects
- project managers are provided with the responsibility and authority to manage
- the organisation has invested in skills transfer to provide internal project teams with the tools and techniques needed to manage projects from concept to commissioning.

For the organisation that has not yet taken the steps needed to balance the management of its work portfolio it is suggested a start should be made to reform the organisation. Underpinning the reform process should be the application of 'best practice' project management. Having a seat at senior management is necessary for reform, but is not sufficient particularly for all but the smallest organisations.

The reform process, although starting at the top, needs to be applied much lower in the organisation and specifically at project team and project support levels. A particularly effective way of handling project management reform is to create a project support office (PSO). Establishing a single PSO or a PSO within each department is likely to be determined by the size of the organisation and the volume of projects handled by each department. A not untypical structure for reform for the larger organisation is shown in Fig. 2.1.

The organisational concept assumes that senior management would be the heads of the various departments, including the director of projects, normally reporting to the equivalent of a chief executive. The diagram shows project managers (PM) using allocated resources from various departments to create the team and/or support a project that is within that PM's remit. The PMs would have a reporting role to the director of projects, but should also have a reporting role to whoever is the sponsor for a project.

Each departmental PSO reports to the director of projects (DoP) on all matters pertaining to the reform process. A PSO would be expected to plan, operate and report on its activities as set out in a Manual of Procedures for the PSOs. The role of each PSO would be to provide a support function to its Department's projects as defined in a charter between the DoP and each PSO. The primary focus of a PSO

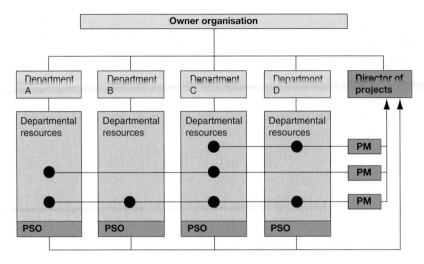

Fig. 2.1 *A not untypical structure for reform of a larger organisation.*

should be 'skills transfer' and not 'becoming a specialist operational unit'. Skills transfer to the individual should be the foundation of any organisation's operational reform.

The DoP and the PSOs would share certain aspects of the five reform practice categories referred to earlier. An indication of how these practices could be suitably dealt with is given below.

Policy guidelines

The preparation of policy guidelines for the management of projects is likely to be the sole responsibility of the DoP. Working with senior management and using the PSO as support the policies would normally be presented to senior management for discussion and in the form of recommendations.

In Part 3 each project management procedure commences with a policy statement that, by and large, would be developed by the DoP.

Working processes and procedures

The management procedures contained within a corporate handbook of project management procedures would form the basis for the management of all the organisation's projects. If such a handbook does not exist then it has to be developed.

A project manual (see procedure CN-004 in Part 3) would be designed and created specifically for each project. The manual would fully reflect the guidelines of the corporate handbook of procedures. Whereas the corporate handbook provides guidelines for all projects, a project manual is tailored to match the needs of a specific project. Experience gained on using the procedures and any suggestions emanating from project team personnel would be communicated to a committee established to review the corporate handbook content.

In-house support

Supporting project teams would primarily be a PSO responsibility. The facilitation of various project workshops, providing advice on the interpretation and application of a handbook procedure, providing assistance in the planning and control of projects, and helping in any aspect of a project's management would form the core of the PSO's project support.

Auditing projects

It is expected that the DoP and the PSOs would be responsible for the periodic auditing of projects. It is recommended that all auditing would be undertaken using two people. Two individuals with experience of such work would audit each project at least once in every stage of a project's life cycle. It would be a PSO duty to ensure that a project team responds to the recommendations contained in audit reports and, when they exist, the external service provider project teams.

Training

A structured training programme in project management for the relevant department staff engaged on project-related work is an important aspect of the reform process. Staff training in the project management processes and the application of the corporate handbook procedures would be the responsibility of the DoP using the PSO resources as support. Because training is likely to utilise a high level of DoP and PSO effort, training may be provided selectively; those individuals who are likely to make the greatest impact being given priority. A duty of the DoP and the PSOs would be to assess individual ability and identify individuals to progress through the various training levels to certification and beyond. It is paramount that skills transfer be available to those individuals providing the greatest benefit to the reform process and in doing so demonstrate the application of 'best practice' project management to their project work.

Project team and its structure

Organisational concepts

There are several possible project organisation structures that can be found in the definition and execution of projects. The three major options that are found are:

- functional
- task force
- matrix.

A brief explanation of each of these approaches is given below.

Functional project structure

Functional structures, by their very nature, are hierarchical or vertically structured. Functional structures for projects operate with clear division between the professional disciplines and the divisions of definition and implementation. In other words, there are as many divisions (or departments) as there are disciplines needed to undertake a project. A functional leader or manager usually leads each division.

This type of structure works when the definition and implementation do not fully overlap, i.e. when there is a minimum of interaction. It does not work well when there is a requirement for integration of a project's disciplines. It is principally for this reason that functional structures are not effective when applied to projects.

Weaknesses of functional project structures include:

- slowness to adapt to changes
- minimum appreciation of overall project objectives
- overly rigid operating rules
- potential for introducing and maintaining functional bias.

Many functional leaders may tend to overoptimise their particular speciality to the possible detriment of the overall project. Functional structures are not good proving grounds for the development of project managers.

The strengths of functional project structures include:

- high professional, functional, standards can be achieved
- there is an opportunity for ensuring the incorporation of the latest functional technology
- the functional structure is likely to be highly recognisable if it is a mirror image of the corporate organisation.

It is worth stating that when dealing with project structures within the overall corporate organisation there can be a part or a whole of the organisation that is organised along one or more of the three structures under discussion. The functional structure can be helpful when the owner acting as the project manager with minimum staff depends on others for the functional expertise.

Project task force structure

The task force project structure works well when a self-sufficient project organisation is required. These types of structure are increasingly being utilised by public sector and private sector owners where full-time task forces are staffed with individuals who are employees of either the owner or an external company.

The strengths of the task force structure include high adaptability, the formation of an excellent team spirit, and, a high level of understanding of the overall project objectives. The task force is also good for generating close personal relationships, and it can be responsive to change (i.e. new ideas and methods).

The weaknesses of the task force structure include the problem of no functional quality checks and the feeling of indeterminacy (not really belonging) felt by the people involved. Team members may have only a limited period within the task force and then return to their 'home base' or the division from which they came. Task forces work best when all the team members can be physically located within the same area and away from their home base.

Matrix project structure

This project structure is a cross between the functional structure and the task force structure and represents an attempt to preserve the strong points of each. The matrix endeavours to solve the conflict between the operating line organisation as represented by a project manager and the functional staff by opening up lines of communication at all levels. Project responsibilities, such as scope, cost and time schedules, are the responsibility of a project manager. Functional objectives, such as quality assurance, design standards and internal company policies, are the responsibilities of the functional manager.

The matrix structure fosters an excellent climate for developing project managers and it allows control of both craftsmanship and project objectives. The matrix structure is appropriate when both project accountability and functional expertise are required. It works best when experienced and people-oriented managers are involved and when functional and project authority can be explicitly defined and divided.

People and team skills

The concept of bringing together a group of people on a temporary basis to achieve specific goals has been used probably since the beginning of time. During the classical periods of Chinese, Egyptian, Greek and Roman history, very impressive results were achieved and many of the fundamentals of this process were used. It was not, of course, called project management in those days, but that's what it was.

It is therefore a fact that something, or some things, are at least equally significant as, if not of greater significance than, the modern trappings of project management. By 'modern trappings' we refer to the use of computers and the modern project management procedures, such as network scheduling, risk analysis and value management, which were not available or used until the last 30 years or so. These 'some things' are a project's organisation structure and the personnel within this structure, i.e. the project people.

Years ago, an individual in charge of a project had only to be technically competent in a single discipline. A few centuries ago the master mason was in charge of building works (a project manager) and he did everything. In more recent years the competent architect, working with several master craftsmen, was the project manager. These were times when the time schedule for a project might have been decades, labour was relatively inexpensive and projects were not complicated. As projects have become complex and technically sophisticated, so they have become multidisciplinary in nature. Invariably, modern projects are also subject to tight time schedules and constrained cost budgets.

Today's project managers know that having a strong discipline background and a knowledge of the procedures and techniques are not the complete answer to running a successful project. The astute project manager knows that his or her personal attributes and the ability to lead, motivate and integrate a project team are equally important factors.

A project manager's success or failure on a project can be based on three factors:

- a solid foundation in a discipline appropriate to the type of project for which the manager is responsible
- a strong background based on project management techniques of planning, scheduling and cost management
- competency as a manager in a project environment.

A project manager would typically be well trained in a specific discipline. He or she may well have been very successful in that discipline, and this fact probably contributed to his or her ultimate selection as a project manager. A project manager's knowledge and experience in project management should include project management elements such as planning, organising the work, scheduling, estimating, monitoring, controlling and reporting.

A project manager's competency would ideally contain all or most of the following:

- concern for performance
- leadership qualities
- consistently high values
- hard worker
- get and keep quality people
- communication skills
- good discipline
- effective work systems
- enthusiasm
- sensitivity to interpersonal relationships.

As a project manager's training may have been more haphazard than the formal discipline of education, much of a project manager's management knowledge is likely to have been through self-initiative; in other words, he or she is likely to have been self-taught.

Project managers need to have strong skills in the following areas:

- communication
- organising
- team building
- leadership
- coping (dealing with stress)
- technology of the specific project under consideration.

Project management requires good communication to be effective. Communication in a project environment may take any of several forms or combinations, depending on the requirements and the situation. Three types of communication are generally used in projects: oral, written and visual. In communicating, project managers need to be just as good at listening as they are at persuading others to do certain things.

They need to be highly proficient in planning, goal setting and analysing; the elements that are seen as being prime project organising skills. The process of goal setting begins with a project manager establishing clear goals in his or her mind and then ensuring that they are understood in the minds of the team members. As it is time that drives projects, a project manager and the rest of the team need always to be focused on future work. Future work is what is important; what has already happened is only important with respect to how it affects the future.

A major responsibility of a project manager is making decisions. During the planning phase of a project there are always key decisions which have not been made. A project manager should identify these decisions, schedule a date by which each decision must be made, and assign the responsibility for making it.

Everyone, including a project manager, must learn to distinguish the important tasks (self-imposed, large number of people, dealing with the future) from the urgent tasks (e.g. an individual action from the past that should have been carried out previously). It is important that a project manager responds to these urgent tasks, sometimes moving them up the priority list and trying to find a way to minimise their number and their impact on the work day.

In setting project goals it is worth noting what the four characteristics are:

- the goals must be defined and measurable
- a completion time has to be set
- the resources to be used have to be allocated
- the desired level of quality has to be determined.

A project manager needs to be the sort of person who can develop motivation in a project group and who has the ability to create a 'spirit of belonging' or of being part of something exciting.

Everyone in a project team wants to do a good job. In general, if a person understands what is wanted, the person comes much closer to fulfilling that expectation. If the person has an understanding as to why something is wanted and what it is to be used for, the chances of satisfying the goals are increased.

In general, a close group of people working together is usually more productive and has higher morale than the same people working separately. It follows, therefore, that performance can be enhanced through building a team or teams to undertake projects.

A prerequisite for team building is the visible commitment of top management to the team concept. Any company that is engaged in the management of projects would have to see team building as a necessity because of the technical complexity and multidisciplinary nature of projects.

A project manager is ideally someone who has leadership skills. Therefore he or she is someone who has vision and can see the 'big picture'; in other words, they can see beyond the detail of today's situation. Their leadership skills include setting good examples, being very energetic, being able to delegate and being positive in what they do.

Project management is concerned with accomplishing things through others by performing the functions of planning, organising, directing and control. Leadership adds another dimension by introducing extraordinary motivation for the followers.

However, it should be noted that managers can always manage without having to be leaders and leaders can lead without being good managers. The preferred combination of having a project manager that is a good manager as well as a good leader is not common. The principles of good management can be taught, but leadership cannot as it is instinctive. It is also found that good leaders generally become better leaders with added experience.

Having the ability to cope with the traumatic happenings that can be an everyday occurrence in projects is also a required attribute. Being flexible, being creative, being patient and being persistent are all attributes that need to be applied from time to time in different project situations.

All of us are negotiating every day of our lives. With so much practice we should be very good at it. The problem is that we do not realise what we are doing. We do not go about it in an organised way. Most of the time we come away from negotiations having done a poor job, ending up with much less than we could have obtained. Most people do not really know what they want as a result of negotiation. They have not established the limits they are likely to settle for. For them, negotiation is merely arguing to get the better of an opponent. One important rule of negotiation that must be learnt is to concentrate on the issues and not on the people. We must learn to avoid being overly emotional in our negotiations. There is a real need to make negotiations 'win–win'. In other words, one party must not feel that it has come away from a negotiation having lost something at the expense of the other party having gained something. Unless both parties come out of a negotiation feeling that they can live with the final resolution, there has not been a successful negotiation.

Last, but not least, a project manager needs to have project knowledge and be experienced in the type of work that the team is required to handle as part of their functional responsibilities. In other words, if a project is for the design and installation of a new IT system, then it is advisable that the project manager has had IT experience.

Work breakdown structure of a project

The third structure in this triad is the product structure of the work activities that need to be undertaken to deliver a project and satisfy the owner's requirements; this structure is known as the work breakdown structure. The work breakdown structure is a method of defining and organising work to achieve the scope of work of a project. The term and associated acronym, WBS, is being used increasingly in modern project management applications.

The WBS also establishes the framework for the total project communication process. It is used for thinking about and building project activities that are required to satisfy and complete the objectives. Without the utilisation of a WBS the chances of failure in successfully achieving the owner's objectives are increased.

The WBS is used in projects to:

- identify the major end products or end deliverables needed to accomplish a project's objectives
- identify and define the detailed tasks required to produce the end deliverables
- assign responsibility for task accomplishment to specific organisations or individuals
- provide a framework that facilitates the planning and scheduling of project work, and the allocation of resources to that work
- help in monitoring project cost, schedule and technical performance
- through the orderly summation of anticipated work performance provide a structure for selected levels of control
- identify and, if necessary, re-plan work requiring special attention.

Two choices exist for formatting the WBS. It can be prepared and presented in the format of a vertical list; in other words, set out in the same way as the contents page of a textbook. Or the WBS can also be prepared as a tree-type presentation.

The vertical layout approach offers two advantages. It is easy to assemble it and it also provides the advantage of a condensed approach. It can fit on the fewest pages and page breaks are easy to follow. The tree format also has two advantages. It offers the familiarity needed to ensure that it is used effectively, and it provides a graphic presentation of the structure of a project. This visual aid assists in structuring a project.

Either way, the WBS defines all the activities, equipment, services and data required for producing a project's deliverables. It is structured according to the way the work might be undertaken and reflects the way that project costs and data are to be summarised and reported. Descending reporting levels provide more detailed information of the work-item tasks.

The individual work items specified at each level are called 'elements'. The elements at the level at which costs or related work items are accumulated are called 'work packages'. Work packages are made up from elements that consist of activities and detailed tasks. Tasks are the lowest level of project activity in that they are virtually incapable of further subdivision or material items that are determined by a project team to be grouped together for doing the work to achieve the predetermined objectives. A properly constituted work package has the following characteristics:

- it represents significant units of work at levels at which the work is to be executed
- it is unique and is clearly distinguished from all other work packages
- it is chargeable to a single cost account
- it is the responsibility of a single supervisor, constructor or subcontractor
- It has defined start and completion dates and, as required, intermediate milestones that represent physical works
- it has budgeted values expressed in monetary units, people-hours or some other quantifiable units
- its duration is long enough for the accomplishment of significant quantities of work but short enough to regulate the work in progress to an optimal level

Table 2.2 *A rule of thumb for determining the lowest level of decomposition of a WBS: linking activity (task) duration to the overall length of a project*

Project duration	Smallest activity (task) duration
6 months	1 day
1 year	2 days
3 years	1 week

- it is mutually supportive of other detailed manufacturer (or erector, builder, etc.), designer, vendor and owner schedules
- it supports the cost estimating function by providing cost information at summary levels and in terms that exactly reflect the way in which the work was estimated.

Once a project's team starts creating the WBS they are likely to wonder how low into the WBS they must go; in other words, how far the decomposition must be taken. The answer to this, to a large extent, depends on how closely the team must monitor a project. If a project is very complex and is critical, then there would be a need to decompose the project work to a very low level. If, when undertaking this decomposition, the team is not clear on what a particular activity refers to, they must investigate lower into the work scope structure. If responsibility for the activity cannot be clearly assigned, it is always recommended to go lower with the WBS decomposition. If there are indications that an activity's duration, resources and costs cannot be estimated with reasonable accuracy, then the decomposition should go further.

Another rule of thumb for determining the lowest level is by linking activity duration to the overall length of a project. For instance the rough guideline given in Table 2.2 may be used. Of course, in this rule of thumb any activity that has a duration less than that stated and is an activity that is critically important to a project should not be excluded from a project's work scope or from the WBS. Rules of thumb are just that, and should be used with great care and prudence.

Part 3

Project management procedures

General comments

The following comments are intended to assist the Handbook holder in understanding the context and the application of the project management procedures that follow in this part.

Before commencing to consult the procedures, the holder is recommended to read or refer back to the section in Part 1 called 'The handbook and how to use it' (see p. 1-1). The holder's attention is particularly drawn to the section 'The Handbook as a set of guidelines' (see p. 1-2). A primary intention of the procedures is that they should provide inspiration for the development of a set of project management protocols that would be suitable for the project-based organisation, a project team or an individual project manager to adopt. The procedures should be of particular importance to project-based stakeholders who do not have any formal documentation on how projects are to be managed.

Another primary intention, as explained in the Preface and Part 1, is through the alumni of Handbook holders to create a virtual think-tank where the experiences of project management procedure use and application, and other experiences of holders, can be shared. By registering (see 'Registration of Holders', p. 1-1), it is planned that the Handbook benefits from the collective knowledge and skills of the alumni. It is planned that any additional procedures or any modifications to the Handbook that are a result of this collective knowledge sharing will culminate in regular updates of those sections of the Handbook that are affected.

The procedures have been separated into 10 knowledge areas; this reflects the eight knowledge areas used by the Project Management Institute (PMI) in their PMBOK, to which the *health and safety* and *value knowledge areas* has been added. For holders who are more familiar with the Association for Project Management's (APM) body of knowledge, 4th edition, a means of referencing the procedures against the APM's PMBOK is given in 'Referencing against the APM PMBOK' (see p. 3-34 and Table 3.1).

Procedure coding system

Each knowledge area is defined by two alphas, e.g. *communications management* is *CN*. Each knowledge area has been provided with a set of numbers that are used as unique identifiers for the procedures within a knowledge area. For example, procurement management has been allocated 061 to 080, and within that range a single number has been allocated to a commonly found procedure, e.g. 065 deals with the bidding process and is titled *Bidders conference*.

As any new procedure is developed it should be allocated an alpha numeric, its assigned code. The assigned code would depend on the knowledge area within which the new procedure resides and the next number in the available series.

If the procedures within a knowledge area exceed the number range allocated, then it is possible that the complete register of procedures may need to be re-coded.

Procedure format

A procedure consists of, on average, between five and six pages and provides the related narrative, process flow diagrams, standard forms, and sometimes exhibits that assist in understanding how to apply the procedure and complete the standard forms.

Headers and footers

Each page of each procedure has a header and footer. The header contains the procedure title that is linked to the Handbook content. The footer contains the procedure's code and page number, and the title of diagrams, forms and exhibits. The footer also gives the revision number and date of issue of a procedure; any replacement procedures will be provided with a new revision number and issue date.

Policy statement

A representative statement of policy has been prepared for each procedure. These statements generally explain what the procedure is, the reason for the procedure and how the procedure should be used when managing a project. On average a policy statement is about six paragraphs long.

The collective policy statements that have been provided offer the basis for inspiration to those organisations, teams and individuals that do not have formal operational project management policies but would wish to develop their own. For a specific procedure the policy statement provided could also be used as inspiration for developing a new one; alternatively, it could probably be used as it appears, with little change or modification to the content.

Outcome

The outcome (or outcomes) of a procedure is some deliverable that is the culmination of the input of effort and the use of resources. Because of the significant interconnections between procedural outcomes in any stage of a project, other allied procedures are normally referred to in the outcome section.

Process

The process within a procedure refers to the steps needed to turn a policy into an outcome. The process is presented as a two-column list headed 'person' and 'responsibility'. *Person* refers to a project's stakeholders, such as the project manager, sponsor, service provider and contractor, who would be involved in the process. *Responsibility* refers to the actions that are required from each stakeholder to respond to a step within a process. Each step is described as a narrative. In many procedures, but not all, the process is further clarified by showing the narrative in a flow diagram format.

The flow diagrams are formatted as vertical columns that separate the stakeholders involved in a particular procedure. The activities or actions by a stakeholder appear as rectangular boxed statements in that stakeholder's column.

Questions, in which an output could be 'yes' or 'no' appear as diamond-shaped boxes. References to other procedures appear as rectangular dotted-outline boxes and are shaded. Connecting lines between activities shows the sequence in which the activities should generally be performed. The direction of flow is generally from the top of the page to the bottom.

Stakeholders

There are a number of stakeholders that appear within the range of procedures, but an attempt was made to restrict the range. The more common ones are the study or project manager, project team, sponsor, senior management, department head, executive manager, PSO (project support office), facilitator, auditor, SP (service provider), contractor and external entity.

Standard forms

Each procedure has one or more standard forms that can be used for tracking, recording and storing information. These standard forms consist of boxes within which there is a requirement to respond to questions, fill in lines or windows, tick boxes, etc. that need to be completed. Each standard form has a unique number that is referred to in the associated process.

Exhibits

To the rear of some procedures is one or more exhibits that are meant to be further aids in understanding the procedure and how to use it. These exhibits are mainly completed tables that would be output from applying a procedure; in other cases the exhibits are blank templates that, if required, can be used by the Handbook holder.

Referencing against the APM PMBOK

Table 3.1 lists the Handbook procedures in the left-hand column and on the right-hand column contains the six management topics that are the APM's PMBOK, namely: strategic, control, technical, commercial, organisational and people. The cells within the resulting matrix indicate with a tick the APM PMBOK management topics that are addressed by a particular project management procedure from the Handbook.

Handbook philosophy

The Handbook procedures have been prepared assuming that the procedures author is the performing organisation. The performing organisation is that organisation which has the overall responsibility for ensuring the satisfactory delivery of a project. Another term that is used interchangeably with performing organisation is 'owner' or 'owner organisation'. The use of the term 'internal' would,

Table 3.1 Handbook procedures and the APM PMBOK

Handbook of Project Management Procedures	APM — Project management body of knowledge					
	Strategic	Control	Technical	Commercial	Organisational	People
Communication (CN)						
001 Communications management plan	✓		✓			✓
002 Project registration		✓				
003 Initiate a workshop		✓	✓	✓	✓	✓
004 Project manual		✓			✓	✓
005 Project coding and filing system		✓				
006 Performance reviews (services)		✓				
007 Performance reviews (works)		✓				✓
008 Earned value management		✓	✓	✓		
009 Change report and change order		✓	✓	✓		
010 Project auditing	✓	✓	✓	✓	✓	✓
011 Serve a way-leave notice	✓					
012 Vary a development plan	✓					
Cost (CS)						
021 Cost management plan	✓					
022 Budget type versus project stage		✓	✓	✓		
023 Cost breakdown structure (CBS)		✓		✓		
024 Budgeted cost of work scheduled (BCWS)		✓		✓		
Human resources (HR)						
041 Staff management plan	✓					
042 Project organisation and roles					✓	✓
043 Role assignments and staff selection					✓	✓
044 Staff training programme					✓	✓
045 Selection, appraisal and reward						✓

Table 3.1   Handbook procedures and the APM PMBOK (Contd)

Handbook of Project Management Procedures	APM — Project management body of knowledge					
	Strategic	Control	Technical	Commercial	Organisational	People
Health and safety (HS)						
051 Health and safety management plan	✓		✓		✓	✓
Procurement (PT)						
061 Procurement management plan (services)	✓			✓		
062 Advertise to procure a service				✓		
063 Request for proposal document				✓		
064 Prequality potential SP candidates				✓		
065 Holding a bidders conference				✓		
066 Evaluate external service proposals				✓		
067 Specifying time and price requirements (services)				✓		
071 Procurement management plan (works)	✓			✓		
072 Request to participate (works)				✓		
073 Request for tender (works)						
074 Appointing a contractor						
075 Recording the works		✓		✓		
076 Communications during the works		✓		✓		
077 Reporting on the works		✓		✓		
078 Works measurement and payment certification				✓		
Quality (QY)						
081 Quality management plan	✓			✓		
082 Product quality assurance	✓		✓	✓		
083 Quality improvement response	✓		✓			

Risk (RK)

101 Risk management plan
102 Identify and qualify risk sources
103 Quantitative risk assessment
104 Risk response plan

Scope (SE)

121 Study and project charter
122 Conceptualising alternative options
123 Evaluating and ranking options
124 Project requirements and information document (PRID)
125 Work breakdown structure (WBS)
131 Delivering the operations manual

Time (TE)

141 Time schedule management plan
142 Project planning
143 Estimating activity duration
144 Scheduling the plan

Value (VA)

161 Value management plan
162 Value planning exercise
163 Value engineering exercise
164 Value review

therefore, imply internal to the performing organisation and the use of the term 'external' means outside the performing organisation.

The appointment of a sponsor and the assignment of a study manager to lead a team for a concept study to deliver a PRID (project requirements and information document) has been assumed to be sourced from internal human resources. The rationale for this approach assumes that the performing organisation has the knowledge, know what they want and, in general, how it is likely to be achieved (see 'External support', p. 3-39).

Corporate policies

Most organisations that handle projects need to reform the way they handle such work. Accordingly, it is assumed that any reform should be based on using 'best practice' project management processes. The Handbook and its procedures have therefore been developed to provide a 'best practice' approach, and in that regard certain policy protocols need to be established and respected by the performing organisation. These protocols fall under certain headings and are commented on as follows.

The role of corporate management

The initiative to introduce new working procedures is, on its own, inadequate. What is essential is serious intent by senior management to reform the organisation structure and commit the organisation to change. To achieve significant success in project outcomes it is imperative that corporate departments engaged in conceptualising and executing projects need to be more project focused. As part of the reform process there may be a need to reform department structures so that what becomes important are *goals* and not *roles*, if that is what is currently important. Associated with this structural change should be a total reform of how to handle communications. A general communications policy for each department should encompass the communications management plan for each project; this is described in procedure CN-001.

Corporate management should identify a sponsor for all new and existing projects. An appointed sponsor becomes responsible to senior management for the performance of each and every project they have been assigned to. Sponsors do not directly run projects — project managers have that role. Managers of projects should be identified and assigned through a study charter, if at the pre-investment phase, or through a project charter, if at any subsequent phase. Any charter document (study or project) needs to cover the delegation of responsibility and authority, so that the named project manager can be effective in delivering a project's requirements. Corporate management must use the opportunity of delegating the procedural sign-offs to a project manager. This delegation should be confirmed within a project charter, and this effectively means that the project manager signs all project orders, with whatever exceptions have been reserved for the sponsor.

Corporate management and their project managers need to be aware of the 'gateway' acceptance/rejection that should be the role of a project support office (PSO) to determine at the end of each project's current stage. Such checks ensure that no project team is disappointed as they reach the end of a stage and that they have engaged immediately with the PSO to ensure the procedures being used, or planned to be used, are in accordance with requirements. See Part 2 for additional description of the role of a PSO.

Corporate management would need to ensure that all new projects comply with the working standards and practices and all existing projects, irrespective of their current project stage, should use selected procedures. Procedures to be used in any stage should be agreed with the PSO. Senior management should be diligent in directing project managers and their teams to work with and respect the role of the PSO.

Delegated authority and responsibility

It is essential that authority is delegated to the project manager level, because it is at that level where the day-to-day effectiveness of decision-making impacts on project planning, execution and control. The project management working standards and practices require the PSO to monitor and audit project managers, their teams and their projects, and report their findings to the sponsor and/or corporate management. This arrangement should provide corporate management with the surety that the delegated function is being properly applied.

The study, or project, charter is normally the basis for defining the responsibilities/authorities of both the sponsor (appointed by corporate management) and the study (project) manager on each project. The sponsor would be expected to draft the charter.

It is anticipated that authorities are delegated to a project's manager for preparing all project document instruments and in taking responsibility for all, or most, project sign-offs. Where there are constraints on a project's manager regarding his or her responsibility and authority, then the charter is where it should be stated.

External support

The performing organisation should direct and lead the important formative stages of any project — its concept and feasibility development. It is during these stages when various options are investigated to arrive at the 'best option'. If external resources are required, such human skills should only be engaged because there is a skills shortfall or because the performing organisation does not have particular expertise. Except for small projects, such skills should be seconded to work directly with a project team and be located within the performing organisation's premises.

The requirements for external supplies, services or products that are to be procured for a project should be required to comply with a project's procurement strategy and other applicable project management procurement procedures. In the range of external support, at one end some projects may have no requirement to procure anything external, and in the extreme case may require everything to be procured, including a project's management. Supplies, services and products provided to a project should always be procured so that any external human resource, who is a stakeholder, becomes part of the core or secondary project team that is responsible for planning, executing and controlling a project.

The engagement of any external resource for a self-contained package(s) of work should be procured using an RFP (request for proposal). The RFP requires each appointed SP (service provider) to undertake the assigned work using procedures that are the working standards of the performing organisation. This means that SPs are required to provide planning and control information for their work, in the same way as the performing organisation requires such information from contractors. It should also be a requirement that the SP is appointed for one stage only and does not have the expectation of progressing automatically into subsequent stages.

The size, type, complexity and risk to the performing organisation of a project and any other special requirements should determine the form of contract used to procure a contractor. There is no reason to continue to use traditional forms of contract that are no longer appropriate. In many instances these forms have been a significant reason for project failure. Other contracts, such as the NEC (New Engineering Contract), offer a more cooperative form of contract and are not adversarial.

This Handbook has been developed based on the assumption that external services are not normally included in a project's management which, it has been assumed, is provided by the performing organisation. The reason for recommending that the performing organisation retain a project's management is because the performing organisation's personnel are likely to be best placed to understand the organisation's business, operational philosophies and the associated technologies.

Advisory panels

As stated previously, projects should be managed through the nomination and appointment of a single entity — a project manager. If a project is large or complex, or if a project manager is in need of specialist knowledge that he or she cannot claim to have, it may be necessary to appoint a small panel of experts from whom a project manager can obtain advice. The role of such panels should be advisory, not decision-making.

The use of such names as *steering committee* should be avoided particularly, as it is a project manager, the single responsible person, who should determine the strategy and tactics and manage the day-to-day work of a project. The reason for this recommendation is that research indicates that the use of a single entity to manage a project has a very high correlation in achieving successful project outcomes.

Using a project life cycle as the basis for understanding

The life cycle is a good starting point in the explanation of the Handbook procedures. The difficulty encountered is that there is no single life cycle that reflects all projects. Each development area within which projects are found have their own traditional and familiar life cycle and, within each area, there are terms used that are specific to that area. Each project is also likely to have its own terms for the stage deliverables. In other words, there is no such thing as a generic life cycle that covers all project types.

The assumed strategy of the performing organisation in handling a social need (public sector organisation) or a business need (private sector organisation) is that they adopt a life cycle consisting of stages with a deliverable at the end of each stage. As each development sector is likely to have its own life cycle, number of stages, terminology for stages and deliverables, it is not possible to refer to a generic life cycle that accommodates all sectors. The Handbook assumes a capital works life cycle of eight stages; this cycle, the stages and their deliverables are shown as Route Map A in Part 4.

Phases and stages
The eight-stage project life cycle can be aggregated into a three-phase cycle of: (1) pre-investment, (2) definition and (3) implementation. *Pre-investment* accommodates the concept and feasibility stages. *Definition* covers the stages of design phase 1, statutory and legal, design phase 2 and procurement. *Implementation* refers to the two stages of construction and commissioning. The terms 'phases' and 'stages' are not interchangeable; a stage is part of a phase.

The reason why the life cycle from project start to project finish should be divided into phases and stages is so that a project can be better managed. What the concept of life cycle division and subdivision does is break a project into a number of definable chunks, each of which can be scoped and planned, and, very importantly, the deliverables can be specified at the end of each phase and stage. By 'chunking' a project's life cycle the bigger picture of the final deliverable and what a project is required to achieve is not diminished or forgotten. Chunking means that, while continually ensuring a project's management will deliver the predetermined requirements (i.e. the final outcome), a project team and the project stakeholders are afforded the opportunity to focus on the management of the current stage, leading to that stage's deliverable(s).

As the Handbook is likely to be of greatest use to the organisation handling capital projects, it would seem pertinent to use a life cycle that reflects such projects. Accordingly, an eight-stage life cycle has been adopted; other projects, and the organisation handling other types of project, may need to adopt different life cycles.

Whichever cycle is adopted it is still appropriate to use relevant procedures from the Handbook. It is likely that a core of no more than, say, half a dozen procedures would be applicable during any one stage. The procedures used in a current stage should be an amalgam of certain procedures that were used in the preceding stage plus new introductions to satisfy particular aspects of the management requirements of the current stage.

The eight-stage life cycle, project stage names and the stage deliverables referred to in the Handbook are for a capital works development project, and they are

Table 3.2 *The eight-stage life cycle: stage names and the stage deliverables*

Stages	Abbreviation	Deliverable
Concept	CT	Project requirements and information document (PRID)
Feasibility	FS	Feasibility report
Outline design	D1	Design part 1 document
Statutory and legal	SL	Project manager's (PM) certificate
Detailed design	D2	Design part 2 document
Procurement	PR	Letter of appointment or signed contract
Construction	CN	Substantial completion certificate
Commissioning	CO	Operations manual

listed in Table 3.2. Although these stage names and deliverables vary from one organisation to another, it is worth studying the stage names, their sequence, the abbreviations used and the deliverables. The process and the data and tracking documents (standard forms) that are the project management procedures within the Handbook use this lexicon.

Other life cycles

For projects that are not of a capital works development type the stage names may well change, but the project management procedures within a particular stage ostensibly still apply. For instance, a not untypical sequence of stage names for an IT project is listed in the first column in Table 3.3. The second column in the table gives the capital works life cycle used in this Handbook, and the horizontal shaded bands show the stage connections between the two different types of project. The capital work stages that are not included in a band are generally not applicable to an IT project. It is invariably found that the procedures that would be used in the PR stage of an IT project would be the same, or very similar, to those used for a capital works project. Based on this example it can be seen that there is much more that is common in comparing different life cycles than there are potential differences between different types of project.

Gateways and deliverables

Each life cycle stage should be viewed as having a gateway at the end of each stage. The inclusion of gateways ensures that projects have control points that determine project compliance and project progression. Progression to a subsequent stage without having satisfactorily passed an audit or some other means of approving compliance with the Handbook's procedures would be the basis for censure and

Table 3.3 *Comparison between IT and capital works projects*

IT project	Capital works project
CT: Concept	CT: Concept
FS: Feasibility	FS: Feasibility
	D1: Outline design
	SL: Statutory and legal
	D2: Detail design
PR: Procurement	PR: Procurement
CA: Contract analysis	
SC: Systems configuration	CN: Construction
SI: Site implementation	
TG: Testing	CO: Commissioning
HO: Handover	

possible delay. The gateway concept, if used proactively, can significantly improve the management and successful outcome of a project.

It would normally be a Project Support Office's (PSO) responsibility (see Part 2) to ensure that at the start of each stage the correct project management procedures to be used have been identified. The PSO would also be responsible for checking the proper application of the procedures, and before a project can be cleared through a gateway to the next stage a project should satisfy all compliance checks.

Part 4 of the Handbook contains route maps of the life cycle and the procedures that can be used during a stage. Route Map A shows the capital works life cycle, the stages and the deliverable at the end of each stage. The Handbook's procedures support this life cycle. The stage deliverables are captioned in the form of a flag at the end of each stage. The terms used are those that have been adopted for use in the Handbook, but the holder, or corporate organisation, can of course adopt his or her own terms or create new terms.

A facsimile of Route Map A — capital works life cycle, its stages and the deliverable at each gateway — is shown in Fig. 3.1.

Procedures during a stage

The relationship between the life cycle and the procedures to be used in a stage can perhaps be best explained by looking at an example. The flow diagram in Fig. 3.2 shows the project management procedures for the CT (concept) stage of a project.

The flow diagram for the CT stage shows 15 procedures in a particular sequence, commencing with 002 (project registration) and ending with 124 (PRID). Within this sequence is a block of eight procedures that together are the core strategy for

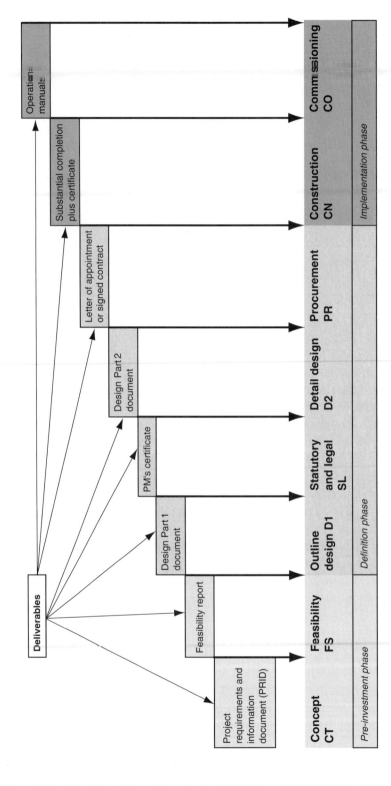

Fig. 3.1   A facsimile of Route Map A — capital works life cycle, its stages and the deliverable at each gateway.

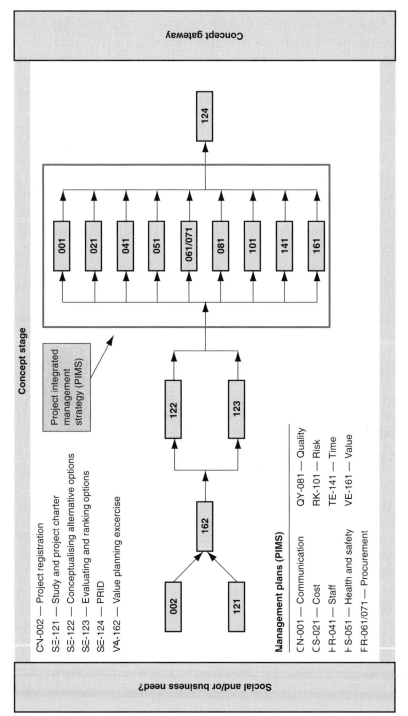

Fig. 3.2 Project management procedures for the CT stage of a project.

planning the management of a project: these eight procedures are referred to as the PIMS (project integrated management strategy). PIMS normally appear in subsequent stages because the applicable procedures within PIMS need to be re-applied to capture the state of a project in each stage.

Some of the PIMS procedures may not be required for a project. For instance, if a project is being undertaken using internal resources without recourse to any form of external service or purchase then there is no procurement activity and hence procedures PR-061 and PR-071 are not required.

Assuming corporate management have responded to a project opportunity by indicating a first-stage evaluation (concept) study, then by initiating procedure CN-001 the study becomes registered and funds and resources allocated. Use of procedure SE-121 creates the *study charter* that documents the assigned study manager authorised to deliver the PRID. Procedures SE-122 and SE-123 give guidance on how the alternative options that would satisfy the requirements should be handled and on how to compare and rank each of the options, respectively. As stated, PIMS is that group of procedures that cover each of the knowledge areas that provide the overriding strategies for each knowledge area and their respective management plans. In other words, PIMS is the core set of procedures documenting what has to be managed and how it is planned to manage. The concept stage is completed when the PRID, procedure SE-124, is signed-off. At that point the study should have reached the concept gateway.

Project management skills transfer

A structured training programme in project management for relevant corporate staff engaged on project-related work should be provided (see procedure HR-044, p. 3-149). Staff training in using the project management process and the application of the Handbook procedures would normally be the responsibility of a PSO. Because training utilises a high level of PSO effort, the training courses provided should be undertaken for selected participants.

A related role of a PSO is to assess individual ability and identify individuals who should progress through the various levels from, say, 'knowledge level' to 'expert level'. It is essential that skills transfer be made available to those staff in the performing organisation who are more likely to provide the greatest benefit to the reform process and in doing so demonstrate the application of 'best practice' project management to their project work. Such skilled individuals can then be seen as role models for others to emulate.

It is normally a PSO responsibility to ensure through auditing that all project managers are applying 'due process' as set out in a project management handbook. If necessary, it can also be a PSO responsibility to independently report to corporate management on the performance of projects and their teams in the application of 'due process'.

Procedure register

Ref. No.	Title	Pages	Issue date	Revision
Communications procedures (CN)				
CN-001	Communications management plan	3	01 Mar 04	0
CN-002	Project registration	5	01 Mar 04	0
CN-003	Initiate a workshop	6	01 Mar 04	0
CN-004	Project manual	5	01 Mar 04	0
CN-005	Project coding and filing system	4	01 Mar 04	0
CN-006	Performance reviews (services)	5	01 Mar 04	0
CN-007	Performance reviews (works)	5	01 Mar 04	0
CN-008	Earned value management	6	01 Mar 04	0
CN-009	Change report and change order	5	01 Mar 04	0
CN-010	Project auditing	6	01 Mar 04	0
CN-011	Serve a way-leave notice	5	01 Mar 04	0
CN-012	Vary a development plan	5	01 Mar 04	0
Cost procedures (CS)				
CS-021	Cost management plan	3	01 Mar 04	0
CS-022	Budget type versus project stage	6	01 Mar 04	0
CS-023	Cost breakdown structure (CBS)	4	01 Mar 04	0
CS-024	Budgeted cost of work scheduled (BCWS)	4	01 Mar 04	0
Human resources procedures (HR)				
HR-041	Staff management plan	5	01 Mar 04	0
HR-042	Project organisation and team roles	6	01 Mar 04	0
HR-043	Role assignments and appointments	7	01 Mar 04	0
HR-044	Staff training programme	6	01 Mar 04	0
HR-045	Selection, appraisal and reward	4	01 Mar 04	0
Health and safety procedures (HS)				
HS-051	Health and safety management plan	4	01 Mar 04	0
Procurement procedures (PT)				
PT-061	Procurement management plan (services)	6	01 Mar 04	0
PT-062	Advertise to procure a service	7	01 Mar 04	0
PT-063	'Request for proposal' document	5	01 Mar 04	0
PT-064	Prequalify potential service provider candidates	6	01 Mar 04	0
PT-065	Holding a bidders' conference	4	01 Mar 04	0
PT-066	Evaluate external service proposals	6	01 Mar 04	0
PT-067	Specifying time and price requirements (services)	4	01 Mar 04	0
PT-071	Procurement management plan (works)	4	01 Mar 04	0
PT-072	Request to participate (works)	8	01 Mar 04	0
PT-073	Request for tender (works)	5	01 Mar 04	0
PT-074	Appointing a contractor	7	01 Mar 04	0
PT-075	Recording the works	5	01 Mar 04	0
PT-076	Communications during the works	5	01 Mar 04	0

Ref. No.	Title	Pages	Issue date	Revision
PT-077	Reporting on the works	4	01 Mar 04	0
PT-078	Works measurement and payment certification	8	01 Mar 04	0
Quality procedures (QY)				
QY-081	Quality management plan	4	01 Mar 04	0
QY-082	Product quality assurance	5	01 Mar 04	0
QY-083	Quality improvement response	9	01 Mar 04	0
Risk procedures (RK)				
RK-101	Risk management plan	4	01 Mar 04	0
RK-102	Identify and qualify risk sources	6	01 Mar 04	0
RK-103	Quantitative risk assessment	6	01 Mar 04	0
RK-104	Risk response plan	6	01 Mar 04	0
Scope procedures (SE)				
SE-121	Study and project charter	6	01 Mar 04	0
SE-122	Conceptualising alternative options	5	01 Mar 04	0
SE-123	Evaluating and ranking options	5	01 Mar 04	0
SE-124	Project requirements and information document (PRID)	3	01 Mar 04	0
SE-125	Work breakdown structure (WBS)	4	01 Mar 04	0
SE-131	Delivering the operations manual	2	01 Mar 04	0
Time procedures (TE)				
TE-141	Time schedule management plan	3	01 Mar 04	0
TE-142	Project planning	3	01 Mar 04	0
TE-143	Estimating activity duration	4	01 Mar 04	0
TE-144	Scheduling the plan	5	01 Mar 04	0
Value procedures (VA)				
VA-161	Value management plan	4	01 Mar 04	0
VA-162	Value planning exercise	5	01 Mar 04	0
VA-163	Value engineering exercise	13	01 Mar 04	0
VA-164	Value review	4	01 Mar 04	0

Communications procedures

This section contains twelve procedures that deal with certain aspects of project communications and their management. The procedures are:

CN-001   Communications management plan
CN-002   Project registration
CN-003   Initiate a workshop
CN-004   Project manual
CN-005   Project coding and filing system
CN-006   Performance reviews (services)
CN-007   Performance reviews (works)
CN-008   Earned value management
CN-009   Change report and change order
CN-010   Project auditing
CN-011   Serve a way-leave notice
CN-012   Vary a development plan

A brief overview of each procedure and what each procedure sets out to achieve is given below.

CN-001: Communications management plan

For any project, procedure CN-001 sets out to determine what should be the communication network and who should obtain what project information, in which format, with what frequency, and what each person or organisation is expected to do with the information once it has been received. CN-001 also provides a plan for document style ('document' here covering a range of productions from e-mails to reports), updating and revising information, and a project filing system (see procedure CN-005). The outcome of this procedure is the project's *com-plan*.

CN-002: Project registration

Before any corporate initiative is taken that commits a significant expenditure of effort to investigate the response to a need or opportunity and/or shall commit the organisation to undertake a project, it is necessary that such investigations or projects be registered. Registering ensures that a job number is provided, against which resources can be allocated, a sponsor assigned, and a study/project manager identified and appointed to lead the management process. The outcome of this procedure is an official job number and approval to get started.

CN-003: Initiate a workshop

A major aspect of successful project management is drawing together, from time to time, all the relevant stakeholders in a project to create, to solve and to decide on certain aspects of a project's scope, risk, cost, etc. Workshops, facilitated by someone without project bias, are considered to be the most appropriate way of providing all relevant personnel with the opportunity to make their contribution, to add to the contribution of others, and to debate and question matters that are of concern.

CN-004: Project manual

For most corporate endeavours, studies and projects that require the assignment of more than two or three people a study manual or project manual needs to be developed by the study/project manager. The manual is the basis for communicating the project scope, constraints, team roles, responsibilities and authorities, and other important factors to the team and other stakeholders. The manual should always be current and up to date and should be held by all appropriate stakeholders.

CN-005: Project coding and filing system

All studies and projects should have an identifier (job number) and a coding hierarchy that facilitates the filing of various types of communication and information. Procedure CN-005 provides a format that could be used by the organisation or individual not having such a system, or could be helpful to those seeking inspiration on developing their own communication system.

CN-006: Performance reviews (services)

This procedure sets out a methodology for establishing the means of, and reporting on, tracking performance and forecasting the out-turn cost of a procured external service that is providing support to the project owner or performing organisation. The procedure is predicated on ensuring that the requirements for performance reporting of an SP (service provider) are clearly specified in the associated RFP (request for proposal) document.

CN-007: Performance reviews (works)

This procedure is almost identical to that set out in procedure CN-006, but is for use where the external entity is a contractor, supplier or vendor that is providing equipment, materials or specialist effort associated with works contracts.

CN-008: Earned value management

This procedure is complimentary to CN-006 and CN-007; it explains earned value and its application. Earned value is the recognised preferred method of measuring how much work has been accomplished on a project or any subproject or definable package of work. Procedure CN-008 sets out to demystify the theory and show how it is used to assess an owner's project team activities, SP's work actions and a contractor's scope of work. It shows how performance to date is measured and, based on the result of past trends, how to forecast time and cost to completion.

CN-009: Change report and change order

Variations, or more commonly changes, to a project need to be proactively identified and assessed. This procedure has the potential for two steps. The first step requires a change report to be prepared from which the project manager either accepts or rejects the planned change. The second step may require the preparation of a change order. An accepted change report generates an official change order; a rejected change report is used to inform the initiator that the potential change has been rejected and why.

CN-010: Project auditing

This procedure calls for the independent assessment of a project at each stage in its cycle from concept to commissioning, and is normally undertaken by two PSO facilitators. Project auditing is the means for checking and ensuring that the project management working standards (corporate handbook of procedures) is current and up to date, the appropriate procedures have been/are being applied, and the outcomes of procedural application are meeting best-practice standards and the project's requirements.

CN-011: Serve a way-leave notice

This procedure is for use by public authorities. It provides a protocol for handling the project relationship between a local authority and landowners when the local authority plans to cross private land with a works that is required to satisfy a social need, such as a road, pathway or pipeline. The administration of the way-leave procedure needs to be planned and be effective as insufficient lead time and lack of proper documentation can lead to project delay and frustration. The steps in this procedure and the time duration of each step must be appropriately reflected in a project's plan and schedule (see procedures TE-142 and TE-144).

CN-012: Vary a development plan

This procedure is for use by the public authorities. This procedure addresses three aspects relating to the use of land for any project that is to be located at the surface level or just below surface level. To satisfy public concerns about land use and to comply with a public authority's need to inform the public and keep them informed, the first aspect that this procedure deals with is confirming concurrence with, or notifying variation(s) to, a prescribed development plan. The second aspect that the procedure records is all matters pertaining to the impact that a project under consideration may have on the environment. The third aspect covered by this procedure relates to documenting land purchases by agreement and by compulsory purchase.

CN-001: Communications management plan

Policy

This procedure should be used at the commencement of all potential projects to plan the creation, collection, dissemination, storage and circulation of information that is formed by, or through, the existence of a significant project.

The outcomes from the communications management plan for each project need to become a section or appendix within that project's 'project manual' (see procedure CN-004). A copy of a project's manual should be provided to each stakeholder associated with that project. It should be the responsibility of each project manager, or the designated team member, to create the content for the document that becomes the communications management plan, abbreviated to *com-plan*.

The com-plan for a study should be developed in the concept stage and the com-plan for a project should be developed for and during the feasibility stage and updated as a project progresses through its life cycle.

It is essential that a project's com-plan reflects the organisational breakdown structure (OBS) by ensuring that responsibilities and reporting relationships are compatible with the way in which information needs to be created, transmitted, received, etc. The com-plan should be the primary system that determines, enacts and controls the flow of communications; an inadequate com-plan can lead to a poorly administered project and could be the cause of serious difficulties being encountered.

The preferred first-choice technology to be used in all project communications should be electronic (e.g. electronic documents, electronic drawings, electronic presentations). The second-choice technology would normally be workshops of project stakeholders assembled to address such matters as scope of work, methodologies, risk, value, schedules, budget costs and exception matters such as safety. The third-choice technology is likely to cover a range of methods, such as paper documents and meetings, which are normally determined by need, the technology availability, staff experience, simplicity of project, and so on.

Where possible a project should use a dedicated electronic model, such as Primavera Expedition, for the handling of information and communications. For the larger project, the one having many stakeholders, and with numerous documents and an extensive communications network, such a model is likely to be a prerequisite and should be decided on as early as possible in the life of a project.

Outcome

The outcome of the com-plan should include, but not be limited to, the following:

- an identification of a project's stakeholders and an analysis of their roles within a project
- a communications filing structure that reflects the breakdown of a project or some other significant aspect that is unique to a project
- the template styles to be used when transmitting letters, internal memos, faxes, e-mails, etc.
- the methodologies to be used in gathering and receiving information

- the distribution system that sets out what communication is presented in what format, goes to whom and is copied to whom, under what means of transmission, and within what time constraint
- the method to be used in updating and revising information and the attendant system for onward transmittal, circulation and/or storage.

In developing these outcomes it is important that any templates used are compatible with templates from other project management areas. For instance, in developing the com-plan for a project it might be found useful to superimpose communication flows on the project's responsibility assignment matrix (RAM) (see procedure HR-042).

Process

Reference to *project manager* can also mean *study manager* when a project is at the pre-investment phase. *Stakeholder* means any party, or entity, within the performing organisation, and it will also mean other external entities and statutory authorities that may impact on, or be impacted by, the project under consideration.

The following process should be used:

Person	Responsibility
Project manager	Responsible for developing the com-plan for a project. A project's manager may designate a member of a project team to undertake this task; in such circumstances the project manager signs-off on the actions of the other.
	The collection of all input documents needed for the com-plan should be recorded in box 1 on the form CN-001/1.
	Once the com-plan is complete, the responsible project manager completes box 2 and signs-off the form CN-001/1. A copy of the com-plan should be circulated to each named stakeholder and/or those individuals named and incorporated within the 'project manual'.

Box 1

Project/Study name _____   Job ref. # [   ]

Project/Study manager _____   Sponsor _____

Current project stage   ☐ CT   ☐ FS   ☐ D1

- Input documents to the com-plan

Documents	Availability Yes	No	Explain
_____	☐	☐	_____
_____	☐	☐	_____
_____	☐	☐	_____
_____	☐	☐	_____
_____	☐	☐	_____

Signed _____ (project manager)   Date _____

Box 2

Com-plan summary

	Yes	No	
- Project stakeholders Stakeholder register attached	☐	☐	Explanation
- Project filing system Document attached	☐	☐	Explanation
- Document styles Document attached	☐	☐	Explanation
- Receiving, transmitting and distribution system Document attached	☐	☐	Explanation
- Updating and revising information Document attached	☐	☐	Explanation

Com-plan circulated by [_____]   Date _____

Circulated to

Signed _____ (project manager)   Date _____

CN-002: Project registration

Policy

This procedure is the first procedure to be used on all newly identified opportunities by the performing organisation.

It should be used when senior management generally agrees that there is an opportunity and either a study should be carried out to investigate and document solution options or, less commonly, when a project needs to be initiated to create expeditious change. The identifier of an opportunity can be anyone within the corporate body, an external adviser, a customer, a financial agency or any other potential stakeholder.

If initiating a study, or a project, is the generally accepted response to the opportunity then senior management need to identify and assign a sponsor who is required to kick-off the initial action covered by procedure CN-002. The sponsor can be any individual within the performing organisation who senior management are prepared to entrust the direction of the study/project to.

It is a corporate requirement that an investigation and study of all possible solution options (alternatives) needs to be a prerequisite to initiating the subsequent stages of any potential project and prior to a commitment to allocate major capital funding. Only in very extenuating circumstances can this requirement be circumvented. It is always possible that none of the options studied may be found to be technically and/or financially attractive. This is referred to as the 'do nothing option'. However, when this is not the case it is likely that the most feasible and economically attractive option identified from the study is likely to become the eventual project to be designed, implemented and commissioned.

The sponsor's role is to kick off the study or project by complying with this procedure. The kick off includes identifying who the study (project) manager should be, creating a study or project charter for the manager, and ensuring that the manager is provided with the resources necessary to undertake the work to meet the requirements. Thereafter the sponsor has the role of keeping a 'watching brief' on the study (project), but the primary responsibility for auditing and checking the study (project) performance, and the processes being used, should be the project support office (PSO). The PSO needs to report status, etc., to the sponsor on an on going basis set by either the calendar or by exception (as needed) reporting.

In conjunction with defining the sponsor's role, senior management are required to delegate any powers and authorities to the sponsor that he or she may need. This should normally include responsibility and authority for ratifying the financial budget for the study (project) and sign-off authorisation for all payments to be made against the budget.

Outcome

The outcome of this procedure should be a registering of the study or project to be undertaken. By registering the study (project) a 'communication structure' is established against which future transmissions, documents, etc., need to be referenced.

Another outcome, if it is required, is the identification and assignment of individuals who have the necessary skills to supplement a team of corporate personnel. These skills may be obtained through service provider firms or companies, vendor organisations, implementation contractors, etc., and would be a response to an in-house skills shortfall.

Yet another outcome is the initiation of the concept stage of the project when a series of options should be assessed for order-of-magnitude comparisons.

A requirement of the project management process is the delegation of the senior management function. The function and powers delegated, initially from senior management to the sponsor, need in turn to be transferred to the study/project manager with whatever reservations are felt to be necessary and appropriate by the sponsor. This transfer needs to be recorded and documented in the study or project charter (see procedure SE-121).

Process

Reference to a *study* will mean when the matter under consideration, the scheme, is at the pre-investment phase, i.e. the concept and/or the feasibility stages. *Study manager* will also mean *project manager* when a scheme bypasses the pre-investment phase and is taken directly into the outline design or a subsequent stage. *Sponsor* means the individual within the performing organisation who has been identified by senior management as the person who will be the study manager's link to senior management.

The following process should be used:

Person	Responsibility
Corporate	Having identified that there is an opportunity or need to be satisfied and the response being the possible launching of a project, senior management communicates the requirement to the appropriate department or unit, referred to as the 'performing organisation'. Corporate or department management identify and assign a sponsor to the study.
Sponsor	With advice from the PSO, if required, notes the assigned job number to the new opportunity and discusses the study with the person who would be best suited to manage the study (i.e. the study manager). The sponsor completes box 1 on form CN-002/1 and sends the original to the study manager and retains a copy for the PSO and the sponsor's own file.
Study manager	Performs an assessment of the study resource needs that should be required to obtain order-of-magnitude schemes that could respond to the need. Once this assessment has been carried out the study manager completes box 2 on form CN-002/1 and sends a copy of the form to the sponsor.
Corporate	Senior management delegate powers and function to the sponsor for the project under consideration.
Sponsor	Creates a study charter (see procedure SE-121) that documents the agreed delegation of powers and function to the study manager.

Study manager	The personnel resources are assembled to undertake a concept study of the options that would possibly satisfy the social need. The investigation is carried out to a level of accuracy that would allow comparative evaluations of the options and would provide a more definitive focus on the order-of-magnitude 'best option'. The best option may then be the basis for a next stage 'feasibility assessment'.

The appropriate data, analysis and finds are contained within the outcome report, the project requirements and information document (PRID) (see procedure SE-124).

(See procedure SE-122 for protocols to be followed in analysing options to identify the best or preferred option.)

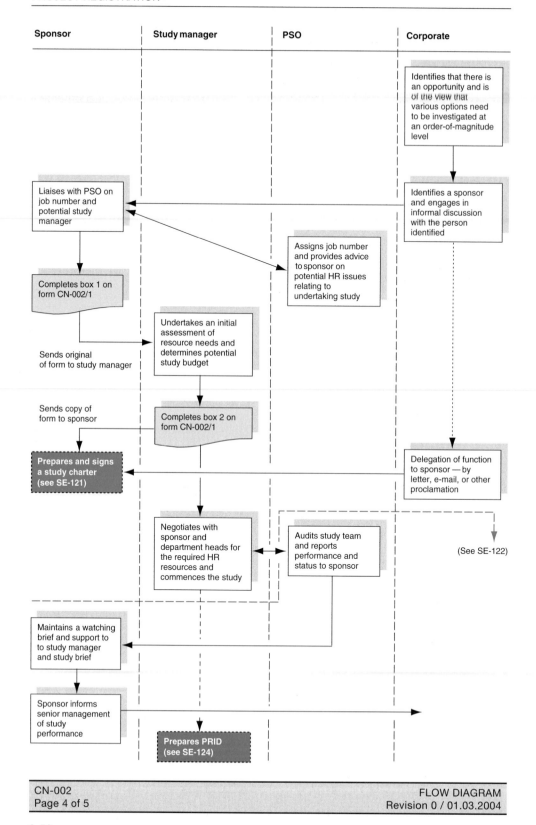

Sponsor	Study manager	PSO	Corporate

Identifies that there is an opportunity and is of the view that various options need to be investigated at an order-of-magnitude level

Liaises with PSO on job number and potential study manager

Identifies a sponsor and engages in informal discussion with the person identified

Assigns job number and provides advice to sponsor on potential HR issues relating to undertaking study

Completes box 1 on form CN-002/1

Undertakes an initial assessment of resource needs and determines potential study budget

Sends original of form to study manager

Sends copy of form to sponsor

Completes box 2 on form CN-002/1

Prepares and signs a study charter (see SE-121)

Delegation of function to sponsor — by letter, e-mail, or other proclamation

Negotiates with sponsor and department heads for the required HR resources and commences the study

Audits study team and reports performance and status to sponsor

(See SE-122)

Maintains a watching brief and support to to study manager and study brief

Sponsor informs senior management of study performance

Prepares PRID (see SE-124)

CN-002	FLOW DIAGRAM
Page 4 of 5	Revision 0 / 01.03.2004

Box 1

Scheme name _____ Job ref # [_____]

Identifier of social need _____ Sponsor _____

Proposed study manager _____ Assigned ☐ Yes ☐ No

Constraints on study/study manager

Signed-off _____ (sponsor) Date _____

Box 2

HR resources needed and budget for concept study

Name	Division/organisation	Hours	Date	Amount

Other external assistance (specify)

Total cost of concept study £ [_____]

Time schedule for concept study

Start date [_____] Finish date [_____]

Significant milestones (describe)

Other important issues

Signed-off _____ (study manager) Date _____

CN-003: Initiate a workshop

Policy

This procedure should be used when there is a need to hold a project stakeholder workshop. The general purpose of a workshop is to obtain the collective response from all stakeholders at a single gathering to a significant project issue or to advance some aspect of a project's development.

The persons nominated to attend a workshop should be those individuals with hands-on experience of the project; and not necessarily the most senior management personnel. There may, however, be a need to engage individual senior management where strategic or corporate input is needed.

Workshops should be the modus operandi for creating responses to a wide range of issues confronting project teams. The issue for which a workshop is initiated may be a general one, such as to determine the content of a request for proposal (RFP), or it may be specific, such as to undertake a quantitative risk assessment.

Workshops should be referenced in accordance with the stage of the project to which they apply. Workshops, for a single project, should be numbered numerically, starting at 1 with the first workshop. Workshops suggested by service providers (SPs) or any other external stakeholder need to be sanctioned and managed by the performing organisation. Such workshops should be referenced with an 'E', or some other suitable suffix.

Workshops must be very well planned. As an input to each workshop a brief document of relevant information to all attendees is recommended. When available the document should be sent to all attendees so that it is in their possession at least 24 hours before the workshop commences.

Workshops that are planned to have a large attendance of performing organisation personnel and external stakeholders might best be held at a neutral location. A neutral location may also be appropriate when the workshop has to crucially capture the undivided attention of the attendees or is needed to bond the disparate elements of a project team. Over-nighting at the workshop venue may be necessary, particularly for value management workshops which can be up to 5 days long.

An experienced person from the project support office (PSO) should normally be assigned to facilitate a workshop. The facilitator should ensure that all relevant tools and techniques are used during the workshop. The output of each workshop shall be a concluding document that reflects the workshop proceedings, the findings and the actions to be taken with regard to the issue under consideration.

Outcome

This procedure initiates the process for holding and facilitating project workshops. This procedure deals with the initiation of the workshop and not the process of what happens during the course of the workshop.

Each project workshop provides a forum for drawing together of knowledgeable stakeholders, both within the performing organisation and in other external organisations, to engage, within a single location, in a structured process that is managed by a facilitator.

The workshop process should be directed towards resolving or agreeing what action to take on whatever was the predetermined issue or initial purpose for holding the workshop.

Process

Project manager can also mean *study manager* when the workshop is held in the concept or feasibility stages of a project. The project manager is the individual who is identified within the project charter. The project manager has the primary responsibility for deciding on the need for workshops and when they should be held.

The following process should be used:

Person	Responsibility
Project manager	Identifies that there is a need to hold a project workshop and completes box 1 of the standard form CN-003/1, and sends a copy of the form to the PSO.
(Corporate)	The project manager considers an off-site location versus an in-house location for the workshop. May seek the assistance of corporate if an off-site location is preferred. If an in-house venue is suitable then the project manager makes the necessary arrangements.
	The project manager develops a briefing paper for the required workshop (see exhibit CN-003/2).
(PSO)	If required, the project manager liases with the PSO regarding the structure and content of the workshop briefing paper.
Project manager	Decides on workshop objectives, attendee stakeholders, date, start time, etc. The project manager contacts the stakeholder organisations and/or departments, who nominate appropriate participants to be invited to the workshop. Alternatively, the project manager decides who is to be contacted and makes arrangements directly with each participant.
	The project manager is responsible for developing, preparing and sending to all participants, including the PSO facilitator, whatever pre-workshop documentation may be required.
PSO	The assigned facilitator initiates the plan to lead the workshop. The facilitator checks the list of materials and equipment resources and sets a pre-workshop reminder to take action on the plan. Advises the project manager of the facilitator's requirements to run a workshop.
Project manager	Completes box 2 on form CN-003/1 once all potential attendees have been notified and the pre-workshop documentation has been sent. The form is filed within the project files.

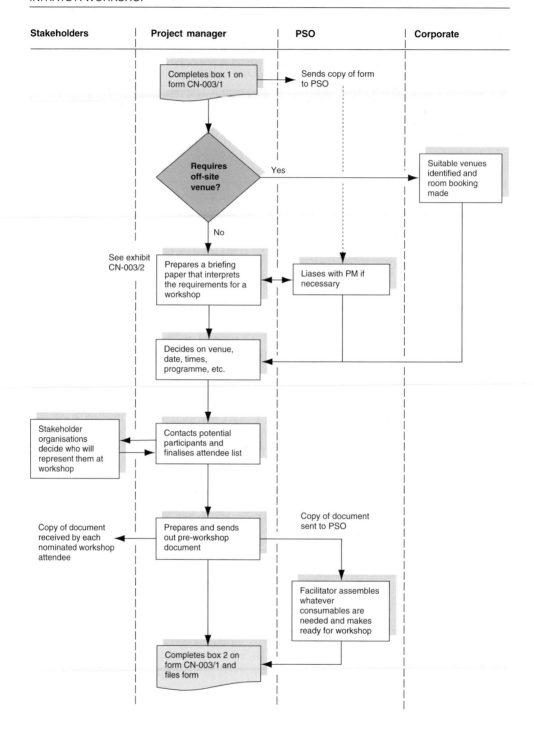

Stakeholders	Project manager	PSO	Corporate

Completes box 1 on form CN-003/1

Sends copy of form to PSO

Requires off-site venue?

Yes

No

Suitable venues identified and room booking made

See exhibit CN-003/2

Prepares a briefing paper that interprets the requirements for a workshop

Liases with PM if necessary

Decides on venue, date, times, programme, etc.

Stakeholder organisations decide who will represent them at workshop

Contacts potential participants and finalises attendee list

Copy of document received by each nominated workshop attendee

Prepares and sends out pre-workshop document

Copy of document sent to PSO

Facilitator assembles whatever consumables are needed and makes ready for workshop

Completes box 2 on form CN-003/1 and files form

Box 1

Project name _____	Job ref. # [ ]

Project manager _____

Current stage of project   ☐ CT   ☐ FS   ☐ D1   ☐ SL   ☐ D2   ☐ PR   ☐ CN   ☐ CO

Workshop issue(s)

Preferred date for workshop   [ ] Earliest   [ ] Latest

Box 2

Workshop code number _____   Assigned facilitator _____

Briefing document produced   Yes ☐   Date [ ]   No ☐

If no _____ (reason)

Venue   ☐ External   ☐ In-house   Agreed date [ ]   Start time [ ]

Location [ ]   Booked by [ ]

In-room equipment required

Invited attendees (if required use back of Form)

Name	*Organisation/section*

Pre-workshop document

☐ Drafted   ☐ Signed-off by _____   Date _____

☐ Checked   ☐ Signed by _____   Date _____

☐ Dispatched   ☐ Signed by _____   Date _____

PROJECT SUPPORT OFFICE

Briefing paper
Project X
Workshop #5

The project manager of project X is interested in investigating the issues associated with the following matters:

- the contractors newest revision of the construction programme which is expected to be submitted in a few weeks;
- the anticipated operability of the plant on hand-over to the owner.

To facilitate such an internal investigation it is planned to hold an initial 1 day brainstorming workshop in order to identify and quantify project issues/risks/opportunities that may arise between now and the commissioning date which it is mooted will extend from August 2002 to November 2002. A tentative date for the workshop has been set for Wednesday 26 September 2001. The proposed venue will be a large conference room in the owner's head-office.

Workshop location

The workshop should be held in a proper training room that is complete with a number of desks, chairs and flipcharts, and walls suitable for mounting large sheets. The large training room in Block Y would be an ideal location. Large felt-tip pens, large yellow post-its, blue-tack, flip chart sheets, and paper and pencils will need to be available. Within the room should be drawings, tender documents, feasibility reports and all other historical reference material which pertain to this project.

Refreshments and a sandwich lunch should be pre-arranged so that the team will not be interrupted and can work continuously on the day's events.

Workshop attendees

Only those who have worked on or are working on the project and who have a detailed knowledge of the two matters under consideration should be nominated to attend. Those in attendance should have been selected because they can speak authoritatively and deal effectively with these project matters. They should, of course, be selected because of the undoubted contribution they will be able to make to the workshop process.

It is planned that person z of the Project Support Office (PSO) will facilitate the workshop.

Pre-workshop action

Person z would spend part or all of the proceeding day studying layout drawings and the documentation available for this project. In particular, a copy of the contractor's latest revision of construction programme and the process steps leading up to hand-over along with whatever supporting information the constructor wishes to provide should be available.

The contractor will be required to provide each nominated attendee with a copy of all information that they plan to submit for discussion at the workshop. This information should be made available to the attendees at the latest two days before the workshop date.

Workshop deliverables

It is planned that the workshop will provide the leaders of the projects with the following:

- an identification of any and all project issues between now and the end of hook-up — these issues will require to be classified so that a limited range of response types can be identified;
- a qualitative evaluation of the identified issues;
- a plan that could be followed by which the issues will be handled;
- a management plan to be used by the project team for the remainder of the project work until hook-up.

Workshop process

The facilitator's plan for the workshop is to work through the following process:

1. briefly explain the targets of the workshop and the planned process;
2. the contractor presents an explanation of the tabled construction programme;
3. the attendees are set-up in appropriate sub-groups to discuss/debate a part of the project and its associated programme (each sub-group should have a balanced mix of owner/ service provider/contractor);
4. assemble in plenary session to listen to each sub-groups' issues and document an aggregated list of all issues raised;
5. categorise the issues as low/medium/high;
6. develop a response plan to each issue category;
7. agree the content of a management plan and immediate action to be recommended to the owner;
8. the contractor presents an explanation of the physical work to be undertaken between September 2001 and hand-over to the owner;
9. items 3 to 8 inclusive are repeated but this time are undertaken in association with the physical components to hand-over and the planned operability of the completed facility.

Other comments

1. There have been three workshops already held for this project. #1 was a strategy workshop, #2 was an EIS workshop, and #3 was an operations and maintenance workshop. Workshop #4 to be held on Wednesday 12 September 2001, which will be a companion to the planned workshop, will deal with construction costs to completion and include claims assessment. Therefore, this workshop is being referred to as #5.

2. Each attendee will be expected to bring to the workshop the personal files that they have on this project that could have a bearing on their input and effectiveness.

3. A 09:00 h start is proposed, and it is likely that the workshop could last 10 hours — be prepared for a long day. No one should be nominated who has not made arrangements to devote themselves totally to achieving the owner's requirements and interests for this workshop.

CN-004: Project manual

Policy

It should be a mandatory requirement for all projects, except very small projects where only a few people are involved, to have a *project manual*. A project manual is a document that provides common understanding to each stakeholder on the standards and procedures that are to be used by all entities involved in the project. The volume and content of a project manual should be commensurate with the size and complexity of the project, and the level of management that is needed to plan, execute and control the associated project activities.

When a future project is in the early stages of its development, the manual should be referred to as a *study manual*. The study manual serves the same purpose as the project manual. Hereinafter, this procedure uses the term 'project manual', but the terms 'project manual' and 'study manual' are synonymous.

A project manual is a document developed by each project's manager and/or team and it is a distillation and tailoring of all appropriate and necessary project management procedures contained within the corporate handbook of project management procedures. It is from the handbook that project manual authors find guidance to create project manuals that are designed specifically for each project.

A handbook of project management procedures is the corporate policies and guidelines that are used for developing policies and procedural needs for managing a broad range of projects. A handbook contains information that should be privy to only corporate personnel and it would generally be inappropriate to copy or divulge the handbook's content in whole, or in part, to external and third parties. A project manual, on the other hand, is a document for use by all stakeholders, including external and third parties. If appropriate, a *confidentiality agreement* should be drafted and each recipient of a project's manual required to sign this agreement (see exhibit CN-004/3).

The manual needs to be updated and re-issued as required and as a response to changes and revisions to its content. Project stakeholders should be required to have a current revision of any project's manual.

Outcome

The outcome of this procedure is a document, referred to as the project manual, which is used by the project manager to communicate primary project data to all stakeholders engaged in the project and to ensure consistent working standards by the project team. See exhibit CN-004/2 for an example of the likely content of a project manual.

The project manual should contain, but not be limited to:

(1) the product and deliverables of the project, including constraints, milestones, control points, etc.
(2) the approach to be used in carrying out the project work and in achieving the deliverables
(3) conditions of assignment of the project team and external entities
(4) project schedule and project budget
(5) communications management plan (see procedure CN-001)

(6) the applicable range of specially tailored project management procedures that should be used on the project under consideration using the corporate handbook as a guide.

Item 6 can be considered as an appendix in a project's manual. However on a large, complex project it is likely to be more appropriate to contain item 6 material in a separate document (e.g. within a volume 2 of the project manual).

Process

Reference to *project manager* can also mean *study manager* when the project is at the pre-design stages. *Stakeholder* means any party, or entity, that is a core project resource, and it will also mean any secondary or tertiary party that impacts on, or is impacted by, the project under consideration.

The following process should be used:

Person	Responsibility
Project manager	Develops the project's project manual or, when necessary, designates a project team member to undertake this task; in such circumstances the project manager signs-off on the actions of the other.
	The collection of all input documents needed to create the project manual is recorded in box 1 on form CN-004/1.
	Once the project manual is complete, the project manager completes box 2, signs-off form CN-004/1 and circulates a copy of the manual to each stakeholder or each identified project manual holder.

Box 1

Project/Study name _____		Job ref. # [_____]

Project/Study manager _____ Sponsor _____

Current stage of project   ☐ CI   ☐ FS   ☐ DI

- Input documents to the Project/Study Manual

Documents   *Availability*
                                               Yes   No   Why?

Project communications plan _____   ☐   ☐   _____
_____   ☐   ☐   _____
_____   ☐   ☐   _____
_____   ☐   ☐   _____

Other comments

Signed _____ (project manager)   Date _____

Box 2

- Project/Study Manual summary

List of contents	*Title*	*Prepared by*
Section No.		
Appendices		

- Control copies of Project Manual sent to/held by

Copy number	*Issued to and signed by (name)*	*Organisation/section*	*Revision — date*

Signed _____ (project manager)   Date_____

CONTENTS PAGE

CONFIDENTIALITY AGREEMENT

As a holder of the project manual for this project I will maintain all project information in strict confidence unless and until such time as such information is or becomes known publicly. I will not be the initiator, or in any way be responsible for, the information contained within the project manual becoming public knowledge.

I will not, without the prior written permission of the project manager, furnish to any third party any materials embodying or made by use of any information in this project manual. Nor shall I use any such information for other than project purposes, so long as such information is to be maintained confidential hereunder. All project information provided to me by the owner in documented, or any other tangible form, shall be returned to the owner by me at the request of the project manager or upon completion of the project whichever comes first.

I agree that, to the extent that I develop any project management technique for this project on my own initiative, or in conjunction with the project manager or project team, all such information related thereto shall be the sole and exclusive property of the owner and its assigns. I hereby assign to the owner any rights I may have or acquire in such techniques.

No termination of any relationship between my employer and I, as the signatory and holder of the project manual, shall relieve me of any obligation hereunder with respect to project information either disclosed to me by the owner or developed by me for the owner prior to such termination.

This AGREEMENT is entered into by the project manager on behalf of the owner. The AGREEMENT shall be governed by and construed in accordance with the laws of .... and the parties hereto shall submit to the non-exclusive jurisdiction of its Courts in relation to any dispute or claim hereunder. Kindly indicate your acceptance of the foregoing by signing and dating this form and returning it to the project manager.

Accepted by: *Signature*   *Date*

01   Πηιλιπ Μαγυιρε   ....

02   Μιχηαελ Πηιλλιπσ   ....

03   Φρανκ Μυρραψ   ....

04   Ειλεεν Βραδψ   ....

05   Γερρψ Δοηερτψ   ....

06   Βερτ Ηαμιλτον   ....

07   Δοννελλψ Τυρπιν Αρχηιτεχτσ   ....

08   Μιχηαελ Πυνχη & Παρτνερσ   ....

09   Βυρο Ηαππολδ   ....

10   Αυστιν Ρεδδψ & Χομπανψ   ....

CN-005: Project coding and filing system

Policy

A corporate register of studies and projects should be used to capture events such as:

- all new studies and projects
- referencing the management, technical, administration and finance processes of all projects
- referencing the products of each process
- archiving all documents, drawings and files.

All 'documents', namely reports, procurement books, drawings, correspondence, e-mails and other means of hard-copy communication, are required to display an alpha-numeric code that facilitates filing and archiving of project information. It is the responsibility of the initiator of any communication on a project, whether based internally or externally, to ensure that the appropriate code is used. It is the responsibility of each project manager to ensure that his or her project's communications are appropriately coded. A part of a project support office's (PSO's) auditing duties is to carry out periodic checks to ensure compliance is being maintained.

A possible coding hierarchy, or levels, are 1st (department), 2nd (project type), 3rd (project number) and 4th (life cycle stage); the 5th and 6th levels are to be used for file names with <C, B, D, or O> being the primary title and <aaaaa> being a secondary file title.

The filing of project documents is likely to be a function of many different aspects that are unique to a project. An example of how the 5th and 6th levels of coding may be used is as follows:

Primary level (5th)

(C) Correspondence (letters, e-mails, memos, etc.)
(B) Books (reports, SP's document submissions, tender documents, etc.)
(D) Drawings (sketches, general drawings, detail drawings, etc.)
(O) Other (reference materials, brochures, etc.).

The primary file division therefore contains C, B, D and O files. The B, D and O files are likely to require secondary structures for each project that is determined by the project manager and project team. However, for ease of interpretation and for consistency the secondary level for correspondence files should be common across a specific department's projects.

Secondary level (6th)

The secondary level titles (or categories) should be very dependent on the characteristics of the project and on the project's current life cycle stage. A possible guide to each project's secondary level correspondence is the following structure:

- communications in
- communications out
- costs and funding
- third-party matters, planning and statutory requirements

- progress meetings and reporting
- project team and personnel issues.

Each of the secondary level files should contain at the front of the file a summary of the content as the content is placed in the file. This summary should contain a means of cross-referencing file items; an example of summary headings would be:

				Action			
Ref. #	Date	In/out	Name from	Required	Taken by	Date	Ref. #

Style

Letter, memo and e-mail formats should be in accordance with corporate policy, should use whatever font type and size are applicable and, of course, should display the project code.

Outcome

Each study and/or project should be assigned a seven character alpha-numeric identifier to be retained throughout its life cycle from concept through to completion and, if appropriate, through its operational life to retirement. The identifier should be arranged in a hierarchy, such as:

- digits 1 and 2 (alpha — upper case) should indicate the *corporate department or initiator*
- digits 1 and 2 should be followed by a hyphen
- digits 3 and 4 (alpha — uppercase) should indicate the *project type*
- digits 3 and 4 should be followed by a hyphen
- digits 5, 6 and 7 (numeric) should indicate a *unique number*.

Any project referencing and communication system should conform to a coding hierarchy. An example of a coding system for the roads department of a local authority is shown in the table below:

KEY:
RD - department
QQ - national roads, RR - other roads, SS - bridge construction,
TT - bridge refurbishment, UU - roads maintenance
	Department
	  Project type
	    Project number
	      Lifecycle stage
	        File name					

Project name/communication hierarchy	1st	2nd	3rd	4th	5th	6th
project 001 - 'name'	RD	QQ	001	CN	C, B, D or O	aaaaa
project 005 - 'name'	RD	RR	005	CO	C, B, D or O	aaaaa
project 008 - 'name'	RD	RR	008	CN	C, B, D or O	aaaaa
project 009 - 'name'	RD	RR	009	CN	C, B, D or O	aaaaa
project 010 - 'name'	RD	RR	010	CN	C, B, D or O	aaaaa
project 012 - 'name'	RD	RR	012	D1	C, B, D or O	aaaaa
project 023 - 'name'	RD	TT	023	FS	C, B, D or O	aaaaa
project 024 - 'name'	RD	TT	024	CT	C, B, D or O	aaaaa
project 026 - 'name'	RD	SS	026	CN	C, B, D or O	aaaaa
project 027 - 'name'	RD	SS	027	PR	C, B, D or O	aaaaa
project 029 - 'name'	RD	UU	029	CT	C, B, D or O	aaaaa

The 1st, 2nd and 3rd levels together are: the alpha-numeric that registers the project and states the department within which the project resides or is sponsored by; the type of project; and the unique number assigned to the project. For example, RD-TT-023 indicates a bridge refurbishment project within the roads department and the unique number 023 indicates which project it is and its name.

It is advisable that the project life cycle stages (4th level) becomes a natural reference for all planning and control, execution of work, and for the management of documents. Using the capital works project life cycle stages of CT (concept), FS (feasibility), D1 (outline design), SL (statutory and legal), D2 (detail design), PR (procurement), CN (construction) and CO (commissioning), it can be seen that RD-TT-023 becomes RD-TT-023-FS, as the project is at the feasibility stage. As the 4th level changes during a project's progress it is not appropriate that this level should be part of the coding for registering projects.

Process

Reference to *project manager* can also mean *study manager* when the project is at the pre-design stages. *Department head* refers to the person responsible for a *department*. *Executive manager* refers to the senior administrator within a department.

The following process should be used:

Person	Responsibility
Department head	Instructs the establishment of a study/project register in accordance with CN-005/1 that is held centrally by the department's administration and is controlled by an executive manager.
Executive manager	Retains and maintains a study/project register in accordance with the templates contained in form CN-005/1 and from box 1 issues study/project managers with the next available unique number.
Project manager	Advises the executive manager on the title to be used for the study/project.
Executive manager	Includes the title within the register and at the end of each month circulates the department personnel with any new entries by reissuing the updated register. Completes box 2 of form CN-005/1.
	Also circulates this updated register status to the corporate library, or the PSO, who should hold the corporate register for all studies/projects from all departments.

Box 1

Department [   ]   Dept code [   ]

• Register of studies/projects

Project type	Year of initiation	Code number	Project name

Box 2

• Register (all departments) issue and re-issue

Date	Revision number	Issued by	Issued to (staff grade)	Copy to library or PSO

CN-006: Performance reviews (services)

Policy

Any external entity providing a service to a project, referred to as a *service provider* (SP), should be required to communicate their progress every period, normally at the month's end, unless a different calendar time is otherwise agreed. A report, referred to as the *SP's status report*, should be created to match a project's needs. A project's communications management plan and/or a project's manual should provide requirements on the status report format, frequency, etc., and the recipients who are to be circulated with each report.

The scope of work for all external services should be prescribed to a common method of presentation set by the project manager and his or her designated alternate from the project team. In that regard each request for proposal (RFP) and the subsequent contract between the owner and the service provider (SP) should be explicit in requiring:

- an acceptable work breakdown structure (WBS) showing each element (work activity)
- a responsibility assignment matrix (RAM) showing who does what to which work activity
- a network diagram of the required work along with the associated mathematical analysis to determine time schedule for each and all activities.

The analysis should provide a time-related bar chart against which resources and the SP's planned charge rates (that which makes up the SP's fee) can be applied to create the format for the SP's status reporting. This format forms the basis for applying the earned value technique for periodic progress monitoring of the SP's performance on a project.

A narrative dealing with the SP's progress is only acceptable when provided as additional information. Such information should be accepted as supportive of a summary of measurable time and cost criteria (earned value) and should be contained in an appendix within the submitted report.

It is the project team's responsibility to ensure that all SPs comply with these requirements.

Outcome

The outcome of this procedure is a direct measure of a project's status at the end of an agreed project reporting cycle. If the reporting period is other than monthly this must be by prior agreement with the project manager. A summary of performance of each work package, consisting of work elements, needs to be presented to the project manager. This should relate the following measurable attributes:

- element's budget
- to-date budget
- percentage complete
- earned value (what has been achieved)
- performance indicator
- current forecast
- current variance.

These attributes should be evaluated for each package element. The overall package performance should be obtained by aggregating the elements within each package. All packages should be aggregated to demonstrate the performance of the overall project; this allows the project manager to assess the SP's performance. A typical template that can be used by the SP is shown in exhibit CN-006/1. The exhibit contains a hypothetical example that shows the procedure outcome and the related calculations.

The following summarises what each column in the template represents (items 1, 2, 3 and 6 are input data obtained from the selected tenderer's submission):

(1) the package name and reference number
(2) the WBS elements (with their code, if available) within the package
(3) the total budgeted amount for each element
(4) the budgeted amount to date for each element
(5) the actual claimed amount (or certified if different) for each element
(6) is optional and is the importance weight (amount of effort) assigned to each element by the organisation undertaking the work
(7) is the physical measurement, as a percentage, of the amount of work completed within an element that is agreed (between the contractor and the project team)
(8) the total of this column is of importance as it gives the weighted value of the percentage work complete of the whole package
(9) the earned value (budgeted cost of work performed (BCWP)) is obtained by multiplying the budget amount (column 3) by the percentage complete work of the element (column 7), dividing the product by 100 and aggregating the sum for all elements
(10) the cost performance index (CPI) is obtained by dividing the earned value (column 9) by the actual budget amount to date (column 5) and summing for all elements
(11) the current cost variance (CV) is the actual cost of the element to date, subtracted from its earned value, and aggregating the sum for all elements to get the packages CV
(12) the current schedule variance (SV) is found by subtracting the budget amount to date for an element (column 4) from its earned value (column 9) and aggregating the sum for all elements.

Although the procedure shows the variables being measured in monetary units (MU) they are really units of work. If it is absolutely necessary to diverge from the use of monetary units, other units can be used (e.g. labour hours). This might be an appropriate approach if the owner is likely to have difficulty in obtaining cost data from potential service providers.

Process

Reference to *project manager* can also mean *study manager* when the project is at the pre-design stages. *SP (service provider)* is the external entity engaged by the owner to perform a specialist service. *Sponsor* means the individual who has been identified by senior management as the person who will initiate the project and report to management on its performance. *Stakeholder* means anyone who impacts on or is impacted by the project.

The following process should be used:

Person	Responsibility
Service provider	Advises the project manager at what time intervals the SP plans to undertake an updating of the SP's performance on the project. A template is set up by the SP that contains the input data in columns 1, 2, 3, and 6.
Project manager	Agrees with the SP the measurement of the principal elements, and any other significant elements, within a work package that provides the input data to columns 4 and 5.
Service provider	At the end of each reporting period enters the input data (columns 1–7 inclusive) into the SP's performance template (see form CN-006/1) and uses this information to calculate the performance data in columns 8–12 inclusive. The SP performance update is shown by the accumulated total of columns 4, 5 and 8–12 inclusive for each work package. This procedure requires the SP to show the total result for the overall project. The completed template is incorporated in the SP's status report and sent to the project manager.
Project manager	Reviews the SP's performance update and sends copies to the sponsor and other stakeholders identified as being recipients of the SP's status reports.
Sponsor/stakeholders	Provides recommendation to the project manager of action to be taken or advice to be given to the SP.
Project manager	Ratifies the offered advice, or decides on an alternative course of action and instructs the SP accordingly.

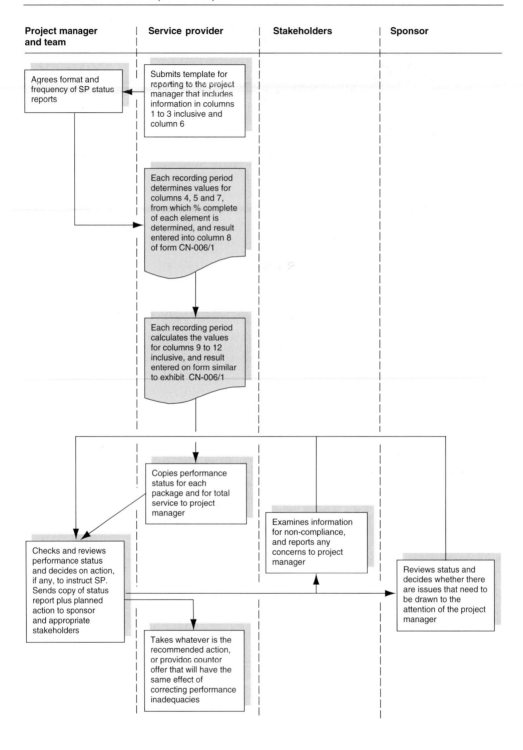

Project manager and team	Service provider	Stakeholders	Sponsor

Agrees format and frequency of SP status reports

Submits template for reporting to the project manager that includes information in columns 1 to 3 inclusive and column 6

Each recording period determines values for columns 4, 5 and 7, from which % complete of each element is determined, and result entered into column 8 of form CN-006/1

Each recording period calculates the values for columns 9 to 12 inclusive, and result entered on form similar to exhibit CN-006/1

Copies performance status for each package and for total service to project manager

Examines information for non-compliance, and reports any concerns to project manager

Checks and reviews performance status and decides on action, if any, to instruct SP. Sends copy of status report plus planned action to sponsor and appropriate stakeholders

Reviews status and decides whether there are issues that need to be drawn to the attention of the project manager

Takes whatever is the recommended action, or provides counter offer that will have the same effect of correcting performance inadequacies

Week No.:

1	2	3	4	5	6	7	8 = 6×7	9 = 3×7	10 = 9/5	11 = 9 - 5	12 = 9 - 4
Package reference/No.	Element name/No.	Total budget amount	Budget amount to date	Actual to date	Element weight	Element % complete	Package percent complete	Earned value	Cost performance index	Current cost variance	Current schedule variance
			BCWS	ACWP				BCWP	BCWP/ACWP	BCWP - ACWP	BCWP - BCWS
Contract 2											
Watertower 2-2-01											
	Plan the work	2,000	2,000	2,000	0.01	100.0	1.00	2,000	1.00	0	0
	Survey site	3,500	3,500	3,500	0.01	100.0	1.00	3,500	1.00	0	0
	Assemble and manage team	27,000	8,100	8,500	0.05	30.0	1.50	8,100	0.95	-400	0
	Civil engineering design	43,500	32,000	42,000	0.19	70.0	13.30	30,450	0.73	-11,550	-1,550
	M&E engineering design	23,700	10,000	12,500	0.06	40.0	2.40	9,480	0.76	-3,020	-520
	Architectural design	10,500	7,000	4,500	0.04	70.0	2.80	7,350	1.63	2,850	350
	general arrgts: tender	6,000	2,000	2,000	0.03	25.0	0.75	1,500	0.75	-500	-500
	general arrgts: contract	22,300	1,500	2,000	0.07	0.0	0.00	1,500	-	-	-1,500
	Detail drawings	38,800	0	0	0.15	0.0	0.00	-	-	0	0
	General specifications	15,000	0	0	0.05	0.0	0.00	-	-	0	0
	Engineering specifications	22,000	0	0	0.09	0.0	0.00	-	-	0	0
	Produce tender documents	10,000	0	0	0.02	0.0	0.00	-	-	0	0
	Evaluate tender returns	18,500	0	0	0.03	0.0	0.00	-	-	0	0
	Contractor appointment	4,200	0	0	0.01	0.0	0.00	-	-	0	0
	Establish site team	3,000	0	0	0.01	0.0	0.00	-	-	0	0
	Supervise contractor	54,320	0	0	0.15	0.0	0.00	-	-	0	0
	As constructed drawings	12,400	0	0	0.02	0.0	0.00	-	-	0	0
	Archive site records	4,500	0	0	0.01	0.0	0.00	-	-	0	0
Package total		321,220	66,100	75,000			22.75	62,380	0.83	-12,620	-3,720

CN-007: Performance reviews (works)

Policy

This procedure is similar to that described in procedure CN-006, except that CN-006 deals with the performance of *service* contracts while CN-007 deals with the performance of *works* contracts.

Any contractor, manufacturer or installation specialist awarded a contract to construct, build, install and/or commission a project should be required to report the project's status and progress at the end of a period, normally at the month's end. The contractor's status report on progress should be to the required format and be communicated to the project manager for the project in question.

The contractor should use either their own in-house earned value management system (EVMS), if approved by the project manager, or where such a system is not approved or does not exist should use the owner's system as set out in the corporate handbook.

The contractor, and any subcontractors, for works contracts are required to provide their scope of work for each project to a prescribed method of presentation. In that regard each request for tender (RFT) and the contract between the owner and the contractor should be explicit in requiring the contractor to produce an acceptable critical path method (CPM) or programme and evaluation review technique (PERT) network of the scope of work along with the associated mathematical analysis. The analysis provides a time-based schedule of activities and tasks against which resources and the planned works costs can be applied to create the format for the required status reporting. This format will be the basis for applying EVMS for progressive monitoring of the contract and for approving payment to the works contractor.

It is the project team's responsibility to ensure that the contractor complies with these requirements.

Outcome

The outcome of this procedure provides a direct measure of a project's status at the end of the agreed project reporting cycle. If the reporting period is other than monthly this must be by prior agreement with the project manager.

A summary of performance of each work package, which consists of work elements (activities and tasks), needs to be presented to the project manager. This should relate the following measurable attributes:

- the budget for an element
- to-date budget
- percentage complete
- earned value (what has been achieved)
- performance indicator
- current forecast
- current variance.

These attributes should be evaluated for each element within a work package. The overall package performance should be obtained by aggregating the elements within each package. All work packages should then be aggregated to demonstrate the performance of the overall project; this allows the contractor's performance to be assessed. The process is designed to encourage works contractors to use effective internal cost and schedule management control systems. A typical template that can be used on a work package is shown in exhibit CN-007/1. The template contains a hypothetical example that shows the procedure and the related calculations.

The following summarises what each column in the template represents (items 1, 2, 3 and 6 are input data obtained from the selected tenderer's submission):

(1) package name and reference number
(2) work breakdown structure (WBS) elements (with their code, if available) within the package
(3) the total budgeted amount for each element
(4) the budgeted amount to date for each element
(5) the actual claimed amount (or certified amount, if different) for each element
(6) is optional and is the importance weight (amount of effort) assigned to each element by the organisation undertaking the work
(7) is the physical measurement, as a percentage, of the amount of work completed within an element that is agreed (between the contractor and the project team)
(8) the total of this column is of importance as it gives the weighted value of the percentage of complete work of the whole package
(9) the earned value (budgeted cost of work performed (BCWP)) is obtained by multiplying the budget amount (column 3) by the percentage of complete work of an element (column 7), dividing the product by 100 and aggregating the sum for all elements
(10) the CPI (cost performance indicator) is obtained by dividing the earned value (column 9) by the actual budget amount to date (column 5) and summing for all elements
(11) the current cost variance (CV) is the actual cost of the element to date, subtracted from its earned value and aggregating the sum for all elements to get the packages CV
(12) the current schedule variance (SV) is found by subtracting the budget amount to date for an element (column 4) from its earned value (column 9) and aggregating the sum for all elements.

Process

Reference to *project manager* can also mean *study manager* when the project is at the pre-design stages. *Contractor* is the external entity engaged by the owner to implement or install some aspect of the project works. *Sponsor* means the individual who has been identified by senior management as the person who will initiate the project and report to management on its performance. *Stakeholder* means anyone who impacts on or is impacted by the project.

The following process should be used:

Person	Responsibility
Contractor	Submits EVMS template to project manager for approval.
Project manager	Agrees format and any other associated aspect, such as submission dates, circulation of copies, etc.

Contractor	Advises project manager when it is planned to undertake an updating of the physical work undertaken and it is agreed to use joint measurement or separate measurement of the works to date. A template, similar to exhibit CN-007/1, is set up by the contractor that contains the input data in columns 1, 2, 3 and 6.
	The value in column 6 is set by the contractor and is usually based on the assessed effort needed to complete a work element. The sum of all work elements in column 6 should equal 1.00 or 100%.
Project manager	Agrees with the contractor the measurement of the principal elements or subelements, within a work package that provides the input data to columns 4 and 7.
Contractor	Enters the input data (columns 1–7 inclusive) into the performance template (see exhibit CN-007/1) and calculates the output data in columns 8–12 inclusive. The contractor's performance update will show the total result of columns 4, 5 and 8–12 inclusive for each work package. The procedure requires the contractor to show the total result for the overall project. The completed template is incorporated within the contractor's status report and sent to the project manager.
Project manager	Reviews the contractor's performance update and sends copies to the sponsor and other stakeholders identified as being recipients of the contractor's status reports.
Sponsor/stakeholders	Provides recommendation to the project manager of action to be taken or advice to be given to the contractor. The project manager ratifies the offered advice, or decides on an alternative course of action and directs the contractor accordingly.
	(Procedure CN-008 provides guidance on the interpretation and how to calculate the cost to date (actual value), the earned value, the variance, and the forecast to complete.)

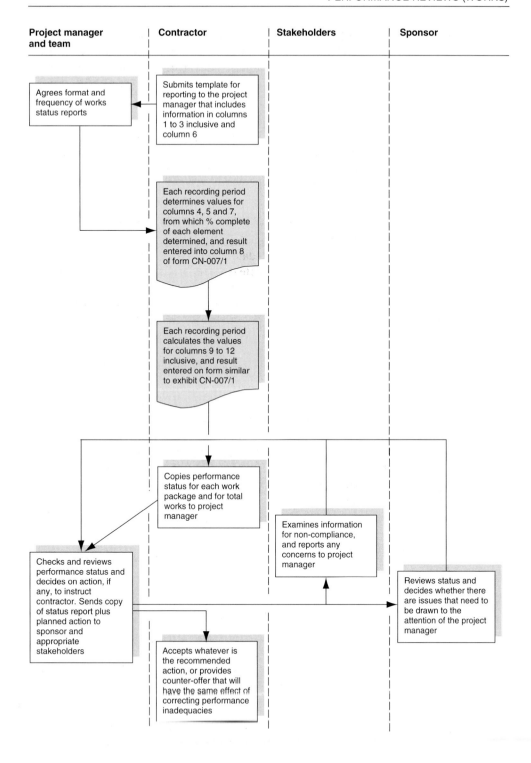

Project manager and team	Contractor	Stakeholders	Sponsor
Agrees format and frequency of works status reports	Submits template for reporting to the project manager that includes information in columns 1 to 3 inclusive and column 6		
	Each recording period determines values for columns 4, 5 and 7, from which % complete of each element determined, and result entered into column 8 of form CN-007/1		
	Each recording period calculates the values for columns 9 to 12 inclusive, and result entered on form similar to exhibit CN-007/1		
	Copies performance status for each work package and for total works to project manager		
Checks and reviews performance status and decides on action, if any, to instruct contractor. Sends copy of status report plus planned action to sponsor and appropriate stakeholders	Accepts whatever is the recommended action, or provides counter-offer that will have the same effect of correcting performance inadequacies	Examines information for non-compliance, and reports any concerns to project manager	Reviews status and decides whether there are issues that need to be drawn to the attention of the project manager

Week No.:

Contract 2 — Reservoir

1	2	3	4	5	6	7	8 = 6×7	9 = 3×7	10 = 9/5	11 = 9 - 5	12 = 9 - 4
Package reference/No. and WBS element code	Element name	Budget amount	Budget amount to date	Actual to date	Element weight	Element % complete	Package % complete	Earned value	Cost performance index	Current cost variance	Current schedule variance
			BCWS	ACWP				BCWP	BCWP/ACWP	BCWP - ACWP	BCWP - BCWS
2-2-01	General site clearance	376,652	320,000	300,000	0.10	88.0	8.80	331,454	1.10	31,454	11,454
2-2-02	Concrete to structure	1,711,448	1,200,000	1,250,000	0.25	65.0	16.25	1,112,441	0.89	-137,559	-87,559
2-2-03	Joints to structure	121,639	96,000	100,000	0.05	78.0	3.90	94,878	0.95	-5,122	-1,122
2-2-04	Under-drainage	98,000	90,000	95,000	0.05	95.0	4.75	93,100	0.98	-1,900	3,100
2-2-05	Ladders, etc.	14,240	0	0	0.01	0.0	0.00	0	-	0	0
2-2-06	Valve house	109,437	15,000	14,500	0.05	15.0	0.75	16,416	1.13	1,916	1,416
2-2-07	Security - site restoration	109,325	8,500	10,500	0.04	8.0	0.32	8,746	0.83	-1,754	246
2-2-08	450 inlet from valve chamber	22,545	0	0	0.02	0.0	0.00	0	-	0	0
2-2-09	450 inlet from 400 branch	49,846	0	0	0.02	0.0	0.00	0	-	0	0
2-2-10	600 inlet from existing 24"	35,755	0	0	0.02	0.0	0.00	0	-	0	0
2-2-11	500-450 outlet (east)	34,268	0	0	0.02	0.0	0.00	0	-	0	0
2-2-12	500-450 outlet (west)	41,674	0	0	0.02	0.0	0.00	0	-	0	0
2-2-13	600 overflow	39,806	0	0	0.02	0.0	0.00	0	-	0	0
2-2-14	450 temporary branch	40,180	0	0	0.02	0.0	0.00	0	-	0	0
2-2-15	Screen chamber	10,000	2,000	2,000	0.01	20.0	0.20	2,000	1.00	0	0
2-2-16	Drill rock cores and test	20,000	20,000	20,000	0.02	100.0	2.00	20,000	1.00	0	0
2-2-17	450 pumping main	175,000	35,000	32,000	0.10	20.0	2.00	35,000	1.09	3,000	0
2-2-18	Pump house	466,160	50,000	45,000	0.18	9.0	1.62	41,954	0.93	-3,046	-8,046
Package total		**3,475,975**	**1,836,500**	**1,869,000**			**40.59**	**1,755,989**		**-113,011**	**-80,511**

CN-008: Earned value management

Policy

It is a requirement for all but very small projects, or projects of only a few months anticipated duration, that earned value should be the process used to measure work progress and forecast to completion. Each service and works contract, which when aggregated together provide performance information on a project, should be subject to the earned value approach.

The earned value approach requires three variables to be measured at agreed dates. The three variables and a suggested 'easy to remember' statement against each are:

- Planned value (also known as budgeted cost of work scheduled (BCWS)): the work that was planned to be done.
- Earned value (also known as budgeted cost of work performed (BCWP)): the work that has actually been achieved.
- Actual cost (also known as actual cost of work performed (ACWP)): the cost of what has been achieved.

These variables are normally measured at the end of each reporting period that are the agreed dates for determining the status of the package (the subproject) or the project that is under consideration. A traditional reporting date would be the end of a month.

At any status date the planned value should incorporate what was planned along with any agreed change orders and other approved variations to the project or part thereof. The earned value and actual value should likewise include all approved variations.

By calculating the difference between the earned value and the planned value (BCWP – BCWS) the time variance will be derived. And by calculating BCWP – ACWP the cost variance will be obtained. Positive variances signify satisfactory performance, and negative variances signify less than satisfactory performance.

Using the same variables, performance indices can be calculated as follows:

Schedule performance index (SPI) = BCWP/BCWS
Cost performance index (CPI) = BCWP/ACWP

Indices of unity (1.0) or greater than unity signify satisfactory performance, while indices less than 1.0 signify less than satisfactory performance.

Calculations of variances and/or indices should be recorded and presented as a graphical or tabular continuum in all progress reports that deal with the package, subproject or the project that is under consideration.

The values of these variables should also be used at the end of each reporting period to calculate a forecast of time and cost to completion of the package, subproject or project under consideration.

Earned value needs to have contractual significance; in other words it needs to be a project requirement. Requests for proposals (RFPs) and requests for tender (RFTs) need to specify what is required to ensure that service providers and contractors adopt earned value when reporting periodically to the owner's project team. The project team also needs to plan their own team activities and incorporate their project management work package with the project's other work packages, so that when aggregated what is being reported on is the total project.

1 Package reference/No. and WBS element code	2 Element name	3 Budget amount
Contract 2		
Reservoir		
2-2-01	General site clearance	376,652
2-2-02	Concrete to structure	1,711,448
2-2-03	Joints to structure	121,639
2-2-04	Underdrainage	98,000
2-2-05	Ladders, etc.	14,240
2-2-06	Valve house	109,437
2-2-07	Security — site restoration	109,325
2-2-08	450 inlet from valve chamber	22,545
2-2-09	450 inlet from 400 branch	49,846
2-2-10	600 inlet from existing 24"	35,755
2-2-11	500-450 outlet (east)	34,268
2-2-12	500-450 outlet (west)	41,674
2-2-13	600 overflow	39,806
2-2-14	450 temporary branch	40,180
2-2-15	Screen chamber	10,000
2-2-16	Drill rock cores and test	20,000
2-2-17	450 pumping main	175,000
2-2-18	Pump house	466,160
Package total		**3,475,975**

Outcome

The outcome of this procedure on a project is very much dependent on there being a contractual commitment by each external entity to comply with the earned value approach, while ensuring that the work effort of the owner's project team is treated as an integral part of the process. The internal working standards and the external agreements and contracts need to clearly specify what is required. Exhibit CN-008/2 (top) contains an example clause that should be included within an RFP; the bottom half of this exhibit is a typical earned value clause that would be found within a tender document leading to a works contract.

With the project requirement for earned value established through the working practices of the corporate organisation this procedure provides the means for measuring how much has been accomplished on a project and each work package within a project. The outcome of this procedure will be a set of calculations that relates resource planning to schedules and to cost and schedule requirements.

From this data, and at set periods during the project, the overall percentage completion for the package can be obtained, along with the BCWS, the BCWP and the ACWP.

Process

Reference will be made to exhibit CN-007/1 to explain the earned value process.

The window which follows shows the basic information that the responsible stakeholder, for some aspect of the project works, would be expected to provide to the owner's project team.

From a work package's WBS the responsible stakeholder creates a template of input data which includes:

- Column 1: WBS element code.
- Column 2: WBS element description.
- Column 3: budget amount per element.

The total of column 3 is the cost budget for the work package under consideration.

4	5	6	7	8 = 6×7	9 = 3×7	10 = 9/5	11 = 9 - 5	12 = 9 - 4
Budget amount to date	Actual to date	Element weight	Element % complete	Package % complete	Earned value	Cost performance index	Current cost variance	Current schedule variance
BCWS	ACWP				BCWP	BCWP/ACWP	BCWP - ACWP	BCWP - BCWS
320,000	300,000	0.10	88.0	8.80	331,454	1.10	31,454	11,454
1,200,000	1,250,000	0.25	65.0	16.25	1,112,441	0.89	-137,559	-87,559
96,000	100,000	0.05	78.0	3.90	94,878	0.95	-5,122	-1,122
90,000	95,000	0.05	95.0	4.75	93,100	0.98	-1,900	3,100
0	0	0.01	0.0	0.00	-	-	0	0
15,000	14,500	0.05	15.0	0.75	16,416	1.13	1,916	1,416
8,500	10,500	0.04	8.0	0.32	8,746	0.83	-1,754	246
0	0	0.02	0.0	0.00	-	-	0	0
0	0	0.02	0.0	0.00	-	-	0	0
0	0	0.02	0.0	0.00	-	-	0	0
0	0	0.02	0.0	0.00	-	-	0	0
0	0	0.02	0.0	0.00	-	-	0	0
0	0	0.02	0.0	0.00	-	-	0	0
2,000	2,000	0.01	20.0	0.20	2,000	1.00	0	0
20,000	20,000	0.02	100.0	2.00	20,000	1.00	0	0
35,000	32,000	0.10	20.0	2.00	35,000	1.09	3,000	0
50,000	45,000	0.18	9.0	1.62	41,954	0.93	-3,046	-8,046
1,836,500	1,869,000			40.59	1,755,989		-113,011	-80,511

Column 6, shown above, is the element weight and is optional information that the responsible stakeholder may provide. The element weight is normally determined as a percentage of the total effort (100%) that would be given to undertake that element.

These data, along with the time schedule for each element, will provide the baseline (the cash flow) for this package of work. The time schedule for an element will be available from the critical path method (CPM)/programme and evaluation review technique (PERT) network analysis, which will give the start and finish dates for an element. The distribution of the cost of an element over its planned time period can be continuous or discontinuous; the responsible stakeholder needs to specify how the cost of an element will be expended.

The input data that are required at the end of each reporting period are shown in columns 4, 5 and 7.

Column 4 is derived from the time–cost relationship for the whole package. The values for each element are less important than the summated total value for the package, which gives the package's planned value or BCWS at the end of a reporting period.

Column 5 shows the actual cost expended against each work breakdown structure (WBS) element, irrespective of what its budget was. The summated values of all these elemental costs provide the package's actual cost, or ACWP.

Column 7 is the measure of physical completion of each element and is evaluated with some care to reflect fairly the degree of completion of each element

Column 8, the package degree of completion, is optional. Column 6, as stated earlier, is also optional. The figures in column 8 are based on the degree of effort that the responsible stakeholder perceives is required to undertake each element. The product of column 6 × column 7, when summated for all elements, will provide an assessment of the percentage completion.

Column 9 is the earned value and is obtained by summating the products of an element's budget amount and its percentage completion (i.e. column 6 × column 7). The SPI (schedule performance index) can be obtained by dividing column 9 by column 4, i.e. BCWP/BCWS, and by referring to the window above this equals 0.9562, indicating that this package is somewhat behind schedule.

Column 10 provides useful information on the CPI for each element. All indices >1.0 indicates satisfactory to good performance and value for money, e.g. the index of 1.13 for the *valve house* indicates that for every monetary unit (mu) spent then what has been earned is 13% greater. On the other hand, the index of 0.83 for the element *security — site restoration* indicates that 17% less value has been achieved for every monetary unit that has been spent on this element. The CPI is a valuable tool that provides the package (project) management with data that help in the project's decision-making.

Column 11 is the current cost variance (CV) and is obtained by subtracting the actual amount to date (ACWP) from the earned value (BCWP) and summing for all elements. The exhibit example shows a CV of −113,011; the negative sign indicating that the project is currently running over budget. The overspend up to the end of the present reporting period is about 6.5%, i.e. (BCWP − ACWP)/BCWP.

The current schedule variance (SV) is obtained by subtracting the budget amount to date (BCWS) from the earned value (BCWP); the elemental SV is given in column 12. The SV in the exhibit example is −80,511; the negative sign indicating the project is running behind schedule. At the end of the present reporting period the project is about 4.5% behind schedule, i.e. (BCWP − BCWS)/BCWP.

Forecasting

New estimates derived from current information are the basis of trend analysis. Estimates tend to improve as actual progress is made. This is due to the completion of activities for which the actual duration and cost become known, as well as to provide better information on workforce productivity and the availability and cost of resources. The indexes for schedule and cost can be used to generate an estimate of the likely situation, in terms of time and cost, of the project at completion.

The estimated cost at completion (EAC) is based on the current trend of SPI and CPI continuing to completion, and is given by

$$EAC = ACWP + (BAC - BCWP)/CPI$$

where EAC is the cost at completion, BAC is the budgeted cost at completion (total of column 3) and ETC is the estimated time to completion, which is given by

$$ETC = ATE + [OD - (ATE \times SPI)]/SPI$$

where ETC is the estimated time to completion, ATE is the actual time expended and OD is the original duration.

By using these two formulae the estimated time and cost to completion can be estimated at any status point or reporting date for a project.

Typical clause content of an RFP when seeking to appoint a service provider (SP)

Earned value will be the required control mechanism for the external service to be provided.

The SP will be required to submit as part of their proposal a detailed work breakdown structure, a relational network diagram of the WBS activities, the diagram should be provided in either CPM or PERT format. From one of these formats a bar chart diagram with associated human resources to be used on the study is required. Planned percentage completion of the study activities versus time elapsed charts (against which actual achievement may be compared, to act as a progress monitor) for his or her conduct of this study will be required. Critical decision/target and reporting dates should be highlighted.

The SP should note that realistic times must be allowed in the time schedule for all necessary consultation and/or decision-making processes involving outside agencies, the public or elected members. Throughout the service period monthly progress reports will be required to be produced and be submitted to the project manager. Where any slippage in the time programme has taken place an explanation for such delays will be required together with a statement as to how it is proposed to recover the loss.

Typical clause content of an RFT when seeking to appoint a works contractor

In performance of this contract the contractor shall within the first month from contract award or contract signature, whichever is the earliest, submit an earned value management system (EVMS) that is approved by the owner's project manager. If the contractor has not been recognised as having an acceptable cost schedule control system then the contractor shall accept and apply the owner's EVMS.

The contractor shall show proper implementation of the EVMS and its procedures that will generate the cost and schedule information for the project manager showing project status at the end of each calendar month.

The elements of the EVMS shall readily allow the comparison of how much work has actually been completed against the amount of work planned to have been accomplished. All work shall be planned, budgeted, and scheduled in time-phased 'planned value' increments constituting a cost and schedule measuring system.

CN-009: Change report and change order

Policy

The approval of any anticipated project change during any stage of a project's life cycle (e.g. concept stage, feasibility stage, detailed design stage, construction process) should be conditional upon this procedure being used.

This procedure needs to be used when it has been identified that there is a change to be reported from what is stated in the request for proposal (RFP), in the case of a study, or a request for tender (RFT), in the case of a project's design, a project's construction, or a project's supervision. Changes to a project can include such matters as scope changes, specification or quality changes, changes in procurement approach, time period changes or cost changes. The basis for determining if there is likely to be a change will be by reference to a project work breakdown structure or other documented configuration that establishes the current scope of work from which all activities emanate. When possible this procedure should be used proactively, i.e. before the applicable change has been instituted or undertaken.

The project manager is required to establish a register for all change reports and for all associated change (variation) orders or rejections. Each change report needs to have a unique number identifier. Each change order issued should likewise be given an identifier, which should be clearly cross-referenced to the change report's unique identifier.

The project manager has the authority to delegate certain aspects of his or her responsibilities within this procedure to a member of the project team, but that can only be assigned if specified in the project's manual (see procedure CN-004).

Outcome

This procedure initiates the process for agreeing to and approving a planned change to some aspect of a project's scope of work or content. The outcome is either an approval or a rejection of a change (variation) report. If the outcome is an approved change to the project then a change (variation) order is established and issued. If the outcome is a rejection then a copy of the change report is sent to the initiating stakeholder along with, if necessary, a rejection explanation. The project manager should catalogue all change reports and change orders, and all issued change orders should be sent to whichever stakeholder initiated the change report.

Process

Reference to *project manager* can also mean *study manager* when the project is at the concept and feasibility stages. *Stakeholder* means any party or entity who impacts on, or could be impacted by, the project.

The following process should be used:

Person	Responsibility
Stakeholders	Any individual or party to the project who identifies that there is likely to be, or they wish to intervene by creating, a change or variation to the project are required to initiate a change report. This is undertaken by completing box 1 on form CN-009/1 and sending it to the project manager.

Project manager	Is required to carry out an assessment of the content of each change report. The assessment will be appropriate to need and will likely include, but not be limited to, the following:

- an examination of the range of technical responses
- an examination of related installability/buildability, etc.
- an estimate of administrative/technical time and the related owner and service provider (SP) costs
- an examination of the impact on the project's time schedule
- an examination of the change's potential effect on the related package cost and the overall construction project cost.

When appropriate the project manager is likely to seek the assistance of the SP and the contractor/vendor in assembling and estimating the impact(s) of the proposed change. All information relating to the impact of the potential change, received from the SP and/or the contractor/vendor, will be filed against the assigned change report number.

Project manager	Once all checking and reviewing have been completed, the project manager will complete box 2 on form CN-009/1 and, along with any supporting information, will review the change report.
Project manager	Decides whether the potential change will be approved or rejected and then completes box 3 on form CN-009/1.
Project manager	Irrespective of an approval or a rejection outcome, a change notice (form CN-009/2) is completed and sent to the initiator of the project change.

All stakeholders are informed of the change order. At the project manager's discretion this will be carried out either formally in writing, by e-mail, or by another approved method, or by sending a copy of the change order.

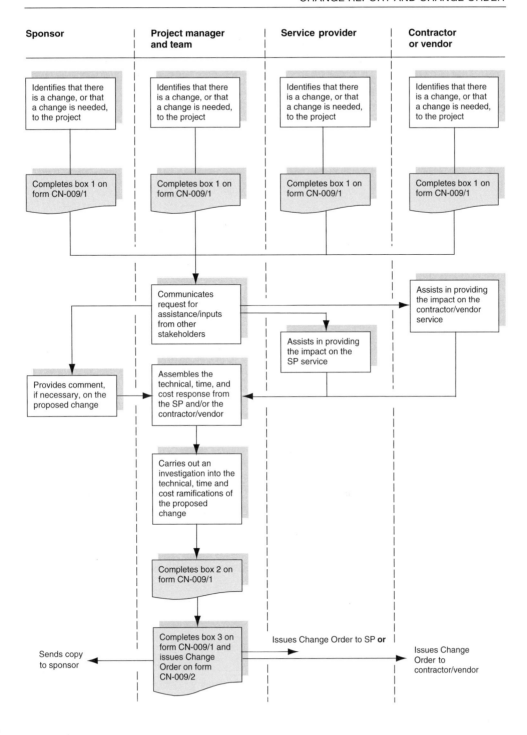

Box 1

Project name _____ Change Report ref. # [_____]

Project ref. # [_____]   Package ref. # _____ Date _____

Current project stage   ☐ CT ☐ FS ☐ D1 ☐ SL ☐ D2 ☐ PR ☐ CN ☐ CO

Urgency of response to change   ☐ High ☐ Medium ☐ Low

Description of change

Reason for change   ☐ Owner request   ☐ Design development   ☐ Construction requirement
                     ☐ Cost reduction   ☐ Schedule improvement   ☐ Safety requirement
                     ☐ Other   Specify

Box 2

• Cost of change — technical costs

Discipline	Name	Rate	Hours	Total cost

• Cost of change — materials and labour

Type	Rate	Quantity	Total cost

Total cost effect to project [_____]

• Effect on project time schedule (programme)

Package completion [_____]

Project completion [_____]

Box 3

Project manager [_____]   [_____]   [_____]
              Accepted   Rejected   Date

Change Order ref. # [_____]   Issued by [_____]

Copied to   ☐ Initiator   ☐ Sponsor   ☐ PSO
             ☐ Others   Specify

Project name _____ Change Order ref. # [_____]

Project ref. # [_____] Package ref. # _____ Issue date: _____

- Description of change

- Reason for change

Change report ref. # _____ Initiator _____ Date _____

- Estimated impact on time schedule

Fully describe

- Estimated impact on project cost

Fully describe

Prepared by _____ Date _____

Approved by _____ Date _____

CN-010: Project auditing

Policy

The project support office (PSO), or a facilitating third party, is required to undertake independent checks on the procedures being used in the study, design and management of a project. Auditing should be conducted on the activities of corporate (internal) project teams and/or external service provider (SP) teams and/or external works teams engaged on the same project. The auditing process, carried out on a *project* at any one time, is normally undertaken within the corporate premises, or project team location if different, and within the premises of the external entities engaged on a project. It is important to undertake the audit wherever the project files are stored.

The auditing process does not include, or represent, an investigation or examination of the corporate entity, firm, practice or company that trades as the external providers of services and/or works.

For each audit there should always be two auditors. The auditors should liase with the project manager or individual that has been assigned responsibility for the direction and management of the project to be audited. The project manager is required to brief the auditors at a pre-audit meeting on the current status of the project and any matters of concern. For external audits the project manager makes contact with the SP, in writing or by e-mail or telephone, advising them that an audit of a particular project is imminent. The auditors independently make contact with the external entities and arrange a suitable day (in the first instance) for commencing the audit. Before the auditing process begins the auditors examine general project documentation, such as the request for proposal (RFP) or request for tender (RFT) and the corresponding proposal/contract.

Three types of audit shall be used for both internal auditing and external auditing: (1) policy, (2) practice and (3) product. *Policy audits* check to determine if written policies and procedures exist that document the corporate working standards for projects. *Practice audits* check the working practices on the project in question against the corporate procedures or working standards. *Product audits* involve evaluation of the deliverables and subdeliverables on the same project. In other words, is the work of the project team and/or external team(s) conforming with delivering the project requirements and in accordance with *best practice* project management?

Auditing of internal team and external team actions and performance on projects should be an on going procedure. Audits should be carried out at least once during each stage of a project's life cycle, and perhaps more frequently on projects that are large and/or complex or, for whatever reason, there is cause for senior management to be concerned. When auditing it is recommended that the audit team use notebook computers to capture the audit elements and any associated discussion. In some audits it may be necessary for each auditor to work independently with an agreed section of the work to be audited, or to deal with a particular section of the SP's personnel. Capturing the information electronically offers a more effective and efficient way to share and aggregate the independent auditors' efforts.

It should be noted that when drafting a project's RFP or RFT to obtain services from external entities, a project audit clause must be included in the RFP/RFT. A project audit clause shall require the appointed party to fully cooperate in any, and all, audits that may be carried out.

It is anticipated that any external personnel's time spent with, and materials photocopied for, the audit team should be to the external party's account, as such costs should not be billable against the project.

Outcome

Auditing is a systematic process that evaluates project work activities to determine whether the actions and related outputs comply with what is required by the owner. The audit also shows whether the project activities and outputs comply with accepted working standards, are being implemented effectively and are achieving the owner's objectives.

In undertaking an audit auditors would be expected to grade the audited elements within each audit type in accordance with the following alpha classification:

- H: high
- M: medium
- L: low.

An H grading indicates that an element is well defined, or is/has been well executed, or whose outcome is rated highly. An M grading indicates an element that could only be rated as average, neither good nor bad. An L grading would indicate an element that is not satisfactorily stated as a procedure or policy, or is one that indicates poor or less than satisfactory work practices, or is likely to produce/has produced unacceptable outcomes.

The response to each grading is:

- H: these audit elements would, more than likely, require no action to be taken by the project team and/or the external entities.
- M: the auditors recommend changes to improve the offending policy, practice or product. In making a recommendation the auditors invite the project team and/or the appropriate external entity to submit a proposal for change, a related time schedule and a date for a re-visit by the audit team.
- L: the owner's senior management seeks a meeting with the project manager, or the senior management of external entities, in order to set out the audit findings, its concerns and the need for urgent and meaningful action to be taken to address serious shortfalls in one or more of the three audit types. The outcome of such discussions would be an agreed plan of corrective action.

Process

Reference to *project manager* and *project team* can also mean *study manager* and *study team* when the project is at the pre-design stages. *Senior management* means top management within the owner's corporate organisation, which also means the performing organisation. *External party* means the entity or entities contracted to the owner to provide a service or provide works.

The following process should be used:

Person	Responsibility
Senior management	From the 'register of project audits' senior management may intervene by directing which project should be audited, or which previously audited project is due its next audit, and advises the PSO accordingly.
PSO	When senior management are non-interventionist the PSO would follow its normal process of deciding on the next audit based on a normal systematic approach and priority of need.
PSO/auditors	The PSO completes box 1 on form CN-010/1. A copy of the form is forwarded to the project manager to be audited for his or her information, and the original is filed in the PSO's audit file.
Project manager	Is required to liase with the auditors regarding the request to audit the selected project and if an internal and/or external audit is planned. A date is agreed for a pre-audit meeting between the auditors and the project manager and this meeting takes place. Either before, or in conjunction with, the pre-audit meeting the project manager should advise the project team and/or the SP's contact for the project of the plan for the project to be audited and that the auditors should make contact to arrange a suitable date.
Auditors	Meet with the project manager, or designated other, who explains the current status of the project, aspects of the project that are performing well and, more specifically, aspects of the project's performance that are not working well. Performance includes matters associated with the technical aspects, management and administration of the project. The auditors, having recorded the project manager's verbal view of the project, are expected to draft notes that can eventually be incorporated in the audit report. The auditors may use these notes as an *aide memoir* during the forthcoming audit.
Project team	Meets with auditors and provides them with the project information and documents that they require prior to undertaking the audit. As part of the audit process a project team member may be required to answer questions raised by an auditor; the responses will be recorded as part of the audit record.
External party	Provides the auditors with the space/room facilities to undertake the audit and makes available files and documents pertaining to their working standards and to the project being audited. The auditors may be required to interview and discuss certain matters with members of the SP's staff, usually on a one-on-one basis.

This should be done with a sensitivity that recognises the staff member's team role and should be undertaken with minimal intrusion into their daily work plans on the audit day(s).

Auditors

On the agreed day the auditors at the owner's premises and/or the external entity's premises introduce the day's audit plan and request, on an on going basis, access to files and other documentation for review and audit search. There may be times when the auditors will require photocopies of certain items; these will be flagged and requested from the project team and/or the external team.

At the end of the first day the auditors should advise the project team personnel of their opinion on the next step, which may be to arrange necessary additional days for continuing the auditing process.

Auditors

Notes are drafted and a grading assigned to each audit element as one of L, M or H. The two auditors agree upon the content of these notes and upon the content of the draft report within which the notes are contained as appendices. The lead auditor will be required to sign-off on the notes and report. Both auditors sign the report.

There would normally be four control copies of the draft audit report; each copy will have a designated control number. It would be anticipated that one copy will be for the sponsor, one copy for the project manager, one copy for the entity that was audited, and one copy for the PSO. The PSO file copy will be the master copy and will be filed within the PSO audit files, which remain in a securely locked filing cabinet at all times.

PROJECT AUDITING

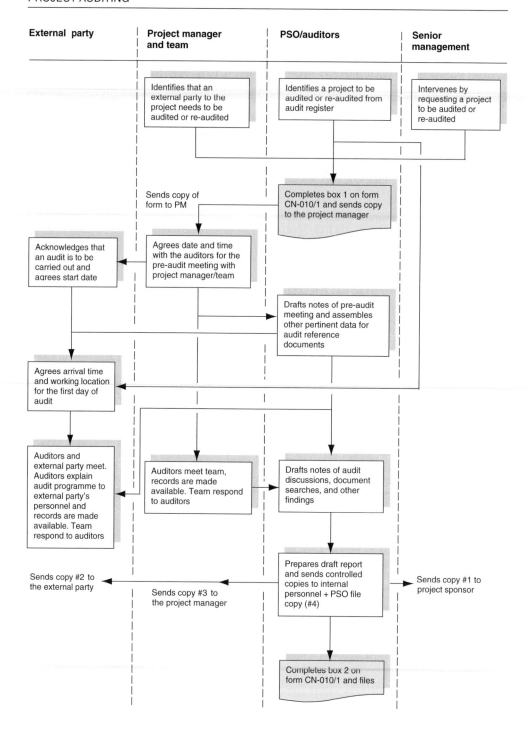

External party	Project manager and team	PSO/auditors	Senior management
	Identifies that an external party to the project needs to be audited or re-audited	Identifies a project to be audited or re-audited from audit register	Intervenes by requesting a project to be audited or re-audited
	Sends copy of form to PM	Completes box 1 on form CN-010/1 and sends copy to the project manager	
Acknowledges that an audit is to be carried out and agrees start date	Agrees date and time with the auditors for the pre-audit meeting with project manager/team		
		Drafts notes of pre-audit meeting and assembles other pertinent data for audit reference documents	
Agrees arrival time and working location for the first day of audit			
Auditors and external party meet. Auditors explain audit programme to external party's personnel and records are made available. Team respond to auditors	Auditors meet team, records are made available. Team respond to auditors	Drafts notes of audit discussions, document searches, and other findings	
Sends copy #2 to the external party	Sends copy #3 to the project manager	Prepares draft report and sends controlled copies to internal personnel + PSO file copy (#4)	Sends copy #1 to project sponsor
		Completes box 2 on form CN-010/1 and files	

Box 1

Project/Study name		Audit ref. #	
Project manager		External parties	

Current project stage   ☐ CT   ☐ FS   ☐ D1   ☐ SL   ☐ D2   ☐ PR   ☐ CN   ☐ CO

Previous audit record   ☐ Never been audited   Last audit ref. _____   Last audit date _____

Comments

Agreed pre-audit date _____   Agreed with PM _____

Preferred audit date _____   Agreed with externals _____

Proposed auditors _____   Auditor 1 (lead) _____   Auditor 2

Form (box 1) completed by _____   Date _____

Box 2

Pre-audit meeting attendees

Comments

☐ Internal audit meeting attendees

☐ External audit meeting attendees

Listing of project material copied and removed by auditors

Summary of audit issues (No. of)   ☐ Low   ☐ Medium   ☐ High

Audit report signed-off by _____   Date _____

Control copies sent to

CN-011: Serve a way-leave notice

Policy

This procedure applies to certain public sector projects. It is used when there is a need to serve a way-leave notice on a landowner for reasons of facilitating planned works that have been sanctioned by the performing organisation. The planned works could be any sort of physical development required to enhance the social environment and address a need (e.g. a new road, a bridge, a sewerage system, a water reticulation system). It is preferred that internal resources should handle the administration associated with serving way-leave notices. This requires various internal departments or sections to coordinate their activities and work effectively and efficiently to administer the creation and issue of way-leave notices.

It shall be the responsibility of a project manager, with the support of the project team members, to ensure that the process steps within this procedure are assigned to the appropriate stakeholder and that the stakeholders undertake their responsibilities. As the project manager has the delegated function to serve way-leave notices it will be a statutory requirement for the project manager to keep the sponsor continuously informed of notices served and their current status.

The project manager has the authority to delegate certain aspects of his or her responsibilities within this procedure to a service provider (SP). However, this should only be assigned if specified in the request for proposal (RFP) and in the terms of appointment with the SP or subsequently as a variation to the contract with the SP.

Outcome

To create a meaningful reaction when a landowner receives a way-leave notice it will be the responsibility of a project manager to have held informal discussions with each landowner to obtain an initial view of their position regarding agreement and/or conclusion of the way-leave notice.

This procedure leads to the issuing of way-leave notices to landowners. The events associated with what may happen after the way-leave notice has been issued is not the subject of this procedure, but is dealt with under procedure CN-012. The alternative reactions by a landowner normally include:

- agreeing to the planned works without reservation
- agreeing to the planned works with accommodation (e.g. some improvement to the property)
- agreeing to the planned works with compensation
- objecting to the planned works.

Process

The following process should be used:

Person	Responsibility
Project manager	Ratifies the route to be taken by the planned works and liases with the appropriate sections within the owner's organisation. Obtains appropriate section sign-offs on a plan drawing of the

layout and concludes the agreed layout. The drawing, along with any preferred sequence of implementation, and with a list of duties required from the other sections (and the SP) is sent to all interested parties.

Referencer

The referencer within the owner's organisation identifies the plots of land and the ownership of each plot along the route or layout of the planned works.

Project manager

Holds informal, initial discussions with each landowner to discuss the planned layout (route) and to obtain, if possible, indications of the landowner's response to the forthcoming way-leave notice.

Referencer

In referencing documentation, provides the plot number and type (see below). For example a typical reference number would be:

Job   Map   Sheet   Plot   Type   Way-leave
729/40 – 902 – 2/2 – 12 – OC – 113

This referencing is to be used by all project stakeholders and in the way-leave register (CN-011/1).

Project manager

Completes box 1 of form CN-011/1.

Service provider

Is required to provide an electronic way-leave map drawn to a scale of 1:1000 and created on a Micro-station platform for use by the project team. The map should contain an A4 fly leaf at the right-hand end, which will contain landowner information, such as name, address, town, land, barony, requirements and description. It should also contain the Ordnance Survey sheet reference number and the plot reference number. There should be a separate way-leave map for each property interest. The SP sends electronic copies of each way-leave map to the project manager as soon as it has been completed.

Project manager

The date of receipt of each way-leave map received from the SP is entered in box 2 of form CN-011/1. The project team assembles the maps and completes a 'notice of intention' and a brief covering letter, both signed by the project manager. Each notice along with its associated map is sealed into an envelope and despatched by post to the addressee. Each envelope should be registered and this registration provides the project manager with the information to complete box 2 on form CN-011/1.

Valuer

Sends a standard 'without prejudice' letter to each landowner officially introducing the owner organisation and the planned project works. A copy of each letter is sent to the project manager who enters the sent date into box 2 of the standard form CN-011/1.

Project manager   At the end of each month, or other appropriate time period, the project manager arranges to send a copy of the most current and up-to-date revision of the completed form CN-011/1 to the sponsor and the valuer.

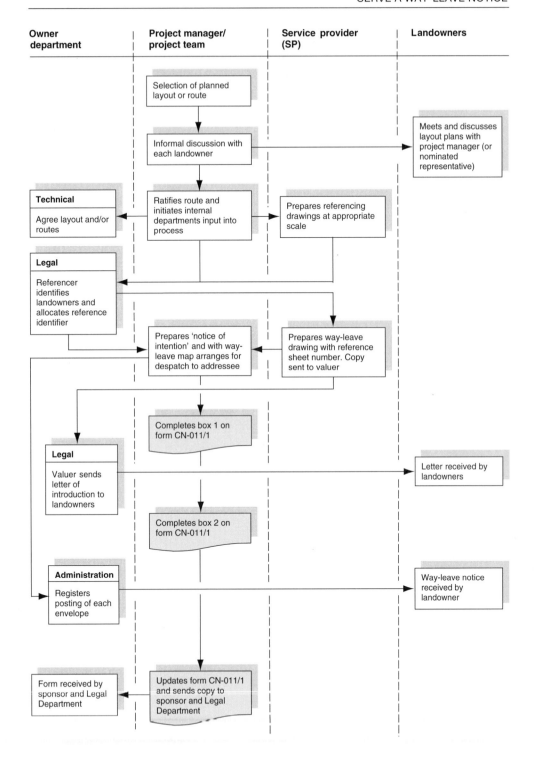

Project _____   Project Manager _____   Sheet ____ of ____

Box 1

Box 2

Reference number	Name	Address (serving)	Date valuer letter sent to landowner	Date way-leave map received	Post office sticker and date stamp

CN-012: Vary a development plan

Policy

This procedure applies to most public sector projects that use the land surface and impact on society and the environment. It assumes that an area development plan (probably part of a national plan) exists which has obtained central government approval for its implementation. The procedure is used to track the typical subsequent process of a local authority's compliance, or otherwise, with an area's development plan, and addresses the matter of land ownership and purchase.

If a project that is included within an area's development plan be subject to change in overall concept, then the variation or variations have to be assessed by the project stakeholders, communicated to the public and the variations adopted as part of the approved project. The adoption of the variation(s) would not be an executive decision but would normally be for the elected members to decide.

The statutory rules that determine whether or not a project requires an environmental impact statement (EIS) are to be adhered to. If an EIS is required then a statement, once prepared, follows a process of presentation to a project's stakeholders and the public and a published notice (national press) of the outcome. If an EIS is not required then it is likely that some other European or local authority assessment process must be adhered to.

Close liaison with a project's stakeholders and the public is essential during each subprocess covered by this procedure and, at the end of each subprocess, it is very important that decisions taken are communicated to the wider public.

The completion of the EIS would normally initiate the serving of way-leave notices (see procedure CN-011), or the acquiring of land. The issue of way-leave or compulsory purchase of land is usually determined by the type of development project. Below-surface projects require way-leave notices to enable work to be carried out on owners' plots of land; on-surface projects require the local authority to acquire land which shall be traversed by a planned project.

Outcome

This procedure can potentially provide a number of outcomes, namely:

- variation to a development plan
- an EIS, or some other report vehicle, if the project is below the threshold for an EIS
- an outline plan for serving way-leaves or the process for the acquisition of land.

Process

The following process should be used:

Person	Responsibility
Project manager	Is responsible for checking a project's current compliance or variance at the time of the concept stage and/or the feasibility stage with what had been stated in the national or area development plan.

	Arranges a workshop of all appropriate stakeholders to examine the project as currently conceived and concludes, if a variance exists, to instruct a review of impact of variations.
Owner department	Works with the project team and various project stakeholders, obtains comments from the public, assesses communications received on the response to the variation, and issues a report to councillors for their adoption.
Project manager	Determines whether an EIS is necessary. If no EIS is needed then some subthreshold process may need to be attended to. When addressed the outcome shall be advertised for communication to the public.
	If an EIS is required, the work associated with preparing the statement, liasing with the stakeholders, facilitating public meetings, etc., and advertising the outcome for public consumption, is the focus of the project manager and team working with other specialists.
	Or
	If an EIS is required and it cannot be undertaken by the internal project team, an external service provider may be appointed using procedures PT-062 and PT-063.
Project manager	If land is to be acquired then detail drawings must be prepared as an input to compulsory purchase orders being served. On behalf of the performing organisation the project manager takes possession of the properties when required and makes all necessary arrangements to secure the lands.

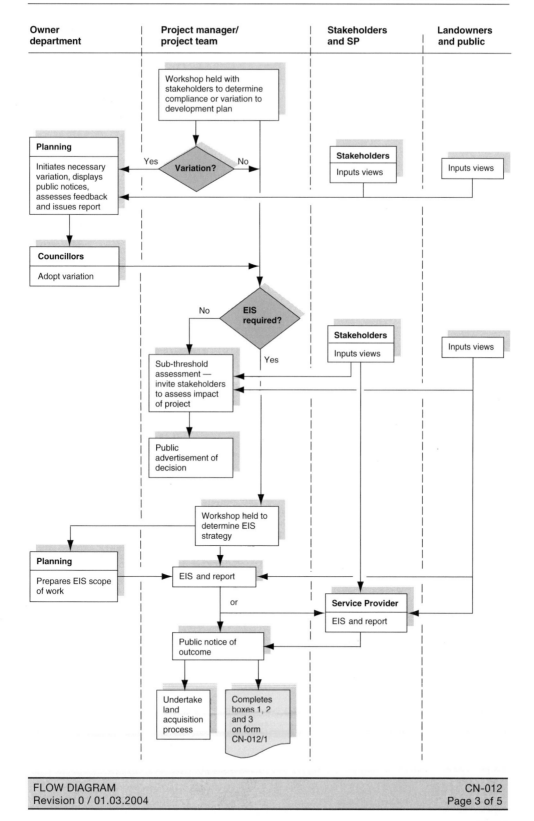

Box 1

Project name [_____]   Job ref. # [_____]

Project manager [_____]   Sponsor [_____]

Current project stage ☐ CT ☐ FS ☐ D1 ☐ SL ☐ D2 ☐ PR ☐ CN ☐ CO

• Workshop to determine compliance with development plan

Name	Organisation/section	Role in relation to project

• Current status on compliance

☐ No change   ☐ Variation (explanation as follows)

Comment

Date of public notice [_____]   Mode of notice [_____]

Date of report to councillors [_____]   Date of councillors adoption [_____]

Signed-off _____ (project manager)   Date _____

Box 2

• EIS required

☐ Yes   ☐ No (use subthreshold process)   Target date for completion [_____]

Subthreshold requirements

EIS stakeholder workshop   Date of workshop [_____]

Name	Organisation/section	Role in relation to project

☐ EIS internal team   ☐ EIS external term   Target date for EIS completion [_____]

Report issue date	Copies sent to	No. of copies

Public notice date [_____]   Mode of notice [_____]

Signed-off _____ (project manager)   Date _____

Box 3

- Land purchase

Ref. #	Landowner name	Address	Drawing ref.	Acquire land	
				By agreement	CPO

Signed-off _____ (project manager)   Date _____

- Acquiring land by agreement

Ref. #	Agreement date		Objections (date)		Decision on objection	Dates	
	Reached	Reference	Sent to agency	Oral hearing		Treat	Enter

Signed-off _____ (project manager)   Date _____

- Acquiring land compulsorily

Ref. #	CPO (dates)		Objections (date)		Objection		Dates	
	Advertise	Serve notice	Sent to Agency	Oral hearing	Decision	Advertise	Treat	Enter

Signed-off _____ (project manager)   Date _____

Cost procedures

This section contains four procedures that deal with certain aspects of project costs and their management. The procedures are:

CS-021   Cost management plan
CS-022   Budget type versus project stage
CS-023   Cost breakdown structure (CBS)
CS-024   Budgeted cost of work scheduled (BCWS)

A brief overview of each procedure and what each procedure sets out to achieve is as follows.

CS-021: Cost management plan

Procedure CS-021 provides the opportunity to predetermine how a project's budget is to be assembled, what each stakeholder will be required to provide, the budget's structure, the method of estimating to be used, the method of measuring variances, etc. This procedure instils the discipline for thinking about and planning a project's budget at all stages except the concept stage (see procedure CN-002).

CS-022: Budget type versus project stage

As a project progresses through its formative stages before becoming a facility, the accuracy variance in developing a budget should be converging towards its out-turn target cost. This procedure provides a system, terminology and accuracy to be achieved on a range of budget types; the five types are defined as 'stage budgets'. A project's budget is described as a five-level hierarchy (summary–package–component–activity–task) separated into direct, indirect and general cost elements. A pro forma template is provided that reflects this hierarchy and accommodates offshore and on-shore divisions, where such divisions would be applicable.

CS-023: Cost breakdown structure (CBS)

When planning a project's budget it is always beneficial to plan the work package structure of the project. This identifies the number of packages, and which package or packages, a stakeholder is responsible for. This procedure determines the macro level of a project's budget cost, while another procedure (CS-024) within the CS series provides the micro level of such budgets.

CS-024: Budgeted cost of work scheduled (BCWS)

A basic element of the earned value approach is to create the time–cost relationship of a package of work and, from that, the total project. It is this 'what we plan to do' baseline against which the performance of the entity or entities that will undertake the work can be judged. This procedure needs to be read in conjunction with the performance review procedures (CN-006 and CN-007) and the earned value procedure (CN-008).

CS-021: Cost management plan

Policy

Any forecasted or recorded costs within a project should be classified, where appropriate, into their cost source. For instance:

- project team cost
- other internal costs (performing organisation)
- external service provider (SP) cost
- specialist adviser cost
- implementation cost (e.g. cost of equipment purchase, construction cost).

In other words, the costs identified within the component sources, also referred to as 'packages', should when aggregated provide the overall cost budget of a study or a project.

The policy on costs should always require:

- the anticipated project costs to be budgeted (the planned cost)
- the true costs at any future reporting date (the actual cost)
- the application of the earned value approach (see procedure CN-008).

These requirements need to be separately identified against each of the cost sources. The corporate policy should also require the aggregation approach for budgets and costs to be an integral aspect of project planning and control.

A cost management plan should be prepared for each study and each project irrespective of size or complexity. In all cases the cost management plan should be a documented, detailed explanation of the inputs that are required to develop project resource estimates and the overall cost budget and how cost variances (the difference between what is planned and what actually happens) should be handled. The cost management plan should also deal with how the periodic analysis of the project cost to date and how the forecast cost to completion should be carried out.

The cost management plan should take account of the significance between the budget to date and actual cost to date. It should provide guidance on the level of accuracy allowable in developing budgets and recording the actual costs as a project advances from the concept stage through its various stages to commissioning and final account stage.

It is the responsibility of the project manager, with assistance from the project team, to develop the content of the cost management plan. The project team may use the support and advice of an SP, specialist advisers, and vendors, contractors, etc., as necessary to create the cost management plan. There are no foreseeable circumstances when it would be acceptable for an SP, or any other external entity, to undertake the development of a cost management plan.

At the early project stages when the various parties to the implementation of a project have yet to be appointed the project team needs to evaluate the project as if the performing organisation was a turn-key contractor. The project team should always evaluate project costs for all cost sources, using the best possible techniques of project estimating and budgeting.

Outcome

The inputs that are required to create the cost management plan include, but are not be limited to, the following:

- an identification and listing of all input documentation that is considered necessary for creating the cost management plan
- the project's work breakdown structure (see procedure SE-125)
- the project's organisation breakdown structure (see procedure HR-042)
- the time schedule for the project (see procedure TE-144).

In developing these inputs it is important that any templates used are compatible with cost templates used elsewhere on the same project. The outcome of this procedure is a cost management plan that documents the following aspects of project cost planning and project cost control:

- the strategy to be used in packaging the project work and project costs within the identified cost sources
- the techniques to be used in estimating the required resources for each work package
- the cost rates to be used against the incremental WBS items
- the methods to be used in monitoring and controlling project costs
- the approach to be used in measuring cost variances
- the approach to be used in forecasting the project cost at completion.

The foregoing is the minimum that the cost management plan should be required to cover.

Process

Reference to *project manager* can also mean *study manager* when the project is at the pre-design stages. *Stakeholder* means any party, or entity, within the performing organisation and it can also mean any external entity that impacts on, or is impacted by, the project under consideration.

The following process should be used:

Person	Responsibility
Project manager	With the assistance of the project team, the project manager develops the cost management plan for the project.
	The collection of all input documents needed for the cost management plan is recorded in box 1 on form CS-021/1.
	Once the cost management plan is complete, the project manager is responsible for completing box 2 and signing-off form CS-021/1. A copy of the cost management plan should be circulated to each member of the project team and to any significant stakeholder that should be privy to such information.
	The salient aspects of the cost management plan should be incorporated within the project manual (see procedure CN-004).

Box 1

Project/Study name _____ Job ref. # [_____]

Project/Study manager _____ Sponsor _____

- Input documents to the cost management plan

| Documents | Availability | | Explain |
	Yes	No	
- WBS	☐	☐	_____
- OBS	☐	☐	_____
- Project time schedule	☐	☐	_____
_____	☐	☐	_____
_____	☐	☐	_____

Other comments

Signed _____ (project manager)   Date _____

Box 2

- Cost budget approach to be used by stakeholders on their work package(s)

☐ Performing organisation | Define

☐ Service provider(s) | Define

☐ Specialist | Define

☐ Contractor | Define

Other comments

- Estimating methodologies to be used

☐ Rates etc. from a similar recent project   Project name/ref. [_____]
☐ Proprietary and published information   Publications [_____]
☐ Bottom-up estimating

- Cost estimating method of resources and rates attached   ☐ Yes   ☐ No

Comments

- Methods to be used in measuring variances, controlling costs, forecasting, etc.

Document attached   ☐ Yes   ☐ No   Comments

Signed _____ (project manager)   Date _____

CS-022: Budget type versus project stage

Policy

It should be a corporate requirement that all projects have cost budgets prepared to accord with a structured cost budget system. The structure of such a system is shown in the table below:

Project phase	Project stage (budget stage)	Budget accuracy (%)	Estimating methods
Pre-investment	Concept (order of magnitude)	±40	Capacity methods
	Feasibility (study)	±20	Top-down and individual factors
Definition	Outline design (D1) (approval)	±15	Bottom-up and specific data
	Detail design (D2) (tender)	±10	Bottom-up and specific data
Implementation	Execution (definitive)	± 3	Detailed calculation and vendor quotes

Decisions to proceed from one project stage to the next are based on an acknowledgement that the estimating accuracy has a higher variance in its early stages and this variance reduces progressively as a project advances through its life cycle. The budget accuracy of project estimates should converge from order of magnitude budgets, which might be derived using capacity data obtained from historically similar projects, to definitive budgets, usually obtained by using costs calculated from disseminating what has been specified along with known vendor prices.

A reliable project cost budget is not normally available until the definition phase or thereafter. Any project budget estimate should be considered as a *target* to be achieved, within an acceptable range of variation, and is used as a yardstick for monetary control.

The methods of estimating used at any budget stage must take account of the accuracy required and be in line with the scheme or project data available at the corresponding project stage. Estimating should always be perceived as a subset of budgeting.

The estimating process should include all direct and indirect costs for equipment, materials, labour, indirect field costs, field office costs, site investigation costs, performing organisation office and administration costs. It should also include the costs of the service provider (SP) (consultant), specialist expert, pre-investment, contingency, escalation, interest during implementation and, if necessary, costs associated with providing working or operating capital.

Outcome

The outcome of this procedure is a progressive project cost budget that can be described under the headings of (1) budget structure and (2) budget stage, along with whatever should be the appropriate estimating methods to be used.

Budget structure

The structure of a cost budget should generally reflect a project's work breakdown structure (WBS) (see procedure SE-125). If a WBS is not available, i.e. the project is at the concept stage or feasibility stage and therefore has not yet been clearly defined, or the available WBS is felt to be somehow inadequate, then a pro forma provided as CS-022/2 can be used.

The pro forma shown is at a summary budget level, i.e. level 1, and is presented for information. Any budget summary needs to be an aggregation of package budgets assembled at a lower level within the WBS. For example, under DC-12 'process building' the further breakdown of DC-12 into level 2, 'project packages', and level 3, 'components', might be along the following lines (incomplete):

Level 2 (project packages)	Level 3 (components)
Process design	Develop scheme design Consultations with environmental/heritage bodies Prepare cost plan and cash flow Owner approval of scheme design Consultations with Planning Officer Submit detailed planning application Prepare detailed design Etc.
Tender process	Prepare tender documents Owner approval of short-list Short-list tenderers Confirm readiness to tender Etc.
Construction works	Site clearance and ground works Sub-structure Services and finishes External works and landscaping Etc.

Estimating of costs performed at level 4, 'activities', or at level 5, 'tasks', should be used in building up the budget for that component, and for all components into a work package. All budgets should be realistically and sufficiently broken down to permit a basis of comparison, and for control purposes, during the current or subsequent project stages.

In addition, the budget should be formulated within three headings, i.e. direct costs, indirect costs and various general cost items. General cost items, such as contingency allowance and currency fluctuations, do not apply to any one package or component but to the overall project. In addition, the pro forma indicates that the three headings are further determined by separating foreign content (outside country of origin) from domestic content (inside country of origin). This provides for the general case, but where a project does not have an offshore element then the budget has only domestic content. Each of the foreign and local contents have been separated into material and installation; these can be interpreted as follows:

- Material: equipment, spare parts, material for the project works, contractor's overhead and profit, etc.
- Installation: labour wage rates, fringe benefits, supplies, temporary equipment not part of the works, equipment suppliers supervision, etc.

Budget stage

The five budget stages of the cost budget system provides a project's cost target, which has a decreasing accuracy range between a lower (optimistic) and upper (pessimistic) limit as the project progresses through its life cycle. Two of the five budget stages happen in the pre-investment phase and before commitment for the project to proceed to the definition phase. The next two budget stages happen during the definition phase. The last cost budget stage is post-procurement of the contractor(s) or, if the works are undertaken using in-house resources, at commencement of the implementation phase.

An explanation of each budget stage and the estimating methods traditionally used are as follows:

- *Order of magnitude* (±40%). These cost budgets are normally determined by using historical methods, such as, cost–capacity curves obtained from project archived data. Order of magnitude budgets serve as a basis for concept consideration of one scheme solution versus other schemes. The order of magnitude budgets for different schemes, needed to satisfy a defined social need, should be carried out using a consistent approach and a common basis of comparison.
- *Study* (±20%). Study budgets are normally based on a top-down approach of decomposing the actual costs of a past, similar project(s) with cost–size scaling upwards or downwards to reflect the study schemes or options under consideration. Each study scheme should be factored upwards to reflect the year(s) covering the period of planned project implementation. The approach used and all assumptions require to be fully documented.
- *Approval* (±15%). Approval budgets are commonly developed at about 30% detailed design completion and after the outline design and total composition of the project has been concluded. Such budgets should, where possible, be based on using a bottom-up approach of applying unit rates against measured quantities of prospective work extracted from the design as envisaged. Equipment cost ratios taken from similar project equipment or recent vendor estimates would normally be used for this budget stage. Where design is not as far developed as it should be or there are aspects of the project's constitution which are still unclear then other methods of estimating, e.g. top-down, may need to be employed.

- *Tender (±10%)*. The tender budget should be a further enhancement of the approval budget, using the bottom-up approach, and be produced when the project design is substantially completed. It becomes the benchmark against which, *inter alia*, tender offers from external bidders are compared during the procurement process.
- *Definitive (±3%)*. The last of a project's cost budgets is the definitive budget. The definitive budget is normally the tender budget modified to reflect the preferred bid and that sum which has been accepted as the 'contract price' for the execution stage of the project. This budget is generally based on specific data, accurate calculations of the work to be undertaken, the use of unit rates and actual vendor quotations. This budget should be continuously updated, probably on a monthly basis, to reflect changes in work scope, variations, claims and other justifiable reasons for budget adjustment.

Process

Reference to *project manager* can also mean *study manager* when the project is at the pre-investment stage. *Stakeholder* means any party, or entity, within the performing organisation and it can mean any external entity that impacts on, or is impacted by, the project under consideration. *SP* will refer to the external specialist consultants engaged to assist the performing organisation. *Contractor* means any external company that has been engaged to undertake the works to produce the project product(s).

The following process shall be used:

Person	Responsibility
Project manager	With the assistance of the project team and other stakeholders the project manager is responsible for developing the budget for the conception stage. This event is recorded in box 1 on form CS-022/1.
	With the assistance of the SP and the project team, the project manager is responsible for ratifying the budget for the feasibility stage. This is recorded in box 1 on form CS-022/1.
	With the assistance of the project team, the SP and other specialists the project manager is responsible for ratifying the budget for the outline design stage. This event is recorded in box 2 on form CS-022/1.
	With the assistance of the project team, the SP and other specialists the project manager is responsible for ratifying the budget for the detail design stage. This event is recorded in box 2 on form CS-022/1.
	With the assistance of the project team, the SP and other specialists, and the appointed contractor the project manager is responsible for checking and ratifying the definitive budget. This event is recorded in box 3 on form CS-022/1.

Box 1

> *Project data*
>
> Project/Study name _____   Job ref. # [_____]
>
> Project/Study manager _____   Sponsor _____
>
> • Concept stage — order of magnitude budget   File ref. # [_____]
>
> Checked by/date [_____]   Signed-off by/date [_____]
>
> • Feasibility stage — study budget   File ref. # [_____]
>
> Checked by/date [_____]   Signed-off by/date [_____]
>
> > *Comments on budget at end of feasibility stage gate*

Box 2

> • Outline design (D1) stage — approval budget   File ref. # [_____]
>
> Checked by/date [_____]   Signed-off by/date [_____]
>
> • Detail design (D2) stage — tender budget   File ref. # [_____]
>
> Checked by/date [_____]   Signed-off by/date [_____]
>
> > *Comments on budget at end of detail design stage gate*

Box 3

> • Execution stage — definitive budget   File ref. # [_____]
>
> Checked by/date [_____]   Signed by/date [_____]
>
> > *Concluding comments on project budget including update periods, etc.*

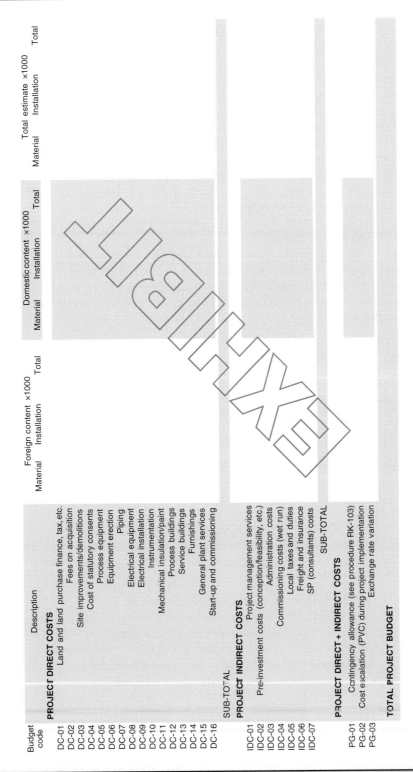

Budget code	Description	Foreign content ×1000			Domestic content ×1000			Total estimate ×1000		
		Material	Installation	Total	Material	Installation	Total	Material	Installation	Total
PROJECT DIRECT COSTS										
DC-01	Land and land purchase finance, tax, etc.									
DC-02	Fees on acquisition									
DC-03	Site improvements/demolitions									
DC-04	Cost of statutory consents									
DC-05	Process equipment									
DC-06	Equipment erection									
DC-07	Piping									
DC-08	Electrical equipment									
DC-09	Electrical installation									
DC-10	Instrumentation									
DC-11	Mechanical insulation/paint									
DC-12	Process buildings									
DC-13	Service buildings									
DC-14	Furnishings									
DC-15	General plant services									
DC-16	Start-up and commissioning									
SUB-TOTAL										
PROJECT INDIRECT COSTS										
IDC-01	Project management services									
IDC-02	Pre-investment costs (conception/feasibility, etc.)									
IDC-03	Administration costs									
IDC-04	Commissioning costs (wet run)									
IDC-05	Local taxes and duties									
IDC-06	Freight and insurance									
IDC-07	SP (consultants) costs									
	SUB-TOTAL									
PROJECT DIRECT + INDIRECT COSTS										
PG-01	Contingency allowance (see procedure RK-103)									
PG-02	Cost escalation (PVC) during project implementation									
PG-03	Exchange rate variation									
TOTAL PROJECT BUDGET										

CS-023: Cost breakdown structure (CBS)

Policy

A cost breakdown structure (CBS) is a core project management procedure that is used when planning projects and is normally prepared by the performing organisation. A CBS should be created as a matrix that draws together the work breakdown structure (WBS) and the project's organisation breakdown structure (OBS). It should clearly show the primary work packages that together form the total work to be undertaken stage by stage to deliver a project's requirements.

A CBS is not a one-off creation; it will change as a project advances through its life cycle by reflecting costs in a current stage of a project. There will therefore be a CBS for each stage of a project. The CBS for a design stage will very be different to the CBS for the construction stage, and so on. As early as possible in a stage a project's costs should be established in the required format.

A CBS is an aggregation of a project's work packages for any stage of its life cycle. A CBS should include the performing organisation's costs and the costs from all external organisations. A CBS is an integration of all costs and provides the structure for presenting the total costs of a stakeholder entity and the total cost of a project package and the overall cost of a project for any stage.

Outcome

The inputs that are required to create a CBS include, but are not limited to, the following:

- the procurement management plan for services and works (see procedures PT-061 and PT-067, respectively)
- the project's work breakdown structure (see procedure SE-125)
- the project's organisation and team roles (see procedure HR-042).

The outcome of this procedure establishes a cost structure for a project in any stage and all stages consisting of:

- the scope of work identified into a series of work packages
- each work package referenced against the 'doer' (stakeholder) of the associated work
- a numerical cost accounting system that can be used to organise, communicate and control the accounts.

The above is the minimum that a CBS is required to achieve.

An example of a CBS for the construction stage of a local community centre project is shown in exhibit CS-023/2. The exhibit shows a matrix combining the WBS (the columns) versus the OBS (the rows). The work packages are shown as shaded boxes. By scanning along a row the packages that a stakeholder has responsibility for can be observed. By scanning vertically the number of work packages can be observed that provide for the work within the first and second levels of the WBS. In the exhibit only the summary level to package level of the WBS has been shown, but within each package (not shown) would be a hierarchy of activities and tasks that provide the detail and the level of costs to be used for developing the package level.

Process

Reference to *project manager* can also mean *study manager* when the project is at the pre-investment phase. *Stakeholder* means any party, or entity, within the performing organisation and it can mean any external entity that impacts on, or is impacted by, the project under consideration.

The following process should be used:

Person	Responsibility
Project manager	With assistance from either the project team or the project support office (PSO) the project manager is responsible for developing the CBS for the project. The collection of all input documents needed for the CBS is recorded in box 1 on form CS-023/1 and signed-off by the project manager.
	Once the salient data needed for creating the CBS are complete, the project manager is responsible for completing box 2 and signing-off form CS-023/1.
	When completed, a copy of the CBS (see exhibit CS-023/2 for a typical example (in-part)) is circulated to each member of the project team and to any significant stakeholder that should be privy to such information; this includes the performing organisation's finance office. A copy of the CBS should be included within the project's 'project manual' (see procedure CN-004).

COST BREAKDOWN STRUCTURE (CBS)

Box 1

Project/Study name _____ Job ref. # [_____]

Project/Study manager _____ Sponsor _____

Current project stage ☐ CT ☐ FS ☐ D1 ☐ SL ☐ D2 ☐ PR ☐ CN ☐ CO

- Input documents

Documents	*Availability*		*Why?*
	Yes	No	
• Procurement management plan (service)	☐	☐	_____
• Procurement management plan (works)	☐	☐	_____
• Work Breakdown Structure	☐	☐	_____
• Organisation Breakdown Structure	☐	☐	_____
• _____	☐	☐	_____
• _____	☐	☐	_____

Other comments

Signed _____ (project manager)   Date _____

Box 2

- Previous CBS

☐ Yes

☐ No

Which stage	File ref. #	Date issued	Signed-off by

- Current stage CBS

Stakeholder organisation/name	No. of packages	Package name

- CBS communicated to

Stakeholder organisation/name	Date sent	Sent by	Method of communication

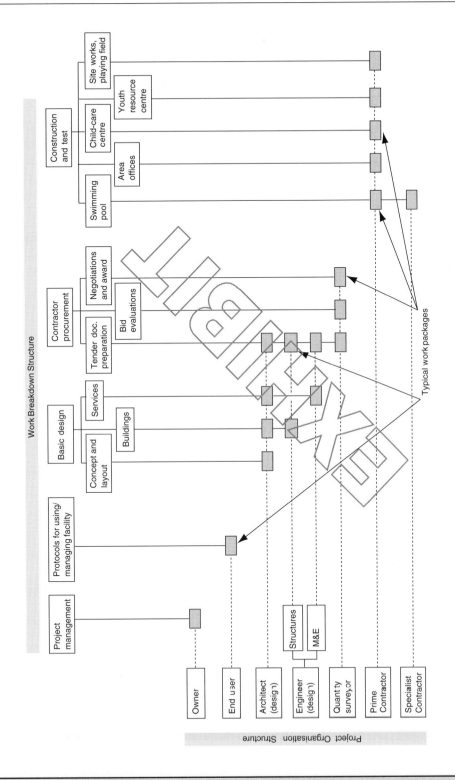

CS-024: Budgeted cost of work scheduled (BCWS)

Policy

The budgeted cost of work scheduled (BCWS) is also known as the 'planned value'. The BCWS of a project is a cost–time relationship derived from each package; adding these BCWSs together provides 'what work has been planned by a set date' and should be used for controlling projects and their subprojects (packages). The BCWS is a cash flow representing the cash value of work achieved and is evaluated periodically at set dates and used as one of the variables in the earned value approach (see procedure CN-008).

Each project package is decomposed to produce the cost of each work element distributed over the associated time period of an element. The unit of time for a cash flow is normally a month, but can be a shorter period for project's of short duration. The unit used for costs should be the currency of the performing organisation or, if more appropriate, the user organisation. The cash flow should be presented as a time-based tabulation of monetary outflows and can also be produced as a line diagram for ease of understanding. Each cash flow should be updated on a continuous basis, to reflect both the historical performance and the past known cost of a project and the forecasted cost to completion. A BCWS needs to take account of all known changes (variations) to a project and all anticipated changes and financial claims.

A copy of a project's aggregated cash flow, both when initially developed and any subsequent revision issues, should be promptly made available to the performing organisation's finance office or corporate section with responsibility for collating all project costs.

Outcome

The inputs that are required to create a BCWS include, but are not limited to, the following:

- the project's budget type
- the work breakdown structure
- the cost breakdown structure
- the project's schedule plan.

The outcomes of this procedure are as follows:

- a time-based dispersion of the budgeted costs of each work package
- the aggregated cost per month of all work and the associated cost of such work for every project stage
- the aggregated sum (cash flow) at the end of each month for the total project duration.

To assist in undertaking performance reviews of a project, the cash flow of project and package costs should be presented as a line graph. Line graphs can also be useful for each cost source, e.g. performing organisation, service providers (SPs), specialist advisers and contractors.

Process

In explaining the BCWS, which is a fundamental part of the earned value process (see procedure CN-008) reference will be made to exhibits CS-024/1 and CS-024/2.

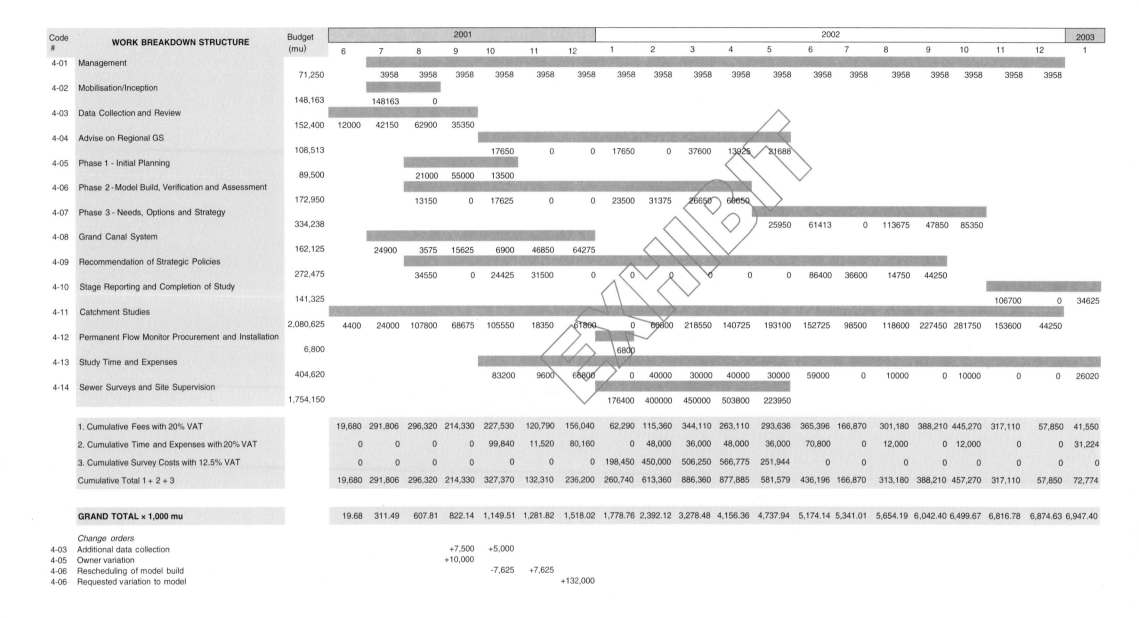

Code #	WORK BREAKDOWN STRUCTURE	Budget (mu)	2001 6	7	8	9	10	11	12	2002 1	2	3	4	5	6	7	8	9	10	11	12	2003 1
4-01	Management	71,250		3958	3958	3958	3958	3958	3958	3958	3958	3958	3958	3958	3958	3958	3958	3958	3958	3958	3958	
4-02	Mobilisation/Inception	148,163		148163	0																	
4-03	Data Collection and Review	152,400	12000	42150	62900	35350																
4-04	Advise on Regional GS	108,513					17650	0	0	17650	0	37600	13925	21688								
4-05	Phase 1 - Initial Planning	89,500			21000	55000	13500															
4-06	Phase 2 - Model Build, Verification and Assessment	172,950			13150	0	17625	0	0	23500	31375	26650	60650									
4-07	Phase 3 - Needs, Options and Strategy	334,238												25950	61413	0	113675	47850	85350			
4-08	Grand Canal System	162,125		24900	3575	15625	6900	46850	64275													
4-09	Recommendation of Strategic Policies	272,475			34550	0	24425	31500	0	0	0	0	0	0	86400	36600	14750	44250				
4-10	Stage Reporting and Completion of Study	141,325																		106700	0	34625
4-11	Catchment Studies	2,080,625	4400	24000	107800	68675	105550	18350	61800	0	60800	218550	140725	193100	152725	98500	118600	227450	281750	153600	44250	
4-12	Permanent Flow Monitor Procurement and Installation	6,800									6800											
4-13	Study Time and Expenses	404,620					83200	9600	66800	0	40000	30000	40000	30000	59000	0	10000	0	10000	0	0	26020
4-14	Sewer Surveys and Site Supervision	1,754,150								176400	400000	450000	503800	223950								

			6	7	8	9	10	11	12	1	2	3	4	5	6	7	8	9	10	11	12	1
	1. Cumulative Fees with 20% VAT		19,680	291,806	296,320	214,330	227,530	120,790	156,040	62,290	115,360	344,110	263,110	293,636	365,396	166,870	301,180	388,210	445,270	317,110	57,850	41,550
	2. Cumulative Time and Expenses with 20% VAT		0	0	0	0	99,840	11,520	80,160	0	48,000	36,000	48,000	36,000	70,800	0	12,000	0	12,000	0	0	31,224
	3. Cumulative Survey Costs with 12.5% VAT		0	0	0	0	0	0	0	198,450	450,000	506,250	566,775	251,944	0	0	0	0	0	0	0	0
	Cumulative Total 1 + 2 + 3		19,680	291,806	296,320	214,330	327,370	132,310	236,200	260,740	613,360	886,360	877,885	581,579	436,196	166,870	313,180	388,210	457,270	317,110	57,850	72,774
	GRAND TOTAL × 1,000 mu		19.68	311.49	607.81	822.14	1,149.51	1,281.82	1,518.02	1,778.76	2,392.12	3,278.48	4,156.36	4,737.94	5,174.14	5,341.01	5,654.19	6,042.40	6,499.67	6,816.78	6,874.63	6,947.40

Change orders

Code		9	10	11	12
4-03	Additional data collection	+7,500	+5,000		
4-05	Owner variation	+10,000			
4-06	Rescheduling of model build		-7,625	+7,625	
4-06	Requested variation to model				+132,000

Creating a BCWS

Having developed the work breakdown structure (WBS) of a package, the elements are listed in a column along with their associated code number, as shown in the first two columns of CS-024/1. The *elements* consist of *activities* and *tasks*, as lower order items in the WBS, but although these items are used in deriving information about the elements it is not necessary for managing and reporting to go lower than element level.

The time periods for all elements within a work package should be derived from a critical path method (CPM) or programme and evaluation review technique (PERT) of all activities and tasks (see procedures TE-142 and TE-144). From the scheduled plan the start date and the finish date of each WBS is determined. The result of such a time analysis is normally presented in bar-chart format. Exhibit CS-024/1 shows the results of such an analysis as shaded bars for a package of work to be undertaken by an SP. The work package is shown as being undertaken over the time period June 2001 to January 2003, a period of 20 months.

The cost of an element is obtained by determining the cost of the related activities and tasks supporting that element. This cost should be the integrated components of the direct, indirect and general cost. The budget costs of the elements are shown in the third column.

Through the time analysis of the element, the usage of resources and from that the planned allocation of cost, it should be relatively straightforward to distribute the budget costs of an element over the planned time period for that element. For example, element 4-03 has a derived budget of 152,400 and this has been allocated over months 1 to 4 (June to September 2001 inclusive) with a distribution of 12,000, 42,150, 62,900 and 35,350, respectively.

By accumulating the elemental costs in any month (adding the amounts in any monthly column) and adding in any other general package costs (see below GRAND TOTAL), the total package costs as a running total can be derived. The running total is shown as the row of figures denoted 'grand total'. This grand total is shown graphically as the black line in exhibit CS-024/2. The running total is also called the 'cash flow' or the 'cost baseline', but the term by which it is colloquially known is the BCWS — the budgeted cost of work schedule. In North America the BCWS is known as the 'planned value'.

Changes to a BCWS

Procedure CN-008 describes how the BCWS is used in determining the performance of a package, project SP or contractor.

When change orders are issued it is necessary to reflect these approved changes within the BCWS. Assume that the package is at the end of month 7. The change orders for this project at this time (end of December 2001) are shown at the foot of the table shown in CS-024/1. The cash flow will have varied in months 4, 5, 6 and 7 by +17,500, –2,625, +7,625 and +132,000, respectively.

The effect of these changes is shown as the coloured line in CS-024/2. All performance reviews of a services type contract (see procedure CN-006) and of a works type contract (see procedure CN-007) need to take into account all approved past changes. The BCWS is therefore a dynamic baseline that needs continually to reflect the approved changes to the initially conceived BCWS.

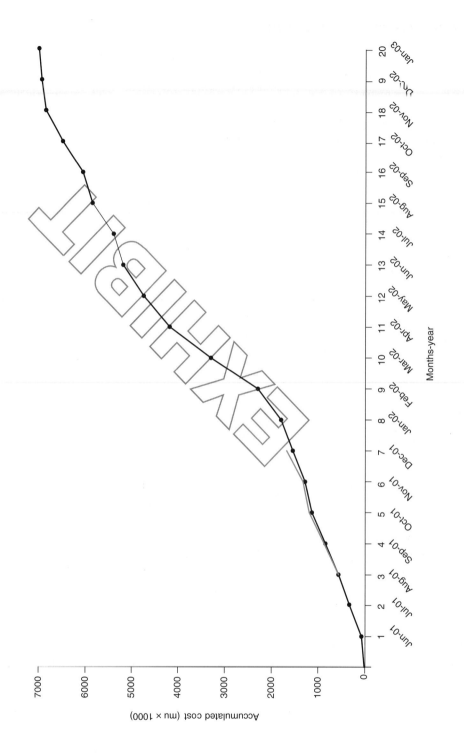

Human resources procedures

This section contains five procedures that deal with certain aspects of the human side of project management. The procedures are:

HR-041   Staff management plan
HR-042   Project organisation and team roles
HR-043   Role assignments and appointments
HR-044   Staff training programme
HR-045   Selection, appraisal and reward

A brief overview of each procedure and what each procedure sets out to achieve is as follows.

HR-041: Staff management plan

A common ingredient of all projects is the requirement for people to carry out work, or to manage the project or manage those that perform the work. This procedure establishes the protocols for the identification, selection, time recording, reward systems, etc., of the indicative project team. Staff employment conditions pertaining within the performing organisation and any other conditions that impact on the stakeholders would be reviewed and documented in procedure HR-041.

HR-042: Project organisation and team roles

Today all but the very small project requires a team of multitalented people to undertake the scope of work and manage the associated processes. It is possible that a project-based organisation, i.e. one regularly carrying out projects, will have internal resources capable of filling many if not all roles. The more traditional operations-type organisation probably uses external resources, more or less, each time a project is required. Whether the work is handled internally, externally or by a combination of both types of resource, this procedure provides the means for determining the team structure and the roles of the team members.

HR-043: Role assignments and appointments

This procedure relates to the process of selecting individuals to perform the specified team roles. Where the roles are filled internally an interview-type selection process is proposed. Where the roles are to be filled by resources sourced from external entities then these parties take the lead in proposing personnel for the identified positions that are ratified by the performing organisation. The procedure requires a formal approach in selecting project team personnel and detailed documentation of each step in the process.

HR-044: Staff training programme

Having a handbook of project management procedures is necessary for the achievement of best practice, but it is not sufficient. Transferring skills to the staff of the performing organisation is also necessary. This procedure offers a three-level approach for appropriate staff members to achieve skill and to reach certification as a project manager.

HR-045: Selection, appraisal and reward

Procedure HR-043 addresses the matter of role assignment and appointment based on the needs of the project, i.e. the roles needed to create, deliver and manage the project. Procedure HR-045 addresses the soft side, i.e. the behavioural aspects, of selecting people for project roles. Successful project teams are as much a product of balanced behaviour characteristics as they are of the selection of the correct usage of the other paraphernalia that is modern project management. The results of psychometric profiling and other methods of assessing personality are recorded along with an individual's project performance.

HR-041: Staff management plan

Policy

This procedure should be used when considering the management of all projects. For such projects a manager can be from any suitable discipline and the team should be assembled from other individuals representing the group needed to undertake the planned scope of work.

A staff management plan is as important as the other associated project management plans (e.g. communications, cost, time, procurement, etc.), and is developed at the concept stage or as early as possible within a project's life. Closely associated with this procedure is the creation of project (and study) charters (see procedure SE-121), and the closely aligned prerequisite of the delegation of the functions of senior management.

Project teams should consist of people who are skilled in the requirements of a project and in its management at whatever stage is current in the development process. Such groupings are likely to consist of a combination of social, technical, economic and management skills, but may from time to time include political skills and other specialist areas. It is assumed that in all, or in most, cases the combination of required skills and experience changes from project stage to project stage. For all projects the leader of a multidiscipline team should have the title of project manager, or study manager if a project is at the pre-investment phase. It is most likely that a project's owner may wish on most occasions to maximise the use of its in-house human resources and minimise the use of external human resources.

The human resources of external entities, who are in contract with the performing organisation, shall be deemed to be included within the intent of this 'staff management plan'. The human resource roles for any project need to be identified at the concept (CT) stage for feasibility studies and at the feasibility stage for design and design services and construction supervision. Once the project roles have been identified individual assignment to the project team becomes official upon the approval of the project manager. Assignment to a project team should always be based on the individual's experience and ability to undertake the team role. Individuals assigned to a project team should be required to be committed for the planned duration of their anticipated involvement.

Performing organisation personnel who are engaged full time for more than 12 months should be considered for some type of financial reward. Typically, successful completion of each individual's contract would warrant the payment of a 'completion' bonus. The project manager should be the arbiter on judging an individual's successful contract completion.

Outcome

The outcome of this procedure is a document that contains directives and guidelines relating to the project organisational structure, and the identification, assignment and development of the personnel needed to undertake the management of a study or a project. The management of a project should be in three parts, namely: (1) the management of the performing organisation's team, (2) the management of any external service providers and (3) the management of any external contractors undertaking works contracts. The management of a study would, in general, only require (1) and (2).

Before a definitive staff management plan can be created, the following inputs should be available:

- the project (study) charter
- delegation of function of the senior management or sponsor
- knowledge of the project life cycle and project deliverables
- an indication of project milestones and control points
- an indicative cost budget and order of magnitude of contingency reserves.

The staff management plan for a project is likely to contain, but is not limited to, the following organisational and HR matters:

- the performing organisation's requirement regarding reporting relationships
- the performing organisation's requirement regarding employment agreements
- the team structure and team roles for the project (study) under consideration
- how the potential nominees for each role are selected
- an outline time schedule of the project, specifically indicating the team roles, the duration of each role, and their start and finish dates
- the benefits and rewards associated with the team roles
- the performance framework for each team role and the overall performance of the project
- the means for enhancing the competencies of team members.

This procedure has a bearing on other project management procedures and therefore should be read together with and related to the following:

- CN-004: Project manual
- HR-042: Project organisation and team roles
- HR-043: Role assignments and appointments
- HR-044: Staff training programme
- HR-045: Selection, appraisal and reward.

The above listing contains essential references, but the procedures listed are not the only ones that may be consulted.

Process

Reference to *project manager* can also mean *study manager* when the project is at the pre-investment phase. *Stakeholder* means any party, or entity, within the performing organisation and it can also mean any external entity that impacts on, or is impacted by, the project under consideration.

The following process should be used:

Person	Responsibility
Project manager	Box 1 of form HR-041/1 is completed.
	Either:
	(1) arranges a workshop of all appropriate stakeholders, or
	(2) uses another means to engage the stakeholders

to examine the approach that should be adopted to determine the content of the staff management plan. In the case of (1) the project manager is required to consult and use procedure CN-003.

Stakeholders

Each entity invited to attend a staff management workshop nominates the attendee to represent them and informs the project manager accordingly. Each attendee is required to make a positive contribution to the outcomes and goals of the prearranged workshop.

Project manager

Upon conclusion of the workshop the project manager completes box 2 of form HR-041/1.

Either as a direct result of the workshop outcomes, or through independent actions, the project manager completes box 3 of form HR-041/1.

The project manager is responsible for circulating a copy of the completed staff management plan to the appropriate stakeholders.

The project manager is responsible for obtaining the sponsor sign-off to the content of HR-041/1 which, along with all other detailed information, constitutes the project's staff management plan.

Box 1

Project/Study name _____   Job ref. # [_____]

Project/Study manager _____   Date _____

Current stage   ☐ CT ☐ FS ☐ D1 ☐ SL ☐ D2 ☐ PR ☐ CN ☐ CO

- Stakeholder group

Name	Organisation/section	Role in relation to project

- HR practices reference documents (performing organisation)

Title	Ref. #	Germane to this project?

Box 2

- Input documents to staff management plan

Document	Availability		Why?
	Yes	No	
1. Study/project charter	☐	☐	_____
2. Delegated function to PM	☐	☐	_____
3. Management/employment policies	☐	☐	_____
4. Project's milestones/deliverables	☐	☐	_____
5. Project's budget/contingency reserve	☐	☐	_____
6. _____	☐	☐	_____

- Pre-workshop (or communication) document

☐ Drafted   Signed-off by _____   Date _____

Circulate to (see stakeholder group box1):

Name	Organisation/section	Date issued

- Workshop held

☐ Yes   ☐ No | Details

Prepared and signed-off by _____   Date _____

Box 3

- Amendments to performing organisation's requirements

☐ Employment

> *Define*

☐ Reporting

> *Define*

☐ Administration

> *Define*

- Indicative team structure

Name	Organisation/section	Team role

- Staff selection process

> *Explanation of approach*

- Staff time allocation schedule

> *Define*

- Benefits and reward system

> *Define*

- Circulation of staff management plan

Name	Organisation/section	Date sent

Signed _____ (sponsor)   Date _____

Signed _____ (project manager)   Date _____

HR-042: Project organisation and team roles

Policy

As stated in the staff management plan (see procedure HR-041), the philosophy of the performing organisation should be to maximise the use of in-house resources for the management of all projects, and where appropriate to maximise the use of other disciplines. This approach helps to reduce project costs and it also contributes to improving the skills and experience of internal resources.

This procedure is used in determining the structure and the team roles of a project. The procedure covers the most complex multidisciplinary team structure composed of performing organisation personnel and external organisations and their personnel. By definition, the most simple project organisation structure requiring only performing organisation resources is covered by this procedure.

The project manager decides on the team structure and the roles of the team required to undertake a study, or the definition, implementation or commissioning, etc. of the next stage of the assigned project.

During the concept stage, when the study manager has been identified and assigned and thereafter, *inter alia*, the staff management plan document has been created, the study manager is required to develop the team structure and the team roles. If possible, this should be undertaken for the whole of a project's life cycle, but should be substantially developed for the feasibility study stage. The structure of the team and the team roles are likely to change for each stage of a project's life cycle. This procedure is therefore applied a number of times during the project's development from concept to commissioning.

Outcome

The outcome of this procedure is a document that contains:

- a project organisation chart
- a responsibility assignment matrix
- a job specification for each project team role.

The project organisation chart is normally a graphical display that shows the roles and the reporting relationships; it is usually known, and referred to, by its acronym OBS (organisation breakdown structure) (see exhibit HR-042/2, which is the study team that carried out the work shown on CS-024/1).

The responsibility assignment matrix (RAM) is the template that links the work breakdown structure (WBS) with the OBS (see exhibit HR-042/3). The RAM provides the means to draw up the specification for the team roles identified in the OBS (see the sample team role specification in exhibit HR-042/4).

Process

Reference to *project manager* can also mean *study manager* when the project is at the pre-investment phase. *Stakeholder* means any party, or entity, within the performing organisation and it can also mean any external entity that impacts on, or is impacted by, the project under consideration.

The following process should be used:

Person	Responsibility
Project manager	Develops the most appropriate organisational structure to undertake a project's scope of work. In doing so the project manager may seek the advice of a number of performing organisation stakeholders. The project manager completes box 1 of form HR-042/1 and, if deemed appropriate, sends a copy to each stakeholder.
Stakeholders	Assist the project manager in his or her decision to select the correct organisational structure with the correct blend of skills, influence and knowledge. Assistance is given in determining the team roles that are needed to meet the project objectives successfully. This support and assistance can be provided either formally or informally.
Project manager	Once the outcomes have been developed the project manager completes box 2 on form HR-042/1 and sends a copy to the sponsor for information and approval.
Sponsor	It is the sponsor's responsibility to ensure that the human resources identified by the project manager are approved and that any necessary action is taken to ensure that they are made available when required.

Box 1

Project/Study name _____ Job ref. # [_____]

• Input documents

Documents	Availability		Why?
	Yes	No	
1. Study (project) charter	☐	☐	_____
2. Senior management's delegated function	☐	☐	_____
3. Staff management plan	☐	☐	_____

• Stakeholders to be involved

☐ None   Why? [_____]

☐ Yes — see below

Name	Organisation/section	Project role or section authority

Box 2

• Organisation breakdown structure   ☐ Attached

Explanation

• Responsibility assignment matrix (RAM)   ☐ Attached

Explanation

• Team role job profiles   ☐ Attached

Explanation

Signed _____ (sponsor)   Date _____

Signed _____ (project manager)   Date_____

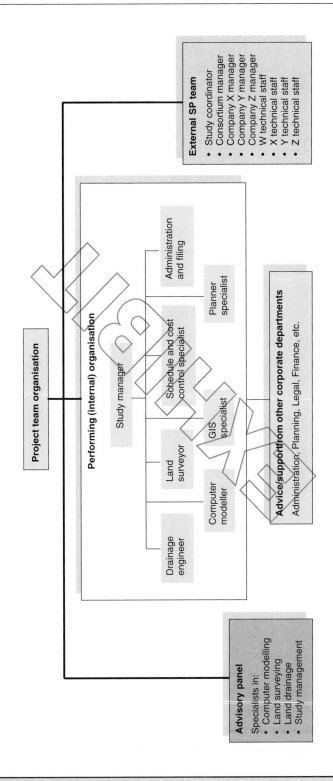

Contract 2 — Watertower 2-2-01

PO — performing organisation

		PO	PO	PO	PO	SP	SP	SP	SP	SP	SP
WBS		PM	Eng. 1	Eng. 2	Tech. Dir.	Manager	Eng. A	Eng. B	Eng. C	Architect	Tech. AA
Package reference/No.	Element name/No.										
2-2-01/001	Attend meetings	Chairs	Yes	Yes	Yes	Yes	Yes	Yes			
2-2-01/002	Prepare perf. reports	S			S	P					
2-2-01/003	Reviews SP's work	A	R	R	R						
2-2-01/004	Approve SP's work	S									
2-2-01/005	Plan the work				P	I	I				
2-2-01/006	Survey site					A/S				I	I
2-2-01/007	Assemble and manage team				A	P					
2-2-01/008	Civil engineering design				S	A	P				
2-2-01/009	M&E engineering design				S	A		P			
2-2-01/010	Architectural design				S	A	P			P	
2-2-01/011	General arrgts (tender)	S				S	A	P	I	I	
2-2-01/012	Ditto (contract)	S				S	A				
2-2-01/013	Detail drawings	S				S	A	P		P	
2-2-01/014	General specifications					A/S	P	P			
2-2-01/015	Engineering specifications	S				A/S	P	P			
2-2-01/016	Produce tender documents	S	P			A	I	I	I	I	
2-2-01/017	Evaluate tender returns	S	P			I	P				
2-2-01/018	Contractor appointment	A/S	P			I					
2-2-01/019	Establish site team	S	R			I			I	I	
2-2-01/020	Supervise contractor	S	A	R							
2-2-01/021	As constructed drawings	S	R	R							
2-2-01/022	Archive site records	S	A	A							

Key for PO: R - reviews SP outputs; A - approves SP outputs; S - signs-off on SP outputs

Key for SP: P - performs activity; A - approves activity; R - reviews activity; I - provides input to activity; S - signs-off on activity

TEAM ROLE SPECIFICATION

Team title	*Role*
Study manager	Responsible for achieving the study aims and the associated goals, and will be the sole authority for the day-to-day management of the study. The study manager will be responsible for approving payments to the SP in accordance with the terms of the contract, and ensuring that any owner requirement has been incorporated into the study activities.
Planner specialist	Responsible for ensuring that all planning input data used in the study are in accordance with existing guidelines. The planner will respond to any planning issues raised, and will ratify any new policies recommended by the service provider (and adopted by the stakeholders).
Drainage system specialist	Responsible for liaising with the SP and LA representatives and other nominated LA specialists on all aspects of the physical infrastructure. This will include, but is not be limited to, catchment data, asset data, event data (rainfall, dry weather flow, storm flow, diversion, etc.), calibration recommendations and installation, etc.
Computer model specialist	Responsible for liasing with the SP to ensure that the model and its verification are fully in accordance with the study requirements. These responsibilities will include ensuring that the SP examines and interprets all possible risk and implementation scenarios.
Land survey specialist	Responsible for shadowing the SP's personnel who have the responsibility for all surveying activities of the existing urban drainage system that will be required. These activities will include viewing of aerial photographs, examination of drawings of zonal infrastructure, physical measurement of coordinates and levels, assessing physical properties of watercourses, etc.
GIS specialist	Responsible for shadowing the SP's personnel who have responsibility developing the geographical information system for the area under consideration. The responsibilities will include liasing with the modelling group in their investigation into gaps in the asset records and ratifying solutions that will be compatible with the owner's existing GIS for water supply and determining the GIS to be used in the study.
Schedule and cost control specialist	Reports to the study manager, and responsible for providing assistance on time and cost control and special support to the study manager on any aspect of the study activities and the management of the study. The specialist will also be available for facilitating required study workshops.

HR-043: Role assignments and appointments

Policy

This procedure deals with the identification, interviewing and selection of personnel to be appointed to previously identified roles within project teams. The performing organisation's project team is required to manage the scope of work covered by the study or project. However, there should be a requirement to assemble all or part of a management team to supervise the work of contractors or installation companies; this procedure also applies to that type of resource option.

The requirement for a project organisation structure is identified and documented under procedure HR-042. This is the case whether the team is:

- a performing organisation team to supervise an external service or external works
- part of a human resource amalgam acting for the owner, e.g. an owner's representative
- supervising the implementation as part of a management entity engaged to act for the owner.

The procurement philosophy should be for the performing organisation to maintain the responsibility of a project's management. Corporate policy should be to avoid engaging an external organisation during implementation to supervise works that the same organisation has designed.

The appointment of performing organisation personnel for project team positions should be on the basis of their overall experience, their detailed knowledge of the project under consideration and their specialist skills. An interview should be held with short-listed personnel for each vacant team role. A selection panel should undertake the short-listing and the interviewing process of candidates. The selection panel would normally consist of the project manager (of the project under consideration), a representative from senior management, and an internal specialist with expertise in the development area of the study or project. The selection process follows a predetermined approach based on this procedure. Each candidate going forward for consideration is advised of the selection process, the criteria for advancement and eventual selection; this information should be available to each candidate before the start of the process. Each candidate in the long list should be informed of his or her evaluation in meeting/not meeting the short-list criteria. Each candidate short-listed should be informed of his or her evaluation in meeting/not meeting final selection.

Any form of canvassing would normally lead to the immediate withdrawal of the offending candidate from any further consideration for the project on which the candidate seeks a position and to which the canvassing relates.

Outcome

This procedure creates the linkages between the preceding staff management plan, the human resource needs of the team needed to undertake a project, and the final selection of individuals to the various team roles. The outcome of this procedure is a notification to all successful candidates for project roles to take up their position by a specified date and report to the project's manager. The outcome also incorporates notifications to all unsuccessful candidates.

Through this procedure it is intended that all performing organisation staff with an active interest in the management of projects should, as often as possible, be given the opportunity to serve in project teams.

This procedure recognises that if an individual needs exposure to projects and needs project management experience then they are not disadvantaged if, in any staff competition, they do not have such experience. However, it should be also be recognised by performing organisation personnel that the larger and more complex projects, and those that present significant risks to the owner, require the most experienced and best qualified personnel. In other words, on certain projects experience and track record in managing projects are significant requirements in the selection process.

Process

Reference to *project manager* can also mean *study manager* when the project is at the pre-investment phase. *Stakeholder* means any party, or entity, within the performing organisation and it can also mean any external entity that impacts on, or is impacted by, the project under consideration.

The following process should be used:

Person	Responsibility
Project manager	Reviews the staff management plan (HR-041) and the outcome of the project organisation and team roles procedure (HR-042). These procedures, along with the procurement management plan (PT-061), are instrumental in determining whether:
	(1) the owner will manage using their own human resources
	(2) an external entity will be procured to manage for and on behalf of the owner
	(3) the management will be part of a human resource hybrid that uses both the owner's personnel and external personnel.
	When (2) or (3) applies:
Project manager	Prepares documentation under selected procurement procedures and therein specifies the extent to which the performing organisation's staff are required to manage external entities or be seconded to external entities.
External entity	The firm or company that is/has been contracted to act for and on behalf of the owner provides a project's organisation chart to the project manager. This chart shows all team roles and those roles that have been identified as being resourced from the performing organisation's staff register. Each role identified is to be complete with a role specification, indicating the associated duties, responsibilities and authority. Other job conditions relating to each role, such as normal work-day, work week, holidays and working conditions, are provided to the

project manager. The result of these actions by the external entity, after any negotiation with the project manager, is recorded in box 1 on form HR-043/1.

Or, when (1) applies:

Project manager	Prepares an internal advertisement for communicating project role opportunities. Prepares an information pack for respondents that gives salient aspects about the project, the project's organisation chart and a role specification for each role available. E-mails or sends hard copy information pack to each respondent. Completes box 1 on form HR-043/1 and sends a copy of the form to the sponsor and/or the external entity.
Senior management	Nominates an individual to the project team selection panel.
Project manager	The selection panel meets and assesses the competence of each candidate against declared criteria. As the leader of the selection panel the project manager signs-off on the panel's recommended short-list of candidates. The project manager informs the respondents who have been/have not been selected for the identified team roles. Completes box 2 on form HR-043/1.
Selection panel	With the project manager as leader, the team selection panel interviews and assesses the short-listed candidates using ranked selection criteria similar to those shown in exhibit HR-043/2. Box 2 of form HR-043/1 is completed and the form filed.
Project manager	The successful candidates are contacted by the project manager and requested to meet the project manager by an appointed time and date. The unsuccessful candidates are accordingly notified.

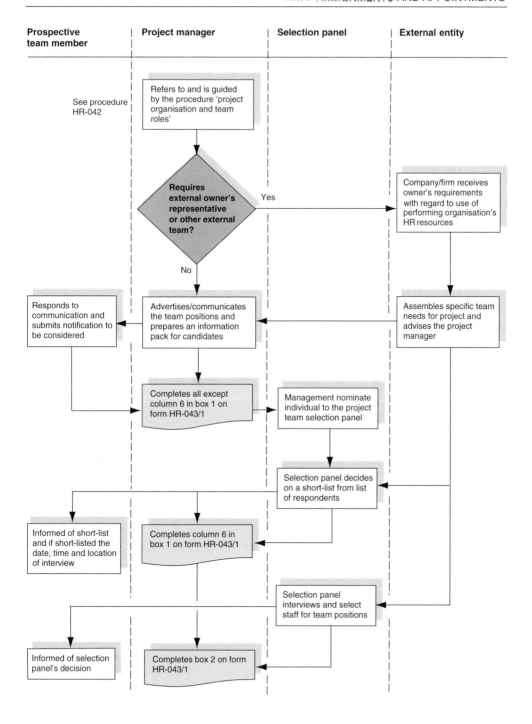

| Prospective team member | Project manager | Selection panel | External entity |

See procedure HR-042

Refers to and is guided by the procedure 'project organisation and team roles'

Requires external owner's representative or other external team?

Yes

Company/firm receives owner's requirements with regard to use of performing organisation's HR resources

No

Responds to communication and submits notification to be considered

Advertises/communicates the team positions and prepares an information pack for candidates

Assembles specific team needs for project and advises the project manager

Completes all except column 6 in box 1 on form HR-043/1

Management nominate individual to the project team selection panel

Selection panel decides on a short-list from list of respondents

Informed of short-list and if short-listed the date, time and location of interview

Completes column 6 in box 1 on form HR-043/1

Selection panel interviews and select staff for team positions

Informed of selection panel's decision

Completes box 2 on form HR-043/1

Box 1

Project/Study name _____ Job ref. # [_____]

Project/Study manager _____ Sponsor _____

Project team | (1) ☐ Solely owner resources | (2) ☐ Solely external resources | (3) ☐ Hybrid of internal/external

• Documentation for (2) and/or (3)

Name of documents sent	Ref. #	Date sent	Sent by

• Information pack sent to candidates

☐ Yes Date sent [_____]

☐ No Explain [_____]

• Register of candidates

(4) Name	(5) Section	(6) Short-listed (yes/no)

• Form copied to ☐ Owner (performing organisation ☐ Sponsor ☐ External entity

Signed-off _____ (project manager) Date _____

Box 2

- Interview panel

Name	Organisation/affiliation	Related expertise

- Short-list interview assessment

Team role position [   ]   Date held [   ]

Candidates name	Current grade	Score	Rank	Informed — date

Team role position [   ]   Date held [   ]

Candidates name	Current grade	Score	Rank	Informed — date

Copy this sheet when interviews held for more than two positions

Signed-off _____ (project manager)   Date _____

1 Ref No.	2 Selection criteria	4 Weight %	4 AA Score	5 AA 3×4	4 BB Score	5 BB 3×6	8 CC Score	9 CC 3×8	10 DD Score	11 DD 3×10	12 EE Score	13 EE 3×12
100	Technical skills	20	1	20	0.75	15	0.75	15	1	20	0.75	15
101	Project management knowledge/training	20	0.5	10	0.75	15	1	20	0.25	5	0.5	10
102	Experience of similar project work	12	0.5	6	0	0	0	0	0.5	6	1	12
103	Communication and interpersonal skills	10	0.75	7.5	1	10	0.25	2.5	0.5	5	0.75	7.5
104	Decision making/problem solving	10	0.5	5	0.5	5	0.75	7.5	0.75	7.5	0.5	5
105	Planning and organising ability	10	0.5	5	0.75	7.5	1	10	0.25	2.5	0.5	5
106	Ability to handle conflict	18	0	0	0.5	9	0.5	9	0.5	9	1	18
	Weighted score of each candidate			53.5		61.5		64		55		72.5
	Ranking of candidates			5		3		2		4		1

score system

1.00 = impressive or more than satisfies
0.75 = better than average ability/competence but not exceptional
0.50 = average ability/competence
0.25 = less than average ability/competence
0.00 = no discernible ability/competence

Explanation of 100 to 106

100 = assessment of ability within area specified by team role
101 = certified as PMP, progress with training modules, PMBOK?
102 = rate H, M or L depending on past exposure to similar project roles
103 = rate 5 min. verbal presentation, check letters, e-mails, etc.
104 = gave test and check weaknesses
105 = rate H, M or L depending on systems used, review of personal 'project file'
106 = question candidate on past relationships with owner, SP, contractors, etc.

HR-044: Staff training programme

Policy

This procedure outlines the training programme to be provided in the discipline of project management. The training programme is structured from introduction level to specialised level and is available to any member of staff who is involved in or likely to become involved in the management of projects. This involvement includes anyone who is an appointed member of a project team or has an assigned role to support a project.

The individual requirements that are needed to enter each level are:

- Level K (knowledge): open to all permanent staff who are engaged in, either part time or full time, or who hold a position that is likely to lead to becoming a member of a project team.
- Level C (competence): open to staff who have satisfactorily completed the level K module, or its equivalent, and who seek to add to their knowledge by gaining skills in the application of the tools and techniques of project management.
- Level E (expertise): open to staff who have satisfactorily completed the level K and C modules and who seek to become certified as a project manager.

Senior management and/or the project management training facilitator are the final arbiter in determining the appropriate level of any individual seeking project management training and in determining his or her suitability to progress to the next level of such training.

This training programme is for the shared benefit of the individual and individual's employer. The individual gains through enhanced management capability and the employer gains through the application of the project management process to corporate projects. Accordingly a training charter (see procedure HR-044/2) states the expectations and undertakings by both parties. The charter should be signed at the beginning of level C.

Outcome

The outcome of this procedure is skills transfer in the discipline of project management to those staff requiring such enhancement.

The overall intention is to increase what can only be described as a current general awareness of the subject within the corporate body, to a level where a significant number of staff have competence or expertise. Recent surveys show that, in some cases, less than 7 out of every 10 staff members have only an awareness of the project management process and know little or nothing of what the process can achieve. It is generally found that in many organisations only a very small percentage of staff could claim to have any competence or expertise in the discipline. So the outcome of this procedure is to redress this general situation through focusing on raising the skills profile of staff.

The modules that make up the project management training programme are shown in the table on the next page.

It is possible that a participant could take between 6 months and 1 year to complete the training programme. The speed of progress is determined by the number of people to be trained, the scheduling and availability of training modules, and the prioritising of training to individuals engaged on live projects.

Modules that make up the project management training programme:

Level	Code	Title	Duration
K	01	Introduction to project management	3 consecutive days
C	02	Scope and time management	2 consecutive days
C	03	Cost and communication management	2 consecutive days
C	04	Risk and procurement management	2 consecutive days
C	05	Human resources and quality management	2 consecutive days
E	06	Team building and leadership	4 consecutive days (inc. Sat. and Sun.)
E	07	Project critiquing	2 consecutive days
E	08	Certification exam preparation	1 day

The outcome of the training is to be directly linked to improved management of corporate projects. Through the charter the individual gives an undertaking to apply the project management tools and techniques. Through the internal auditing of projects (see procedure CN-010) senior management is able to determine the effectiveness of the skills transfer.

Process

Facilitator means the individual(s) assigned to design, develop and facilitate the training programme. *Candidate* means an individual interested in project management training. *Participant* is anyone who has been accepted for project management training.

The following process should be used:

Person	Responsibility
Facilitator	Prepares the training materials on an on going basis for the K, C and E modules.
	Advertises the training programme on the in-house communications system and invites individuals to participate.
Candidate	Each person who is of the view that they need training in project management completes box 1 of form HR-044/1 and sends it to the training facilitator.
Facilitator	Accepts/rejects the application. Acceptances are assigned to modules and the participant is advised of venue, date, times, etc. A copy of the training charter (see HR-044/2) is sent to the participant.
Participant	The participant returns the signed training charter to the facilitator.

Facilitator/participant	At the end of the K level, C level and E level the participant is interviewed to determine satisfaction in the skills transfer, relevance to his/her job, and attitude towards the past and, if appropriate, next level of training.
Facilitator	Tracks the individual's progress through the programme and completes box 2 of form HR-044/1.
	When complete the form is signed by the facilitator and placed in the project management training file.

Box 1

Surname _____	First name _____ File ref. # [_____]

Grade _____ Date appointed _____ Department/section _____

Current project _____ Job title _____

Qualifications in PM ☐ No ☐ Yes Specify _____

• Past PM training

Date	Title	Training organisation

Signed _____ (training facilitator) Date _____

Box 2

• PM training progress

1. Level K completed ☐ No ☐ Yes

Dates attended K01 _____ or dates attended equivalent _____

Planned dates for level K module [_____] Approved by _____

Interview at end of level K ☐ No ☐ Yes ☐ Recommended to progress to next level
☐ Not recommended for next level

Facilitator's comments

2. Level C modules

Date	Title	Attendance

Box 2 continued

2. Level C modules

Interview at end of level C   ☐ No   ☐ Yes   ☐ Recommended to progress to next level
   ☐ Not recommended for next level (see below)

Facilitator's comments

3. Level E modules

Date	Title	Attendance

- Interview at end of level E   ☐ No   ☐ Yes   Date _____

Facilitator's comments

- Professional certification   ☐ No   ☐ Yes

Comments

- Post-training courses

Specify

Signed-off and filed by _____ (facilitator)   Date _____

TRAINING CHARTER

Training deliverables

The employer has developed and will deliver an integrated training programme that is in line with the organisation's project management philosophy and the corporate *Handbook of Project Management Procedures*. The training programme is structured in three levels, namely K (knowledge), C (competence) and E (expertise). The training course has been modulated: level K has 1 module, level C has 4 modules and level E has 3 modules. The progression for participants shall be K to C to E, but it is recognised that many individuals may not wish to proceed beyond level K. Individuals who are involved in directing, managing, working in or supporting projects are the prime candidates for the complete suite of training modules. Participants at any level shall be briefly interviewed at the end of each level to determine their motivation and suitability for progressing to the next level. Each participant, by signing this charter, gives the employer his or her undertaking to learn and apply the transferred project management skills to any project that they may be assigned to.

Employers acceptance criteria

Any candidate for consideration as a participant in this training programme is required to demonstrate:

(1)   that they are a permanent employee;

(2)   their daily work would classify as project work;

(3)   they have the interest and determination to create self-change towards a 'management by projects' approach.

During attendance at any training module each participant is expected to approach the skills transfer process in a positive way and with enthusiasm. Each participant is expected to add to the learning process by contributing to two-person SAQs (self-assessment questions), working in plenary workshops, and in the general debate on the employer's drive towards 'best practice' project management.

Participants acceptance criteria

Each participant anticipates that the training programme delivers its stated objectives at each level of skills transfer, i.e. K, C and E. Before each training module, each participant expects the training facilitator to provide adequate notice regarding venue, date(s) and the content of the daily programme. For each training module, each participant expects to be provided with good quality notes and other documentation that may be retained. Participants also expect the facilitators to be qualified in project management and have considerable ability in providing skills transfer. Each participant expects equitable and fair treatment in any post-discussion relating to his or her training performance.

Agreement

The undersigned, the training facilitator and the participant for project management training, concur with the stated intended deliverables and the acceptance criteria within this Training Charter.

....
For employer   *Date*   *Participant*   *Date*

HR-045: Selection, appraisal and reward

Policy

Procedure HR-043 addresses the selection of project team members based on the job role that they are required to perform. In addition to evaluating a team member's performance, this procedure commences with assessing individual behavioural characteristics as part of the selection process of a project team. A project team should consist of members who are selected based on their job role and on their 'behavioural role'.

To determine a member's behavioural role a range of techniques should be used (e.g. interview, psychometric profiling). In most cases an individual's behavioural role shall be determined using interviewing and the 16PF method of personality profiling. However, results from such tests should be compared against information from other sources. An experienced facilitator shall assess the results of these methods, and the behavioural strengths and weaknesses identified should be discussed with the person concerned.

The job role and the behavioural role shall both be used in the appointment of individuals to become members of a project team.

Once assigned to a project team the process of checking performance shall be carried out at interviews with the project sponsor and project manager at the end of each project stage. For larger projects having long period stages it may be necessary to undertake performance checks at one or more times during a stage.

Differentiation between high, medium and low performance shall be reflected in the performance bonus to be paid either annually when salaries are reviewed, at the end of a project or at the end of a person's assigned role, whichever is earlier.

Outcome

The outcome of this procedure is an input to procedure HR-043, which addresses the matter of appointing individuals to team role positions. A team that has balance in both the roles needed to undertake and manage the scope of work and in the personal working relationships between team members is likely to be more successful than one that is not balanced.

Having been assigned to a team role the subsequent performance of the individual is measured and discussed at interviews held at stage end, role end and, if appropriate, project end.

The procedure provides a basis for rewarding individual effort measured on a scale of high, medium and low.

Process

Reference to *project manager* can also mean *study manager* when the project is at the pre-investment phase.

The following process should be used:

Person	Responsibility
Project manager	Prior to project team appointment box 1 of form HR-045/1 is completed for all potential assignees. This information is photo-copied and distributed to all members of the selection panel.

Selection panel	Panel members decide on the interviewee's suitability for selection to the assigned team role. The interviewers complete box 2 of form HR-045/1 and sign the form. The form is copied to the project manager.
Project manager and sponsor	Upon conclusion of an interview with the team member, box 3 of form HR-045/1 is completed and signed by the sponsor and the project manager.
	It is the project manager's responsibility to ensure that the reward for individual performance is actioned and at the appropriate time.

Box 1

Project/Study name _____ Job ref. # [_____]

Project/Study manager _____ Date _____

Current stage ☐ CT ☐ FS ☐ D1 ☐ SL ☐ D2 ☐ PR ☐ CN ☐ CO

- Project role and assignee

Project role	Period of role	Name of assignee

- Information on assignee

Name:

Birth date:

Nationality:

Education:

Qualifications:

Experience:

- Curriculum vitae   ☐ Attached   Date prepared [_____]

Comments

Box 2

- Project appointment interview

Interviewer's comments

Signed _____ (interviewer)   Date _____

Signed _____ (interviewer)   Date _____

SELECTION, APPRAISAL AND REWARD

Box 3

☐ **Performance tracking and reward**

☐ Stage (CT, etc.)   ☐ *High*   ☐ *Medium*   ☐ *Low*

Comments

Proposed reward	*Action taken*	
	By whom	*Date*

Signed _____ (sponsor)   Date _____

Signed _____ (project manager)   Date _____

☐ Stage (CT, etc.)   ☐ *High*   ☐ *Medium*   ☐ *Low*

Comments

Proposed reward	*Action taken*	
	By whom	*Date*

Signed _____ (sponsor)   Date _____

Signed _____ (project manager)   Date _____

☐ Stage (CT, etc.)   ☐ *High*   ☐ *Medium*   ☐ *Low*

Comments

Proposed reward	*Action taken*	
	By whom	*Date*

Signed _____ (sponsor)   Date _____

Signed _____ (project manager)   Date _____

Health and safety procedures

This section contains one procedure that deals with a project's health and safety management. The procedure is:

HS-051   Health and safety management plan

A brief overview of the procedure and what the procedure sets out to achieve is as follows.

HS-051: Health and safety management plan

This procedure documents the health and safety policy for a project and determines the health and safety issues that need to be the focus of a project's stakeholders and those responsible for a project's health and safety management plan (HSMP). It also provides guidelines on which related health and safety parameters are to be measured to create a meaningful data set. It also is specific relative to safety performance. As health and safety issues change during a project's life cycle, an HSMP may be needed at the beginning of each stage of a project.

HS-051: Health and safety management plan

Policy

The project management team of the performing organisation shall be responsible for ensuring that appropriate health facilities are in place and safety systems are in force, and that they comply with the law and obey statutory regulations. In certain cases, probably determined by the size and/or complexity of a project, it shall be necessary to appoint a safety manager.

The elements that are to be contained within a health and safety management plan are what information, instruction, training and supervision are to be made available and how are these duties to be discharged.

A policy statement must be developed for the study or project to be undertaken and it should be supportive of the corporate policy on health and safety issues. The health and safety policy statement should contain a general statement of policy, the organisation and responsibilities for carrying out the policy, and the arrangements for ensuring the safety and health of the stakeholders engaged on a project.

The health and safety plan needs to specify the health and safety issues that should be a focus for the current stage of a project's development. 'Health' meaning such matters as cleanliness, ventilation, lighting, etc., and 'safety' meaning such matters as obstructions, fire escapes, machinery, fencing, etc.

The data elements on which measurements are obtained for health and safety matters shall be specified. These collected data are to be analysed during a stage of a project and, if appropriate, amalgamated with the data from previous stages. The analysed results are to be used as feedback to the instruction and training and to the approach to be used in determining safety performance.

Outcome

This procedure provides the health and safety management plan (HSMP) for a project. The HSMP describes how a project team, or a safety manager, implements the health and safety policy. In other words, the organisational structure, stakeholder responsibilities, and the health and safety processes needed to provide a healthy and safe working environment are specified for the project under consideration.

Process

Reference to *project manager* can also mean *study manager* when a project is at the pre-investment phase. *Stakeholder* means any party, or entity, within the performing organisation and it can also mean any external entity that impacts on, or is impacted by, the project under consideration.

The following process should be used:

Person	Responsibility
Project manager or safety manager	Arranges a workshop (see procedure CN-003) for attendance by all project stakeholders to determine the management plan for dealing with health and safety.

Stakeholders	Attendees to the workshop contribute in determining:

- a project's health and safety policy statement
- the management procedures to be used
- the content of the HSMP.

Project manager	Uses HS-051/1 to document an overview of the HSMP and completes boxes 1 and 2 as agreement is reached regarding the associated issues.

The project manager, or a nominated other, is assigned the role of ensuring that the HSMP is adhered to, modified as needed, and all stakeholders are compliant.

Box 1

Project/Study name _____ Job ref. # [   ]

Project/Study manager _____ Sponsor_____

Current project stage ☐ CT ☐ FS ☐ D1 ☐ EL ☐ D2 ☐ PR ☐ CN ☐ CO

■ Health & Safety policy statement for project/study

[   ]

• Responsibility for H&S (use ✓)

☐ Project management team
☐ Safety manager
☐ Other (specify)

Explain

[   ]

• Health topics to be addressed

Health issue	Description

• Safety topics to be addressed

Perceived safety issue	Description	Collect data (use ✓)	
		Yes	No

Checked by _____ (project manager)   Date _____

Approved by _____ (safety manager)   Date _____

Box 2

• Safety instruction and training

General safety issue	Project stakeholder names I (internal) E (external)	Frequency	
		Briefings	Training

• Primary data collection

• Accident details

Date	Location	Description of what happened

• Casualty information

Name of casualty	Type of injury	Level of injury

• Attendant circumstances

Details of factors

• Safety performance

Inspection date	Inspector	Unsafe condition	Action required		Re-inspect policy
			Specify	By whom	

Checked by _____ (project manager)   Date _____

Approved by _____ (safety manager)   Date _____

Procurement procedures

This section contains fifteen procedures that deal with certain aspects of procuring external services and/or works. The procedures are:

PT-061   Procurement management plan (services)
PT-062   Advertise to procure a service
PT-063   'Request for proposal' document
PT-064   Prequalify potential service provider candidates
PT-065   Holding a bidders' conference
PT-066   Evaluate external service proposals
PT-067   Specifying time and price requirements (services)
PT-071   Procurement management plan (works)
PT-072   Request to participate (works)
PT-073   Request for tender (works)
PT-074   Appointing a contractor
PT-075   Recording the works
PT-076   Communications during the works
PT-077   Reporting on the works
PT-078   Works measurement and payment certification

A brief overview of each procedure and what each procedure sets out to achieve is as follows.

PT-061: Procurement management plan (services)

When the performing organisation need to procure external technical or professional assistance, the plan on how that should be undertaken and other matters relating to this type of procurement package are described in this procedure. The procurement management plan for services requires statements on such issues as advertising, prequalification, requesting an offer, selection, the control of a service provider (SP) and auditing of an SP.

PT-062: Advertise to procure a service

This procedure follows an EU directive on how to procure an external service. Although these guidelines are primarily for public sector application there is significant potential for helping and inspiring private organisations seeking external assistance. In essence, the procedure seeks to obtain responses to a near-future intention to advertise an RFP (request for proposal).

PT-063: 'Request for proposal' document

For the medium to large project, an RFP (Request for proposal) document, developed by the performing organisation (owner), is needed because the owner's requirements for an external service cannot be covered by a simple advertisement (procedure PT-062). A substantial RFP document normally succeeds the production of a PRID (project requirement and information document), which is covered by procedure SE-124.

PT-064: Prequalify potential service provider candidates

Having a large number of candidates bidding for proposed work for which only one candidate can be successful is highly wasteful of resources and has the effect of increasing overheads, which is passed on through proposal mark-ups. This procedure recommends that any requirement for an external service should normally be competed for by three entities, although there may be circumstances where five or more competitors could be accommodated.

PT-065: Holding a bidders' conference

In most cases the requirements of an owner cannot be fully communicated through documentation. This procedure recommends a conference for bidders be arranged during the bidding period, to facilitate communications from the owner and to give the potential bidders an opportunity to raise questions and seek clarification on the project (study) requirements.

PT-066: Evaluate external service proposals

When proposals to perform a service have been submitted to an owner organisation, a structured method is used for evaluation and ordering so that the preferred offer is identified. This procedure provides a process for determining the criteria against which the proposals would be assessed and how to weight the criteria. Scoring each proposal against the weighted criteria would typically expose the preferred proposal as the one with the highest scoring.

PT-067: Specifying time and price requirements (services)

Built into any RFP should be the owner's requirement regarding what control protocol the successful bidder is expected to comply with. Any external entity providing a service, as part of a project, is expected to plan, execute and control the service's WBS (work breakdown structure) activities and tasks. This procedure relates to the drafting of a suitable clause for inclusion within the RFP, and concludes with documenting the SP's compliance agreement

PT-071: Procurement management plan (works)

This procedure is one of the group of procedures that establishes strategies for the different knowledge areas of a project. PT-071 deals with the procurement strategy relating to works contracts. This includes determining the type of contract to use, the most appropriate method of contract award, and the method of measurement and payment.

PT-072: Request to participate (works)

When external resources are needed to carry out some aspect of a project's implementation, or works, that cannot be undertaken by the owner, an early step would be the identification of suitable external entities that could undertake the owner's requirements. This procedure provides guidance on and assistance with advertising and evaluating submissions so that a short-list of suitable bidders (tenderers) can be developed.

PT-073: Request for tender (works)

This procedure is used when there is a need to procure an external organisation to undertake the supply, installation and commissioning of planned work or to implement some physical aspect of the project. The procedure spans the events from having prequalified and selected an agreed short-list of suitable organisations, to the opening of received tender bids from these organisations. The content of the RFT (request for tender), who is to draft each element of the RFT, the schedule for drafting and matters relating to the succeeding bidding period are all documented in procedure PT-072.

PT-074: Appointing a contractor

This procedure applies at any time during a project's life cycle when there is a need to engage an external organisation to undertake work which is not a service (e.g. supply of equipment, installation, building works). In most cases a contractor will be appointed after a number of capable organisations have been short-listed from a longer list of possible candidates and after the short-listed entities have submitted detailed offers in response to an RFT (see procedures PT-072 and PT-073). The identification of a preferred bidder, i.e. the company likely to become the contracted party, is the result of a robust process of selecting measurable criteria, scoring each bidder against these criteria and the outcome of holding exhaustive discussions.

PT-075: Recording the works

In most cases, the owner has the greatest exposure to capital outflows when a project's current stage is CN (construction). In many cases, when a project's performance closely reflects what was originally planned, recording what happens each day is of little consequence other than 'for the record'. However, when things go wrong and a project's performance does not reflect its predetermined plan, detailed daily records of what actually happened are found to be invaluable. This procedure deals with the keeping of daily project records.

PT-076: Communications during the works

This procedure sets out guidelines on the format and registration to be used for the many forms of communication that are developed during a project's implementation.

PT-077: Reporting on the works

This procedure provides guidance on the structure and format for weekly, monthly and exception reports. The procedure provides a template for logging the measurement of work within a project's WBS that can be used for both a project's performance and a works contractor's claim for payment. The procedure also requires the discipline to register and document the issuing of all reports.

PT-078: Works measurement and payment certification

Although this procedure has been designed for works contracts it is equally applicable to service-type contracts. In most contracts between an owner and external entities there is a need to measure achievements at set times and from these measurements establish performance and how much should be paid to each entity. This procedure provides guidance and templates for both the measurement and the certification processes.

PT-061: Procurement management plan (services)

Policy

The owner should take responsibility for the work to be undertaken in the first stage of any project — the concept stage. From time to time, it may be necessary to engage an individual external expert or experts to assist with the conceptualisation work on a particular project. If during the concept stage external assistance is required, it should be procured using a letter or other suitable means of communication. The payment terms should be on the basis of the time and materials (T&M) needed to undertake the assistance.

This procedure deals with planning the procurement of an SP (service provider) after the concept stage and, if required, for some aspect of the concept stage work. The procedure should be used in the early stages of project development when the owner is deliberating over the professional services that may be needed to plan, execute and control a project. Professional services can therefore relate to such work packages as feasibility studies, scheme design, detail design, preparation of tender documentation, environmental impact studies, specialist analysis and recommendations, and works supervision. For any project it is necessary to determine the extent to which the owner takes responsibility for these professional service work packages and how much the owner wishes to procure from external sources.

The procurement management plan (services) offers the means for determining and documenting strategic procurement matters. The procurement management plan (services) relates to all stages of a project from feasibility stage to the completion stage. It should be the owner's policy to procure external services for a project stage by stage and based on merit. Only in extenuating circumstances should an external SP be appointed for the entire development life cycle of a project through to its completion.

The project manager, with the assistance of the project team and other project stakeholders, should determine the content to be included within a procurement management plan (services), and whether it should be broadly or narrowly focused.

Where appropriate, the procurement directives of the EC and/or the directive notes of any other statutory agency, etc., should be consulted and checked for general compliance and/or guidance. In the event of non-compliance, the project manager is required to advise the appropriate agency and, if the need arises, argue the case for non-compliance.

Outcome

This procedure initiates the process for determining the external professional services required and the procurement processes and steps to be taken. The final outcome will be a procurement management plan (services) that, for most projects, will be a formal document to be used for executing and controlling the external entities who will provide the needed services.

The procurement management plan (services) will provide a documented structure for which service packages are to be procured and, after appointment, the means of control and the auditing of each service provider. The structure of the procurement management plan will include such matters as the advertising requirements, the prequalification process, the bidding process, the selection process, and the monitoring and auditing processes required during the post-selection period.

- *Advertising*: the procurement management plan (services) should state what external services are to be procured. The procurement process to be followed is described in procedure PT-062.
- *Prequalification*: only a small number of interested firms, organisations or individuals should be prequalified to ensure that the bidding effort does not generate a large number of unsuccessful candidates. The strategy for the prequalification process (see procedure PT-064) should be outlined in this section.
- *Proposal request*: any particular requirements relating to creating the RFP and the owner's requirements for the bidding process will be dealt with within this section. The processes to be followed are contained within procedures PT-062, PT-063 and PT-065.
- *Selection process*: the process used by the owner and from which the preferred bidder will be identified should be documented within this section. The associated process is contained in procedure PT-066.
- *Controlling the SP*: this section of the procedure will contain the requirements for monitoring and controlling the service to be provided by whoever will be appointed as the SP. Monitoring the time expended and cost aspects of an SP's commission are covered by procedure PT-067.
- *Auditing*: each appointed SP will be subject to the performing organisation's auditing process (see procedure CN-010). The procurement management plan (services) needs to indicate the auditing strategy.

Process

Reference to *project manager* can also mean study manager when the project is at the pre-investment phase. *Stakeholder* means any party, or entity, within the performing organisation and it can also mean any external entity that impacts on, or is impacted by, the project under consideration. *PMP* refers to the procurement management plan (services).

The following process should be used:

Person	Responsibility
Project manager	Decides on the need to arrange a workshop of all appropriate stakeholders to examine the approach that should be adopted for determining the content of the PMP. The project manager is required to consult and use procedure CN-003. The project manager completes box 1 on form PT-061/1.
Stakeholders	Each entity invited to attend a PMP workshop nominates an attendee to represent them and informs the project manager accordingly. Each attendee is required to make a positive contribution to the outcomes of the workshop.
Project manager	Upon conclusion of the workshop the project manager completes boxes 2 to 4 on form PT-061/1. The project

manager is responsible for obtaining the sponsor sign-off to the content of PT-061/1 which, along with all other detailed information, constitutes the project's procurement management plan (services).

The project manager is responsible for circulating a copy of the completed 'PMP — principal features' to the appropriate and associated stakeholders. The master copy of PT-061/1 will be placed in the project file.

Box 1

Project/Study name _____ Job ref. # [_____]

Project/Study manager _____ Sponsor _____

Planned workshop   Date [_____]   Time [_____]   Venue [_____]

Procedure CN-003 complied with   ☐ Yes ☐ No   Reason [_____]

Workshop code number [_____]   Assigned facilitator _____

Signed _____ (project manager)   Date _____

Box 2

- At what stage is the project?

☐ Concept   ☐ Other stage   Name stage [_____]

- What services need to be procured?

☐ 01. Individual expertise
     Specify: [_____]

☐ 02. Technical feasibility
☐ 03. Financial feasibility
☐ 04. Procurement feasibility
☐ 05. Environmental impact
☐ 06. Legal and statutory
☐ 07. Design — outline or scheme design
☐ 08. Design — detail including specifications drawings
☐ 09. Tender documents and document issue
☐ 10. Tender assessment and preferred bidder recommendation
☐ 11. Contract supervision and administration
☐ 12. Commissioning and training of owner personnel
☐ 13. Contract claims assessment and adjudication

- Advertisement to procure service provider (other than for 01) individual expertise

Advertisement reference number   Service to be provided (use above refs 01 to 13)

[_____]   [_____]

[_____]   [_____]

[_____]   [_____]

Other comments

Box 3

- Pre-qualification strategy

Service to be provided	Pre-qualification			Explanation and justification
	Yes	No	Number[1]	

[1] Number refers to the planned number of pre-qualifiers — recommended 3 or 4 from the pre-qualification process

☐ Pre-qualification information document to be sent to all interested parties
☐ Other approach   Specify below

- Request for Proposal (RFP)

☐ Letter of invitation to procure concept stage expert
☐ RFP document pertaining to the services required

To include heading structure as follows:

☐ Definitions
☐ The current situation
☐ Contracting authorities' requirements
☐ Selecting an expert/a service provider*
☐ Making a submission to undertake the requirements
☐ Other heading   Specify below

* Delete whichever is not applicable

Box 4

- Selection process

☐ The lowest price
☐ Most economically advantageous tender
☐ Other method   Specify below

- Controlling the SP

☐ Earned value technique
☐ Other method   Specify below

☐ Suitable control clause specified in letter of invitation/RFP

Auditing the SP   ⟵——————— Project stages ———————⟶

Audit frequency	FS	D1	SL	D2	PR	CN	CO
Once	☐	☐	☐	☐	☐	☐	☐
Twice	☐	☐	☐	☐	☐	☐	☐
Three times	☐	☐	☐	☐	☐	☐	☐

Other comments   Specify below

Signed by _____ (project manager)   Date _____

Ratified by _____ (sponsor)   Date _____

PT-062: Advertise to procure a service

Policy

Although written primarily for procurement by a public body, the outcome and the process are fundamental and would also relate to procurement by a private sector organisation.

This procedure is used when there is a need to procure the services of an external professional entity, such as a consulting engineering practice, a specialist adviser, a construction management consultant or an owner's representative, that can be accomplished by placing an advertisement.

In procuring such a service the public sector is legally bound to comply with EU Public Procurement Directives. For services contracts or appointments the requirements of these directives need to be complied with.

Having developed the procurement strategy, which is documented in the procurement management plan (see procedure PT-061), a subsequent action is to advertise the requirement to obtain an external service. An integral aspect of the procurement strategy is the award method, i.e. open competition, restricted competition, negotiated procedure or special concession. The award method and other strategic aspects relating to procuring a service provider should be prerequisites to advertising the owner's requirements.

Providing the anticipated cost of a service is large enough, three notices need to be advertised in the supplement of the OJEC (*Official Journal of the European Communities*). The intended OJEC notices should appear before the same advertisement appears in the national press.

For public sector compliance the three notices that are advertised are:

- prior indicative notice (PIN)
- request for proposal (RFP) notice
- award of appointment notice.

A PIN notice is a statement of intent, usually advertised in the OJEC each January, and is for any service contract having an anticipated value of more than Euro 750,000. An RFP notice is required for any service contract having an anticipated value of more than Euro 249,681. Award of appointment notice should be published within 48 days from the issue of a letter of intent or formal contract.

Outcome

This procedure ensures compliance with EU Directive 92/50/EEC and as amended by 97/52/EC. The outcome which relates to advertising to procure a service should be in three stages reflecting the three notice process, i.e. intent, need to obtain proposals, and notification of successful SP.

Process

Reference to *project manager* can also mean *study manager* when the project is at the pre-investment phase. *EU* means the office for the Official Publications of the European Communities, 2 Rue Mercier, L-2985 Luxembourg (fax: 00 32 495719).

The following process should be used:

Person	Responsibility
Project manager	Is responsible for drafting the notices for insertion in the OJEC and the national press. The project manager's responsibility includes checking that the content of all notices is accurately stated and correct and that the EU directive in relation to compliance is adhered to. It is the responsibility of the project manager or, if designated, the project administrator, to arrange with the EU and the national press for the advertisement to be placed in their publications.
	Upon completion and transmission of each of the three notices the project manager is required to complete the relevant section of form PT-062/1.
	An example of an RFP notice is shown in exhibit PT-062/2.
	All insertions in both the OJEC and national press should be copied to the project's sponsor.
	Once the actions associated with form PT-062/1 have been attended to the project manager completes the form and files it in the project files.

Project/Study name _____   Job ref. # [_____]

Project/Study manager _____   Sponsor_____

Estimated procurement value of SP services [_____]

Planned project/study schedule dates   Start [_____]   Finish [_____]

- Award method to be used in appointing SP

  ☐ Open competition   ☐ Restricted competition
  ☐ Negotiated procedure   ☐ Special concession

  Comments

- PIN notice

  ☐ Published   Date [_____]   ☐ Copy attached
  ☐ Not published   Why? [_____]

  ☐ Copied to sponsor
  ☐ Copied to (specify) [_____]

  Comments

Signed by _____ (project manager)   Date _____

- RFP notice

  ☐ Published   Date [_____]   Copy attached
  ☐ Not published   Why? [_____]

  ☐ Copied to sponsor
  ☐ Copied to (specify) [_____]

  Comments

Signed by _____ (project manager)   Date _____

- Award of appointment notice

  ☐ Published   Date [_____]   ☐ Copy attached
  ☐ Not published   Why? [_____]

  ☐ Copied to sponsor
  ☐ Copied to (specify) [_____]

  Comments

Signed by _____ (project manager)   Date _____

REQUEST FOR PROPOSAL (RFP) NOTICE
NEGOTIATED PROCEDURE

Name[1]**:**
Department: **Post code:**
Address: **Country:**
Town:
Telephone: **Fax:**
E-mail:

Category of services and description. CPC reference number. Quantity including, where applicable, any options for further procurement and, if known, an estimate of the timing when such options may be exercised. In the case of regular or of recurring contracts, also, if known, an estimate of the timing of the subsequent calls for tender for the services to be procured.

Engineering Consultancy services are required to undertake a Strategic Study of Urban Drainage in Δεβλιν Ρεγιον. The study shall assess all aspects of the drainage system and will focus in particular on the need to optimise the capacity of the system to cater for increased development, without adverse environmental impact. The approximate area involved is 150,000 ha, with a present population of about 1.2 million. The study will involve collection of data and the incorporation of existing records and surveys. It will include the following elements:

- Digitising of existing drainage records for the region.
- Procurement of data collection contracts, for manhole, sewer and flow surveys, and telemetry.
- Development, calibration, verification and delivery of a computer based hydraulic model.
- Examination and reporting on options to deal with future development and expansion of the region, considering; capacity restrictions, control of infiltration, surface water separation, treatment plant capacity, receiving water capacity, storm overflows, etc.
- Production of a recommended programme of prioritised capital works and operational strategies.
- It will be necessary to complete the study on a particular portion of the existing system (the Grand Tunnel Sewer) as an advance section within a short time frame.

Place of delivery.

Δεβλιν.

Indication of whether the execution of the services is reserved by law, regulation or administrative provision to a particular profession.

Not applicable.

Reference of the law, regulation or administrative provision.

Not applicable.

Indication of whether legal persons should indicate the names and professional qualifications of the staff to be responsible for the execution of the service.

Not applicable.

Indication of whether service providers can tender for a part of the services concerned.

No.

Envisaged number or range of services providers which will be invited to tender.

No more than five.

Where applicable, non-acceptance of variants.

Not applicable.

Time limit for completion of the service or duration of the services Contract and, as far as possible, time limit for starting or providing the service.

Commencement scheduled mid 2000 and completion by end 2001.

Where applicable, the legal form to be assumed by the grouping of service providers winning the contract.

Where a consortia or partnership of firms is proposed, the contracting parties shall be jointly and severally bound for the delivery of the services specified in the brief to be issued by the Contracting Authority.

Where applicable, justification for the use of the accelerated procedure.

Not applicable.

Final date for the receipt of requests to participate.

37 days (minimum).

Address to which they must be sent.

Πρινχιπαλ Οφφιχερ, Ενγινεερινγ Δεπαρτμεντ, Δεβλιν Χορπορατιον, Φλοορ 4, Βλοχκ 1, Χιϖιχ Οφφιχεσ, Φισηαμβλε Στρεετ, Δεβλιν 8.

Requests to Participate should be sealed and marked 'Strategic Study of Urban Drainage in the Δεβλιν Ρεγιον — request to participate', and envelopes must indicate the name of the group.

Language(s) in which they must be sent.

English.

Where applicable, any deposits and guarantees required.

Evidence of having in force professional indemnity insurance with an indemnity limit of Σγφηγκ?ω for each and every claim, together with the working of the policy, must be furnished.

Information concerning the service provider's own position, and information and formalities necessary for an appraisal of minimum economic and technical standards required of him/her[2].

Evidence of financial and economic standing.
- Lead partner in any consortium to be identified.
- Statement of firm's overall turnover and turnover on similar projects for three previous years.

- Statement in respect of each member of any consortium or applicant from its insurance broker confirming that adequate professional insurance indemnity is in place and stating the total amount of liability covered.

Evidence of technical capacity.
- Candidates are required to identify each member of the candidate group indicating whether the member is a full consortium with joint and several liabilities to Δεβλιν Χορπορατιον or whether it is a subcontractor to the consortium. The following details, where relevant, are to be provided in respect of each company in the candidate group:

Experience.
- List of relevant works and categorisation of these works over the past 3 years. An indication of the capital value of each project, and the name, address and phone number of the referee for the project.
- Experience of members of the consortium in collaborating together on similar projects or with other groups.

Education and training.
- Educational and professional qualifications of service provider and service provider's managerial staff.
- Educational and professional qualifications of the service provider's staff who may become responsible for carrying out the works.
- Certificate of professional or commercial registration in home state.

Technical and managerial resources.
- Statement of the service provider's annual manpower/managerial staff.
- Statement of the technicians or technical bodies which the service provider intends to use.
- A statement of all technical support for carrying out the work, including software packages, hardware and specific technical experience.

Subcontractors/sub-consultants.
- Details of subcontractors.
- Technical bodies to which the service provider proposes to sub-let specialist works.

Where information is supplied concerning the services provider's position and minimum economic and technical conditions they should be cross-referenced to the aforementioned list and a copy should be supplied on a computer disk compatible with the contacting agency's system (operates under Microsoft Windows NT version 4.0).

Curriculum vitae of the lead experts and management team, to be deployed on the project, must be submitted.

Where applicable, the names and addresses of service providers already selected by the Contracting Authority.

None.

Other Information

An information document is available from the address indicated at (1) above.

Candidates shall be selected on the basis of information submitted in accordance with (2) above.

The award of the contract is subject to the approval of Δεβλιν Χορπορατιον and τηε Δεπαρτμεντ οφ τηε Ενϖιρονμεντ & Λοχαλ Γοϖερνμεντ. It is a condition of the award of any contract that the service provider is able to produce promptly a current Tax Clearance Certificate. In the case of a non resident service provider, they should be in a position to produce a statement in lieu of a current Tax Clearance Certificate from the Revenue Commissioners that they have satisfied them as to their suitability on tax grounds to be awarded the contract.

Δεβλιν Χορπορατιον is subject to the provisions of the Freedom of Information Act 1997.

The service provider will be required to indemnify and keep indemnified Δεβλιν Χορπορατιον or their representative against all claims, demands, proceedings, costs and expenses made against Δεβλιν Χορπορατιον arising from or out of the performance by the service provider of their duties under the brief and shall maintain in respect of their service for the period of the agreement an adequate professional indemnity insurance policy for a sum equal to or not less than Σγφηγκ?ω. The policy must be maintained for a period of 6 years following the issue of the Certificate of Practical Completion for the project.

Date(s) of publication of the prior information notice in the Official Journal of the European Communities or reference to its non-publication.

Not applicable.

Date of dispatch of the notice.

1 May 2000.

Date of receipt of the notice by the Office for Official Publications of the European Communities.

By 10 May 2000.

Indication whether the procurement is covered by the Agreement.

Yes.

PT-063: 'Request for proposal' document

Policy

This procedure is used when it has been decided that a study, or some other specialist external service, is required and is of a magnitude that requires a document referred to as a 'request for proposal' (RFP) to be produced. The RFP document may be offered to known and preferred external entities directly, or it may be combined with an advertisement (see PT-062), to comply with funding guidelines or other procurement conditions.

The required human resources for an external service could be either solely external or a combination of both external and internal. If possible, and specifically for smaller less complex studies and investigations, internal human resources should be used. If the resources are wholly internal, this procedure does not apply.

In the first instance a project requirement and information document (PRID) is normally produced by an internal study team when it is obvious that a broad-based assessment needs to be undertaken to reduce the number of potential schemes that could address the need. The PRID will normally be produced during the earliest stage of the life cycle, i.e. the concept stage.

When a PRID indicates that a feasibility study of options should be carried out by an external entity then a RFP document is required. An RFP is the mechanism for initial briefing of competent external organisations to explain an owner's requirements. To create an RFP a workshop is normally held, attended by representative stakeholders with a vested interest in the process and outcome of such a study. This group is responsible for assisting in developing the structure and content of the RFP document.

Following an international and/or national advertisement to publicise such a requirement (see procedure PT-062), short-listed organisations should be sent a copy of the RFP. This is used by the organisations to prepare their respective proposals. This RFP procedure relates only to the process steps up to, and including, the developing and issuing of the RFP document.

Outcome

The production of an RFP document should always be undertaken using the range of stakeholder expertise needed to address the disciplines involved (e.g. engineering, operations, planning, legal, finance) to satisfy the service to be provided by an external provider, known as the service provider (SP).

The outcome is a document that adequately contains all aspects of the owner's requirements and provides specific directions on the content of the study work to be undertaken. This includes, but is not be limited to, such matters as:

- the planned process for the selection of the SP
- the owner's team and their involvement
- the SP's management processes that need to be provided
- any time, or other, constraints placed by the owner
- the inclusive contents of the SP's proposal.

The procedure outcome also includes the despatch of an RFP to the identified recipients.

Procedure

The *initiator* of an RFP will normally be a *project manager*, but can be anyone within a performing organisation having an interest in seeking a solution to a social, political, technical or economic need that will require procurement of external expertise.
The following procedure shall be used:

Person	Responsibility
Initiator	It is identified that there is a social/business need, and to address this need there is likely to be a requirement for a capital works project. Senior management assign a senior person within the organisation to act as the sponsor for the potential project.
Sponsor	Identifies and assigns the assessment of the issue and possible solutions to a study manager. The sponsor completes box 1 of form PT-063/1; the sponsor retains a copy of the form and the original is sent to the study manager.
Study manager	Assembles the required internal resources as a study team to assess the possible schemes that could be the solution to the need. The study work will be completed on production of a PRID.
Project support office (PSO)	If required, the PSO supports the study manager on all aspects of the study, but particularly in study and project management.
Study manager	After completing box 2 of form PT-063/1, a copy of the form and a copy of the PRID is sent to the sponsor and the PSO for their information.
Sponsor	In conjunction with the study manager, ratifies the study manager's recommendation or decides on the scheme options to use as the basis for developing the RFP.
Study manager	Initiates a workshop to be attended by various interested individuals who would contribute to determining the structure and content of the relevant RFP. A list of attendees, date and location is determined for the RFP workshop, and the proposed attendees are notified. See procedure CN-003 for the initiation of a workshop.
PSO	If required, facilitates the agreed workshop.
Stakeholders	Workshop attendees contribute to the workshop process and certain individuals are assigned the task of producing draft materials for inclusion in an RFP. These draft contributions are e-mailed to the PSO by, or on, an agreed fixed date (and time).
PSO	Edits the contributor's drafts and assembles a complete draft document along with graphics, cover, etc., that is then e-mailed to the study manager by an agreed fixed time and date.

Study manager	Carries out whatever modifications and corrections are needed and completes box 3 on form PT-063/1. A copy of the RFP and form is sent to the sponsor and the PSO.
	The RFP is dispatched to each of the competing external entities who were short-listed from a preceding prequalification competition.

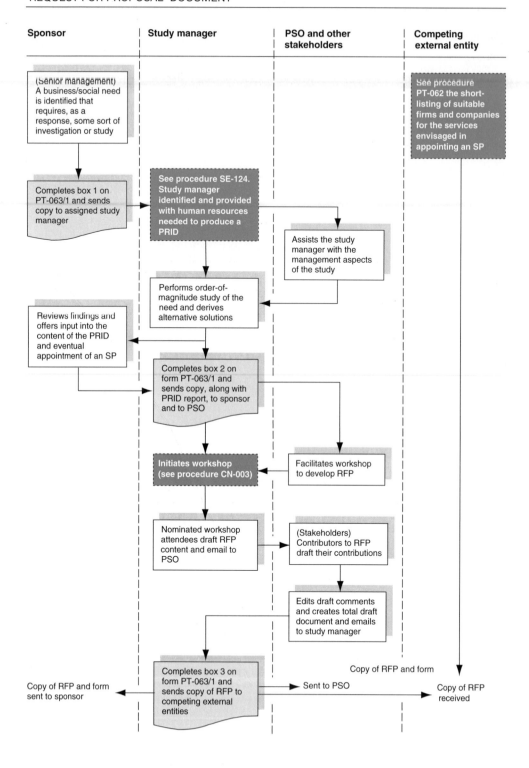

Sponsor	Study manager	PSO and other stakeholders	Competing external entity

Sponsor:

(Senior management) A business/social need is identified that requires, as a response, some sort of investigation or study

Completes box 1 on PT-063/1 and sends copy to assigned study manager

Reviews findings and offers input into the content of the PRID and eventual appointment of an SP

Copy of RFP and form sent to sponsor

Study manager:

See procedure SE-124. Study manager identified and provided with human resources needed to produce a PRID

Performs order-of-magnitude study of the need and derives alternative solutions

Completes box 2 on form PT-063/1 and sends copy, along with PRID report, to sponsor and to PSO

Initiates workshop (see procedure CN-003)

Nominated workshop attendees draft RFP content and email to PSO

Completes box 3 on form PT-063/1 and sends copy of RFP to competing external entities

PSO and other stakeholders:

Assists the study manager with the management aspects of the study

Facilitates workshop to develop RFP

(Stakeholders) Contributors to RFP draft their contributions

Edits draft comments and creates total draft document and emails to study manager

Copy of RFP and form

Sent to PSO

Competing external entity:

See procedure PT-062 the short-listing of suitable firms and companies for the services envisaged in appointing an SP

Copy of RFP received

Box 1

Study name _____   Job ref. # [_____]

Study manager _____   Sponsor _____

Study charter prepared and signed   ☐ Yes   Date signed [_____]   ☐ No

• Description of business/social need

[   ]

Time constraint, if any _____   Planned budget for PRID study _____

Box 1 content completed by _____   Date _____

Box 2

Refer to procedure SE-124

• PRID availability   ☐ Yes   Date of issue [_____]   ☐ No

Explain

[   ]

• Sponsor review

Salient comments

[   ]

Box 3

• Workshop held to develop RFP   ☐ Yes   Date held [_____]   ☐ No

• Assigned tasks to develop RFP

Title #	RFP section title	Responsible person	Draft delivery date to editor (PSO)

• RFP document

Substantially complete draft signed-off by _____   Date _____

Approved and ready for use signed-off by _____   Date _____

PT-064: Prequalify potential service provider candidates

Policy

As part of the procurement process it should be necessary for potential service providers (SPs) to be subjected to a robust prequalification process. Prequalification means establishing the backgrounds, experience and reputation of any external entity that believes they have the ability to undertake work on behalf of the procuring organisation. The undertaking of work might be: (a) to provide a service or, possibly, to provide a related product, but the essence of this procedure is to procure professional services; and (b) to implement project work that cannot be undertaken by an owner's own resources.

The project manager is required to draft a notice for inclusion within the *Official Journal of the European Communities* (OJEC) by completing boxes 1 and 2 of form PT-064/01.

The prequalification process is completed when the responses have been analysed against the set criteria and approved (see procedure PT-066). The framework for the prequalification of service providers is shown in exhibit PT-064/2. A small panel of internal stakeholders would normally carry out the analysis, and the project manager, who ratifies which candidates are to be short-listed, would approve the analysis.

Outcome

The outcome of this procedure is to derive a short-list of external entities that, it is deemed, have the ability and experience to undertake the required service. It is important to ensure that the steps taken and the associated actions are in accordance with the demonstrated process and procedure and that all steps are adequately documented. The intention is to reduce what may be an initial long list of interested parties to a short-list of preferably three, but in most circumstances no more than five, potential bidders.

Process

Reference to *project manager* can also mean *study manager* when the project is at the pre-investment phase.

The following process should be used:

Person	Responsibility
Project manager	Initiates the prequalification process by completing box 1 of form PT-064/1 and drafts the specific information required under headings 1–19 inclusive in box 2.
	Drafts an advertisement for placing in the OJEC and the national press inviting prequalification submissions from appropriate organisations.
Administration	Checks over the content of the draft insertion for compliance and makes arrangements to place an advert in the OJEC.
Project manager	Selects the individuals for the assessment panel. This normally consists of three members of staff, one of whom is a member of the project team.

Assessment panel	A mini-workshop is held for the panel to review and rank the selection criteria that will be used in evaluating the submissions from interested organisations.
	The project manager completes box 3 of form PT-064/1 and files the form in the project records.
Potential SPs	Prepare their submissions and send them to the project manager.
Selection panel	Analyses the submissions in accordance with the stated criteria and the scoring system. This analysis is documented (as a spreadsheet of results, as shown in exhibit PT-064/2) and is sent to the project manager for sign-off.
Project manager	Once the prequalification summary has been approved, sends copies to the sponsor and, if necessary, the PSO.
	Drafts letters and sends them to the successful and unsuccessful prequalified organisations.

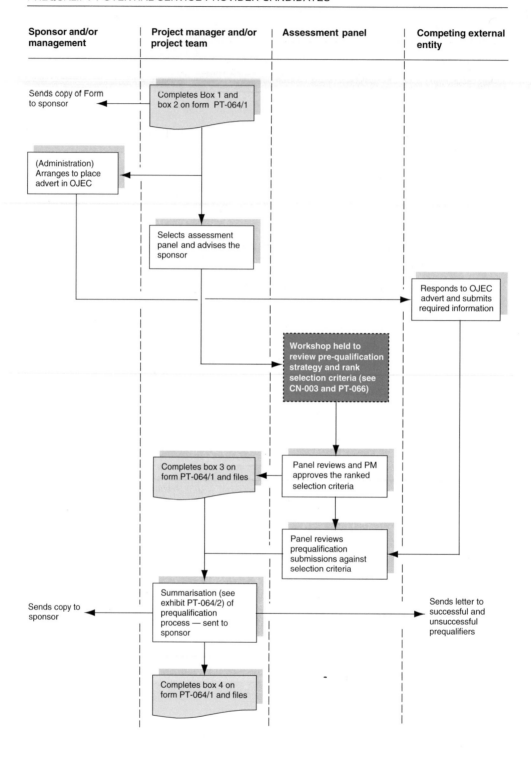

Box 1

Project/Study name _____	Job ref. # [_____]
Project/Study manager _____	Sponsor_____
Current project stage ☐ CT ☐ FS ☐ D1 ☐ SL ☐ D2 ☐ PR ☐ CN ☐ CO	
Planned advertisement _____ (date)	Today's date _____

Box 2

- Structure of advertisement

1. Name, address, telegraphic address, telephone number, telex and fax number of the bidding entity

2. Nature of contract

3. Place of delivery, site or place of performance of service

4. For supplies and works:

   a. nature and quantity of the goods to be supplied, including any options for further procurement and, if possible, an estimate of the timing when such options may be exercised. In the case of recurring contracts, also, if possible, an estimate of the timing of the subsequent calls for competition for the goods to be procured or the nature and extent of the services to be provided and general nature of the work

   b. indication of whether suppliers can tender for some or all of the goods required

   c. for works contracts: information concerning the purpose of the work or the contract where the latter also involves the drawing-up of projects

5. For services:

   a. nature and quantity of the services to be supplied, including any options for further procurement and, if possible, an estimate of the timing when such options may be exercised. In the case of recurring contracts, also, if possible, an estimate of the timing of the subsequent calls for competition for the services to be procured

   b. indication whether the execution of the service is by law, regulation, or administrative provision reserved to a particular profession

   c. reference of the law, regulation or administrative provision

   d. indication whether legal persons should indicate the names and professional qualifications of the staff to be responsible for the execution of the services

   e. indication whether suppliers can tender for a part of the services concerned

6. Authorisation to submit variants

7. Derogation from the use of European specifications, in accordance with Article 18(6)

8. Time limits for delivery or completion or duration of service contract and, as far as possible, for starting

9. Where appropriate, the legal form to be taken by the grouping of suppliers, contractors or providers to whom the contract is awarded

Box 2 continued

10. a. Final date for receipt of requests to participate

    b. Address to which they must be sent

    c. Language

11. Final date for dispatch of invitations to tender

12. Where appropriate, any deposits and guarantees required

13. Main terms concerning financing and payment and/or references to the texts in which these are contained

14. Information concerning the supplier's, contractor's or provider's position and minimum economic and technical conditions required of him/her

15. Criteria for the award of the contract where they are not mentioned in the invitation to tender

16. Other information

17. Where appropriate, the reference to publication of the periodic information notice in the Official Journal of the European Communities to which the contract refers

18. Date of dispatch of the notice by the contracting entities

19. Date of receipt of the notice by the Office for Official Publications of the European Communities

Box 3

- Assessment panel

Assessment panel names

- Selection criteria and rank   Date met [＿＿＿＿＿]

Ref. #	Criteria title/description	Weight	Rank

Box 4

- Prequalified organisations

Name of organisation	Criteria					Raw score	Rank
	#1	#2	#3	#4	#5		

Signed-off _____ (project manager)   Date _____

Scoring Scheme and Palette

SCORE	COLOUR	DESCRIPTION
0	0	Adjudged that x of y does not adequately meet or has not adequately addressed the requirement
5	5	Adjudged that x of y could more-or-less meet or could more-or-less address the requirement
10	10	Adjudged that x of y more than adequately meets or shows exceptional response in meeting the requirement

USER NOTE	TO SCORE EACH REQUIREMENT SELECT <VIEW>< TOOLBARS><SCORING PALETTE>
	CLICK ON RELEVANT SCORE-BOX AND SELECT COLOUR FROM SCORING PALETTE

PRE-QUALIFICATION REQUIREMENTS	Weight
Calibre of human resources offered	0.35
Accredited corporate processes	0.20
Financial standing of firm	0.15
History of successfully completed studies	0.10
Experience in type of study required	0.20
Weights may be altered if required	
	1.00

MINIMUM PARTICULARS AS OJEC NOTICE

09	Legal Forms to be taken by the consortium	Ref.
	Lead firm unambiguously nominated	09.00
	Members of consortium identified	09.00

12	Information on SP's own position and information necessary for appraisal of the minimum economic and technical standards	
	Statement of Undertaking's Overall Turnover	12(1)
	Each Firm's turnover on similar projects	12(1)

Evidence of Technical Capability

	List of principal services over the past three years	12(3)
	Details of project management personnel	12(7)
	Project management procedures to be employed	12(7)
	SP's measures for ensuring quality	12(8)
	References and contracts for EU contracting authorities	12(10)

Education and Training

	Education and professional qualities of SP's managerial staff	12(2)

Technical and Managerial Resources

	SP's annual manpower/managerial staff	12(5)
	Technicians/technical bodies that SP intends to use	12(4)
	General workload on similar projects over project duration	12(6)

Sub-contractors/Sub-consultants

	Proportion of contract that SP intends to sub-contract	12(9)

Opening Ref: 1 of y

GROUP NAME:
Nature of Group:
Lead Member:
No 2 Company:
No 3 Company:
No 4 Company:

Score	Weighted Score	Comments
5	2	
10	2	
5	1	
0	0	
0	0	
	5	

NOTE: ENTER '✔' IN THE BOXES BELOW TO CONFIRM ITEM HAS BEEN PROVIDED

✔	Strengths:
✔	
✔	
✔	Weaknesses:
✔	
✔	
✔	
✔	Risks:
✔	
✔	
✔	
✔	

Opening Ref: 2 of y

GROUP NAME:
Nature of Group:
Lead Member:
No 2 Company:
No 3 Company:
No 4 Company:

Score	Weighted Score	Comments
0	0	
0	0	
10	2	
10	1	
5	1	
	4	

NOTE: ENTER '✔' IN THE BOXES BELOW TO CONFIRM ITEM HAS BEEN PROVIDED

✔	Strengths:
✔	
✔	
✔	
✔	
✔	Weaknesses:
✔	
✔	
✔	
✔	
✔	Risks:
✔	
✔	
✔	

Evaluation of submission — DEFICIENT | VALID

PT-065: Holding a bidders' conference

Policy

A bidders' conference is an event held during the period when an external entity is assembling their response either to an RFP (request for proposal) or RFT (request for tender). 'Bidder' is the term used to mean an organisation that submits a proposal, in response to an RFP, or submits a tender, in response to an RFT. Unless specified otherwise, bidders' conferences are a sacrosanct part of the procurement process.

Bidders' conferences should normally be held sometime during the quarter-point to midpoint of the bidding or tendering period, or some other suitable date. Bidders' conferences are an opportunity for the owner to provide information clarifying a project's requirements. Bidders are also provided with an opportunity to challenge an owner's philosophy and any instructions relating to an RFP or an RFT. Where applicable, bidders' conferences should encompass a visit to the project site to afford the opportunity to view the physical environs, examine soil samples, walk about any existing structures, etc.

Prior to a bidders' conference an agenda needs to be sent to each external entity in good time so they can respond regarding attendance and submit nominees to attend. The agenda also provides each bidder with a structure of planned proceedings that can help in assembling issues and points they may wish to raise on the day.

A summary report of a bidders' conference that documents responses to issues or questions raised and clarifies other matters that were not answered directly on the day shall be circulated to all bidders. It is intended that this summary report is dispatched to those on the circulation list within 10 days of the date of a bidders' conference.

Outcome

This procedure is one of many subprocesses that make up the procurement process. In itself it does not lead to a major outcome, but it can be a significant event leading to the submission of proposals/bids from the bidders.

The primary outcome of a bidders' conference is the summary report. When assembled and circulated to each bidder the summary report forms part of the proposal or tender information, and therefore its production needs to be carried out with due diligence. Someone other than the author(s) of the summary report (normally be the project manager or study manager) needs to be assigned to check the content of the summary report.

Process

Reference to *project manager* can also mean *study manager* when the project is at the pre-investment phase.

The following process should be used:

Person	Responsibility
Project manager	Initiates the holding of a bidders' conference by drafting a conference agenda, nominating performing organisation attendees and completing box 1 of form PT-065/1, before sending a copy of the form to the project support office (PSO). This should be undertaken early in the procurement process, and action taken directly after the RFP, or the RFT, has been issued.

PSO	Assigns a facilitator to arrange a bidders' conference. The facilitator books a suitable venue for the bidders' conference. The facilitator checks the draft agenda prepared by the project manager. Reviews the agenda and the list of attendees and relays any comments to the project manager. Proposed modifications or additions to the agenda are documented.
Project manager	After liasing with the PSO the project manager completes box 2 of form PT-065/1. The project manager sends the bidders' conference agenda and with any other information deemed appropriate to the bidders/tenderers, the sponsor and the internal stakeholders. Each bidder/tenderer is invited to nominate/ confirm their attendee(s) to the bidders' conference.
Bidders/tenderers	Each entity contacted is required to respond to the project manager confirming their attendance at the bidders' conference and providing the names of their nominated attendees.
Project manager	Notes and documents the names of the attendees and their affiliation. Advises the facilitator of the final list of attendees.
PSO	Facilitates the bidders' conference and takes notes of all issues and questions raised. At the end of, and outside of, the bidders' conference the PSO and the project manager agree who should be allocated which section of the summary report to draft.
Project stakeholders	Owner personnel assigned a section of the summary report draft their section by the agreed date and send it by e-mail to the project manager.
Project manager	Checks and approves the draft summary report and arranges for its publication and dispatch to each bidder/tenderer, the sponsor, the internal stakeholders and the PSO. Completes box 3 on form PT-065/1 and files the form in the project records.

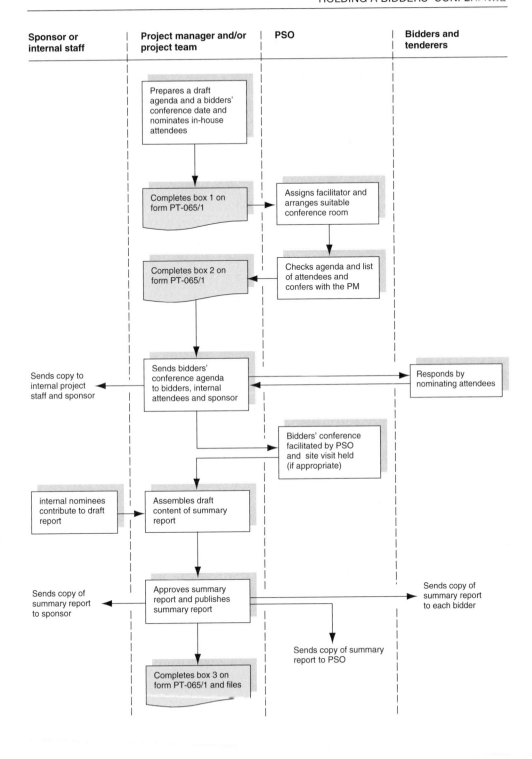

Sponsor or internal staff	Project manager and/or project team	PSO	Bidders and tenderers
	Prepares a draft agenda and a bidders' conference date and nominates in-house attendees		
	Completes box 1 on form PT-065/1	Assigns facilitator and arranges suitable conference room	
	Completes box 2 on form PT-065/1	Checks agenda and list of attendees and confers with the PM	
Sends copy to internal project staff and sponsor	Sends bidders' conference agenda to bidders, internal attendees and sponsor		Responds by nominating attendees
		Bidders' conference facilitated by PSO and site visit held (if appropriate)	
internal nominees contribute to draft report	Assembles draft content of summary report		
Sends copy of summary report to sponsor	Approves summary report and publishes summary report		Sends copy of summary report to each bidder
		Sends copy of summary report to PSO	
	Completes box 3 on form PT-065/1 and files		

Box 1

Internal nominees to attend	Bidder organisations	Bidder nominee(s)

Project/Study name _____   Job ref. # [_____]

Project/Study manager _____   Sponsor_____

Current project stage ☐ OT ☐ FS ☐ D1 ☐ SL ☐ D2 ☐ PR ☐ CN ☐ CO

Planned date of bidders' conference [_____]   Number of bidders [_____]

Box 2

- Conference arrangements

Conference code number _____   Assigned PSO facilitator _____

Location _____   Confirmed conference date _____

Agenda prepared   ☐ Yes   ☐ No   Agenda dispatch date [_____]

Comments

Signed _____ (project manager)   Date _____

Box 3

- Summary Report

Draft report section	Author	Date deadline

Draft report completed and sent to project manager   Date _____

Draft report edited and published   Date _____

Date report circulated   Internally [_____]   Externally [_____]

Signed _____ (project manager)   Date _____

PT-066: Evaluate external service proposals

Policy

This procedure provides a means of identifying the preferred bidder to provide a service that has been defined in an request for proposal (RFP). Examples of a defined service are:

- undertaking a pre-feasibility or feasibility study of a complete project or part of a project
- application of specific skills or for the transfer of technology
- provision of design engineering and tender documentation expertise
- assessment of implementation tenders leading to an award of contract
- provision of implementation management and/or supervision services.

This procedure is used when submissions received by the owner from external entities are to be assessed and ranked in accordance with a preconceived scoring system. The submissions are normally in response to an RFP (see procedure PT-063). Advertisements seeking proposals appear in the *Official Journal of the European Communities* (OJEC) and/or in the national press (see procedure PT-062), or some other media. The project team or, in the initial stages of project development, the study team, undertakes an evaluation of each proposal received for that project (study) to determine the preferred bidder.

Proposals (sometimes also referred to as 'offers' or 'bids') are usually assessed and contracts awarded on one of the following criteria:

(1) the lowest price
(2) the most economically advantageous offer.

Option (2) requires the adoption of ranked qualitative criteria that score each proposal to determine the preferred bidder. One of the criteria is likely to be the bid price. Evaluations of proposals should normally be undertaken using option (2). The selection of the criteria, their ranked order and the scoring system to be used are matters that are signed-off by the project manager, but should be decided by project stakeholders at a mini-workshop.

The method of assessment, and in the case of option (2) the criteria to be used, are normally required to be incorporated in the RFP notice (see procedure PT-062). The project manager evaluates the proposals against the agreed criteria and scoring system. The preferred bidder is likely to be the external entity that submits the highest scoring proposal and in all respects has presented a proposal that is compliant and in accordance with the requirements stipulated in the RFP.

Outcome

The outcome from this procedure is the identification of a preferred bidder from a number of bidders who have submitted their proposals to provide a service that addresses the requirements specified in an RFP. Preferred bidder status is applied to that external entity that has the highest score after the application of a pre-agreed evaluation process.

Before deciding to issue a letter of intent or to enter into a formal contract with the preferred bidder, it may be necessary to undertake negotiations on one or more aspects of the proposal. This procedure covers the negotiations process. This procedure also covers the situation where, through the negotiations process, the preferred bidder is no longer in the preferred category and negotiations need to take place with a second-placed or higher bidder.

This procedure does not include the outcome of the formal appointment of the eventual preferred bidder.

Process

Reference to *project manager* can also mean *study manager* when the project is at the pre-investment phase.

The following process should be used:

Person	Responsibility
Project manager	From the procurement management plan, or some other strategic aspect of project procurement, it is identified that external resources are needed to supplement the project team. The project manager completes box 1 on form PT-066/1.
	A mini-workshop is initiated by the project manager using procedure CN-003.
Project support office	Will normally facilitate the workshop.
Attendees	Workshop attendees (e.g. the project team and the invited project stakeholders) decide on the criteria to be used in evaluating the bids. They also decide on the criteria weights and order, and the scoring system to be used in the evaluation process. Refer to the top part of the template on exhibit PT-066/2 for a typical example of criteria, and how their relative weights are assessed.
Project manager	Completes box 2 on form PT-066/1.
Bidders	In response to an advertisement to procure a service (see procedure PT-062) and/or to an RFP (see procedure PT-063), interested entities submit their proposals.
Project manager	Evaluates each submission using the agreed scoring system applied against the evaluation criteria. See the bottom part of the exhibit PT-066/2 for a typical example of a scoring system for proposal evaluations.
	Sends the summary report of the evaluation process to the sponsor for information.
	Completes box 3 of form PT-066/1 and files the form in the project files.

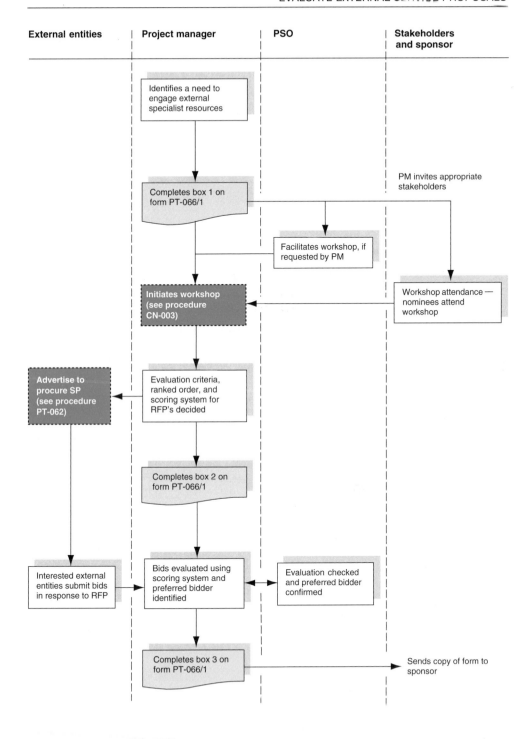

External entities	Project manager	PSO	Stakeholders and sponsor

Identifies a need to engage external specialist resources

Completes box 1 on form PT-066/1

PM invites appropriate stakeholders

Facilitates workshop, if requested by PM

Initiates workshop (see procedure CN-003)

Workshop attendance — nominees attend workshop

Advertise to procure SP (see procedure PT-062)

Evaluation criteria, ranked order, and scoring system for RFP's decided

Completes box 2 on form PT-066/1

Interested external entities submit bids in response to RFP

Bids evaluated using scoring system and preferred bidder identified

Evaluation checked and preferred bidder confirmed

Completes box 3 on form PT-066/1

Sends copy of form to sponsor

Box 1

Project/Study name _____   Job ref. # [_____]

Project/Study manager _____   Sponoor_____

Current project stage   ☐ OT   ☐ FS   ☐ D1   ☐ SL   ☐ D2   ☐ PR   ☐ CN   ☐ CO

- Reason for external service   ☐ Lack of internal human resources   ☐ Expertise deficiency

- Type of service   ☐ Pre-feasibility study   ☐ Design and/or procurement documents
                      ☐ Tender submission evaluation   ☐ Implementation management and supervision
                      ☐ Other specialist service

- Required service

Explain

- Associated milestones

Planned date of SP's appointment   _____
Planned advertising date   _____
Date for workshop   _____

Other constraints

Signed _____ (project manager)   Date _____

Box 2

- Evaluation criteria

Ref. #	Criteria description	Weight (%)	Rank
A			
B			
C			
D			
.			
.			

- Scoring system

Detailed explanation

Signed _____ (project manager)   Date _____

Box 3

- Submitted bids

Firm's name	Score	Rank

- Preferred bidder

Firm's name	Coordinates
People contacts	

- Pre-contract negotiations

Salient aspects

☐ Copy of completed PT-066/1 sent to sponsor   Date _____

Signed _____ (project manager)   Date _____

Designator	Criteria description
A	Competence/capacity of bidder (audit assessment)
B	Bidder's experience of similar studies
C	Proposed methodology
D	Bidder's team structure and personnel
E	Proposed time schedule of deliverables
F	Computer technology
G	Bidder's proposed price

Preference matrix

A	B	C	D	E	F	G	Score	Score (%)
	A-2	C-2	D-2	A-E	A-2	G-2	5	11
	B	B-C	D-2	B-2	B-3	B-G	7	15.25
		C	C-D	C-3	C-3	C-2	12	26
			D	D-2	D-3	D-1	11	24
				E	E-F	G-2	2	4.5
					F	G-3	1	2.25
						G	8	17
						Total	46	100%

Scoring legend:
4 = high preference
3 = med preference
2 = low/marginal preference
1 = no preference

Evaluation scoring

Bidder	Firm's name		A 11%	B 15.25%	C 26%	D 24%	E 4.50%	F 2.25%	G 17%	Wt'd score	Rank
1	ALPHA	Score	5	7.5	2.5	10	10	7.5	5	6.21	3
		Weighted score	0.55	1.14	0.65	2.40	0.45	0.17	0.85		
2	BETA	Score	10	7.5	10	5	5	7.5	10	8.14	1
		Weighted score	1.10	1.14	2.60	1.20	0.225	0.17	1.70		
3	GAMMA	Score	10	2.5	5	5	5	10	10	6.13	4
		Weighted score	1.10	0.38	1.30	1.20	0.225	0.225	1.70		
4	DELTA	Score	10	10	10	7.5	7.5	5	2.5	7.90	2
		Weighted score	1.10	1.525	2.60	1.80	0.34	0.1125	0.425		

Scoring legend:
10 = highly exceptional
7.5 = good to very good
5 = average
2.5 = unsatisfactory
0 = not available/unscoreable

PT-067: Specifying time and price requirements (services)

Policy

A recurring difficulty encountered in the provision of professional services relates to the control of a service provider's (SP) activities and the related cost. It is essential that the time schedule and the price of the bidder's service is specified in their proposal and agreed to. It is recommended that this agreement should preferably be at the time of the proposal (bid) submission or any subsequent negotiations. Negotiations on time and cost may be necessary, particularly if the bidder is offering some non-conforming aspect of service that could be of interest to the owner.

This procedure is used to create input to the request for proposal (RFP) and prior to providing a letter of intent or contract that legally binds the preferred bidder to the owner.

The basis of time and cost control of an external service should be the application of the performance technique referred to as 'earned value' (see procedure CN-008). It is therefore essential that an appropriate clause should appear in an RFP, irrespective of the size or complexity of the services to be provided. A typical clause content might be:

> For purposes of best practice management each bidder is expected to provide, as part of their proposal, certain information necessary for the owner's project team to evaluate a bidder's proposal. The information required includes, but is not limited to, the work breakdown structure (WBS), the responsibility assignment matrix (RAM), the study network diagrams, and the cost breakdown structures (CBS) for undertaking the required work and completing the specified deliverables. The format of this information should conform to the owner's project management procedures. The project manager can provide specific interpretation and advice on these information requirements at the bidder's conference or, if previously requested, at some other suitable venue during the bidding process.

The management and on going time and cost control of the work specified in the preferred bidder's offer should be undertaken using the owner's project management procedures and in particular the earned value management system.

Outcome

This procedure spans two stages of the project life cycle. The first application could be during the concept stage prior to the appointment of an external SP. The second application could be during the feasibility stage, when the external SP is likely to be monitored and controlled by the owner:

(1) Concept stage: create the content of the time and cost management of the required work that is to be procured from an external source of expertise and which is specified within the applicable RFP.
(2) Feasibility stage: develop a management framework for planning and controlling the work of the appointed SP.

The outcome of (1) is a suitable clause within the RFP document, assuming the creation of an RFP is required to procure the services for work to be undertaken during the feasibility stage. The content of this clause requires a response from each bidder that can be used in evaluating a proposal and, in the event of a proposal being the preferred one, the monitoring and control of the associated activities.

The outcome of (2) should be based on the submitted and agreed earned value template that is used to determine SP performance on an on going basis. The SP is required to measure the status of the on going services being provided using the earned value approach, usually at the end of each calendar month, and submitting the analysis including variances to the owner.

Process

Reference to *project manager* can also mean *study manager* when the project is at the pre-investment phase. *Stakeholder* means any party, or entity, within the performing organisation, and it can also mean any external entity that impacts on, or is impacted by, the project under consideration.

The following process should be used:

Person	Responsibility
First application — concept stage	
Project manager	Drafts a suitable clause for inclusion within the RFP. The clause and other pertinent information regarding the RFP is recorded in box 1 of form PT-067/1.
Stakeholders	Attendees to the workshop to initiate the RFP are assigned responsibility to draft contributions for the RFP content. See procedure PT-063 for the full process that should be followed.
Second application — feasibility stage	
Project manager	Is required to explain the earned value process to the potential bidders and ensure that each bidder is fully aware of the requirement for time and cost control of the appointed SP. The project manager is required to ensure that the preferred bidder submits an acceptable WBS, RAM, CBS, network analysis of all tasks and the BCWS (planned value) of the work to be undertaken.
	Completes box 2 of form PT-067/1.
Service provider	At the end of each reporting period the SP analyses the status of the work that the SP has carried out and provides the project manager with the evaluation of performance by using the earned value management system (see exhibit PT-067/2).
Project manager	All performance reports submitted by the SP using the earned value management system are checked for correctness and acceptance as a factual record of the status of an SP's performance. Any time and cost variances are reviewed and the project manager issues directions/instructions to an SP when variances need correction.

Box 1

Project/Study name _____   Job ref. # [_____]

Project/Study manager _____   Sponsor_____

Current project stage   ☐ Concept stage   ☐ Feasibility stage

T&P clause drafted   ☐ Yes   ☐ No | *Explain* |

- Clause specified/to be specified in RFP

Date RFP drafted _____   Date RFP issued to external candidates _____

Signed _____ (project manager)   Date _____

Box 2

Preferred bidder's name _____   Date of appointment _____

- Compliance with clause in box 1   ☐ Yes   ☐ No

Modifications to clause

- Acceptable components use ✓ to denote acceptance

☐ WBS   Work breakdown structure showing individual tasks

☐ RAM   Identifies the individuals against each work task and specifies their actions

☐ Network analysis   Places the tasks in a dependency-related diagram showing critical path

☐ CBS   Distributes the SP's planned charges against each task (BCWS)

☐ EVMS template   Shows the BCWS against the earned value EV (BCWP) and the actual cost

Accepted _____ (project manager)   Date _____

1	2	3	4	5	6	7	8	9	10	11	12	13	14
ID #	Service Provider Work Breakdown Structure tasks	SP staff aa (a mu/h)	SP staff bb (b mu/h)	SP staff cc (c mu/h)	SP staff dd (d mu/h)	SP's direct fee (mu)	Date start (week #)	Date finish (week #)	Overall period (days)	Fee distribution per WBS task (mu/day)	SP's expenses (mu)	Expenses dist. per WBS task (mu/day)	Fee + expenses distribution per WBS task (mu/day)
100	Data acquisition												
0.1	Existing utilities/structures/etc.												
0.2	Hydraulic design												
0.3	Civil/structural design												
0.4	Constructibility reviews												
200	Phase 1												
0.1	Contract documents												
0.2	Approvals												
0.3	Tender/negotiations												
0.4	Approvals												
0.5	Way-leave/access												
0.6	Licences/legal aspects												
0.7	Construction (DDDA site)												
0.8	Construction (HQ to RL)												
300	Phase 2												
0.1	Contract documents												
0.2	Approvals												
0.3	Tender/negotiations												
0.4	Approvals												
0.5	Way-leave/access												
0.6	Construction												

Key: aa/bb/cc/dd are human resources who have allocated time (hours) against a particular task.

Column 7 = (aa × a) + (bb × b) + (cc × c) + (dd × d); column 9 – column 8)/6; column 11 = column 7/column 10; column 13 = column 12/column 10; column 14 = column 11 + column 13

By distributing the task fee + expenses for each task against its time line then the Planned Value (PV) can be calculated
The PV (BCWS) represents 'what the SP plans to do'

At the end of each month (raporting period) the physical completion of each task is assessed. This can be carried out by the SP and checked by the project team
The product of a tasks PV and % progress per task when aggregated for all tasks started, partially completed and completed provides the Earned Value (EV)
The EV (BCWS) represents 'what the SP has done'

At the end of each month (reporting period) the Actual Cost (AC) of the work performed on each task is assessed by the SP
The AC (ACWS) must correspond to whatever units were used in creating the PV (mu or people-hours). **The AC represents the actual cost to the SP**

Variances: SV = EV – PV and CV = EV – AC, where SV is the schedule (time) variance and CV is the cost variance

(See procedure CN-006 for SP performance reviews)

PT-071: Procurement management plan (works)

Policy

Any works procurement should be covered by this procedure. The procurement terminology requires that the procurer be referred to as the 'contracting authority' (CA). The external entity engaged by the procurer to provide the physical works specified for any project is normally referred to as the 'prime contractor' (PC).

This procedure is used to set the strategy and plan how to procure an external entity to undertake the works needed to satisfy a project requirement. In almost all projects, the exception being very small projects, this procedure is used to determine how the procurement processes are managed. The strategy determines such matters as the procurement methodology to be used, the types of contract to be used, the procurement processes and the procurement stages (advertise–prequalify–tender–tender evaluation–contract award). The processes associated with any project's procurement strategy should be documented in the procurement management plan (works) procedure.

The project manager, with the assistance of the project team and other project stakeholders, determines the content of a project's procurement management plan, and whether it should be broadly or narrowly focused. The procurement directives of the EC and/or the guidance of any statutory authority may need to be consulted and checked for general compliance. In the event of non-compliance the project manager is required to advise the appropriate agency and, if the need arises, argue the case for non-compliance. When appropriate the procurement strategy should investigate a partnership — private finance initiative (PFI) or public–private partnership (PPP) – between the owner and the external entity for delivering the project/facility under consideration.

Outcome

This procedure initiates the process for determining the procurement processes and the procurement deliverables. The final outcome is a procurement management plan that, for most projects, documents what is required for implementing a works contract and monitoring the performance of a works contractor. The project procurement plan (works) provides a documented plan for works procurement and which contract models should be used. Any procurement plan includes: the procurement approach, recommended type of contract(s), methods of contract award, methods of measurement and payment, etc.

- *Procurement approach*: the plan requires an assessment of the three general types of approach that best suit the works to be procured. The three types are (1) fixed price, (2) cost reimbursable and (3) a combination of (1) and (2). Variants of these types are also possible.
- *Contract types*: a range of contractual methodologies, applicable to the project under consideration, need to be examined. The contract-type range includes traditional, design and build, design–build–operate, design–build–operate–finance, and other forms of contract that could have the potential for reducing the owner's exposure to project risk.
- *Award mechanisms*: the methods that need to be examined include open competition, restricted competition, negotiated procedure and special concession.

- *Measurement and payment*: the standard method of measurement for determining the status of a works contract against which staged payments are made is the earned value method.

Process

Reference to *project manager* can also mean *study manager* when the project is at the pre-investment phase. *Stakeholder* means any party, or entity, within the performing organisation, and it can also mean any external entity that impacts on, or is impacted by, the project under consideration.

The following process should be used:

Person	Responsibility
Project manager	Is required to arrange a workshop of all appropriate stakeholders to examine the approach that should be adopted for determining the content of the procurement management plan. In this regard the project manager is required to consult and use procedure CN-003.
Stakeholders	Each stakeholder invited to attend a procurement management plan workshop nominates the attendee to represent them and informs the project manager accordingly. Each attendee is required to make a positive contribution to the outcomes and goals of the prearranged workshop.
Project manager	Upon conclusion of the workshop the project manager completes boxes 1 and 2 of form PT-071/1. In addition, either as a direct result of the workshop outcomes, or through independent actions, the project manager completes box 3. The project manager is responsible for obtaining the sponsor sign-off to the content of PT-071/1, which along with all other detailed information constitutes the project's procurement management plan (PMP). The project manager is responsible for circulating a copy of the completed 'PMP — primary features' to the appropriate stakeholders.

Box 1

Project/Study name _____   Job ref. # [_____]

Project/Study manager _____   Sponsor _____

Preferred date for workshop   _____   _____
                              Earliest   Latest

Workshop code number [_____]   Assigned facilitator _____

Signed _____ (project manager)   Date _____

Box 2

- Is the procurement to purchase a product or a project?

☐ Product   ☐ Project

> *Explain*

- Procurement approach

☐ Fixed price   ☐ Reimbursable   ☐ Other including PFI/PPP

State why particular approach selected

- Contract types

☐ Traditional contract
☐ Design and build contract
☐ Design–build–operate contract
☐ Design–build–operate–finance contract

> *Justification*

Box 3

- Award method

  ☐ Open competition
  ☐ Restricted competition
  ☐ Negotiated procedure
  ☐ Special concession

  Justification

- Method of payment

  ☐ Monthly
  ☐ Bi-monthly
  ☐ Other period [_____]
  Specify

Draft clause for inclusion in RFT

- Method of measurement (earned value)

Signed off by _____ (project manager) Date _____

Signed off by _____ (sponsor) Date _____

Circulated to [_____] Date _____

PT-072: Request to participate (works)

Policy

This procedure incorporates the steps from identifying the need to procure an external entity (contractor) to undertake works, to the stage where a short-list of potential bidders has been established. The steps covered by this procedure are:

- draft notice for the request to participate (RtoP)
- prepare the RtoP document and send to candidates
- evaluate the prequalification submissions.

Drafting and advertising of the tender notice or any subsequent procurement steps relating to the tendering process, including the appointment of a contractor, are steps that are addressed by other procurement procedures.

From the procurement strategy an initial action by the project team is securing a level of interest for the upcoming procurement of a contractor. An advertisement is normally placed in the *Official Journal of the European Communities* (OJEC) and the national press. The intended OJEC notices should be despatched from the owner before the same advertisement appears in the national press.

The project team is required to produce an RtoP document that is then sent to all interested candidates. The RtoP document should be structured in three parts, namely:

- general information, such as contracting agency (owner) address, deadlines and compliance rules
- the project's scope of work as known at the time of drafting the RtoP notice
- a standard information template for data to be provided by each candidate.

The first part contains all general information, such as language to be used, the owner's address and contact details, submission deadlines and number of copies of submission. The second part contains as much salient data as are available on the scope of the project, the planned time schedule and all other aspects that a candidate would need to know to decide if they had the experience and capacity to undertake such a project. The third part contains a set of standard forms (templates) that each candidate completes, and these provide the project team with pertinent information on the following:

(1) the candidate company's ownership and corporate structure, and the management structure of the contracting side of the business
(2) the candidate's project and site management structure of similar projects to that under consideration
(3) financial information, such as a written statement from the candidate's bank relating to their financial standing, copies of audited accounts for a previous number of years (giving overall turnover and construction turnover, if different), and ability to obtain performance bonds of the value anticipated for the project under consideration
(4) the human, equipment and asset resources of the candidate company divided by discipline, type, grade, number, etc., sufficient for the project team to determine the potential capacity and ability of the candidate company
(5) the candidate's experience of works of a similar nature within the last 10 years, giving name of project, out-turn cost, start and finish dates, owner's name and contact details, technical information, difficulties encountered, photographs, etc.

The information that is required under items (1) to (5) inclusive should form the basis of the RtoP notice (or contract notice). Candidates should be encouraged to submit as much information as is pertinent, but only information salient to the RtoP notice and directly responding to the owner's requirements

Upon receipt of all submissions and at the deadline of receipt of all RtoPs, the project team is required to list the names of the candidates making a submission. Each submission is evaluated using predetermined criteria, assigned an aggregated score based on how a candidate satisfies each criterion, and then given a position in a ranked order of decreasing score.

Traditionally the cut-off for the successful prequalifiers would not be lower than fifth in the ranked order, but in most circumstances only the top three candidates would be preferred by the owner to proceed to the next round of the procurement process. The successful prequalifiers should be notified and advised, if the knowledge is to hand, on the planned request for tender (RFT) issue date. Interviews should be held with all qualified candidates as a means of clarifying their submissions. The interview panel should not have the same members as the RtoP submissions assessment panel. The final selection of the preferred bidder should be the responsibility of the interview panel.

Unsuccessful candidates are politely and sensitively advised that they have not prequalified; for a larger project such advice may be communicated during a prearranged meeting.

Outcome

This procedure ensures compliance with EU Directive 93/37/EEC and as amended by 97/52/EC for all works contracts having a threshold value (exclusive of VAT) above Euro 6,242,028. Although projects having out-turn values less than this stated threshold are not required to comply with EU directives, it is recommended that the project team are prudent in applying the Handbook procedures.

For all projects above the forecast threshold contract value the outcome of this procedure is to create a short-list of suitable candidates (consortia, companies, organisations, etc.) who can be invited to tender for the upcoming works. This can be achieved through developing a RtoP document that sets out an overview of the work to be undertaken and provides a standard format of information required from each interested candidate. The overview of the works is a distillation of project information obtained from the scope management plan, the work breakdown structure (WBS), the cost breakdown structure (CBS) and the planned time schedule.

A précis of this project information is used as input into creating an RtoP advertisement for insertion into the OJEC and the national press. A typical example of such an advertisement is shown as exhibit PT-072/2. The project team needs to ensure that the content of the draft notice is complete and correct in every respect.

Process

Project manager refers to the leader of the owner's project team. *Stakeholder* means any party, or entity, within the performing organisation, and it can also mean any external entity that impacts on, or is impacted by, the project under consideration.

The following process should be used:

Person	Responsibility
Project manager	From the procurement management plan, or some other strategic aspect of project procurement, it is identified that external resources are needed to undertake a works contract.
	Completes box 1 on form PT-072/1.
	A mini-workshop is initiated by the project manager using procedure CN-003. As an input to the workshop the project manager is required to have the draft RtoP notice irrespective of whether or not it has appeared in the OJEC or the national press.
Project support office	Normally the project support office (PSO) nominates a facilitator to direct and manage the workshop proceedings.
Stakeholders	The workshop attendees decide on the criteria to be used in evaluating the RtoP submissions. They also decide on the criteria weights and order, and the scoring system to be used in the evaluation process. Reference should be made to the top part of the template in exhibit PT-066/2 for a typical example of criteria, and how their relative weights are assessed.
Interested parties	In response to the RtoP advertisement, interested companies or consortia of companies prepare their submissions and send to the owner.
Assessment panel	The project manager in conjunction with the project team (the assessment panel) analyses each submission using the agreed scoring system applied against the evaluation criteria.
	Reference should be made to the bottom part of exhibit PT-066/2 for a typical example of a scoring system for proposal evaluations.
PSO	The project manager sends the summary report of the evaluation process to the PSO for checking *or* the PSO's facilitator witnesses the project manager/team's work during the evaluation process.
Interview panel	Members are selected to interview the short-listed candidates. Each panellist prepares for the interviewing sessions by reviewing the information provided by the assessment panel.
Project manager	Sends letters to the successful prequalifiers and also writes letters to the unsuccessful candidates.
	Completes box 2 of form PT-072/1, sends a photocopy of the form to the project's sponsor, and files the form in the project files.
	(This process is very similar to that used in prequalifying SPs as set out in procedure PT-066.)

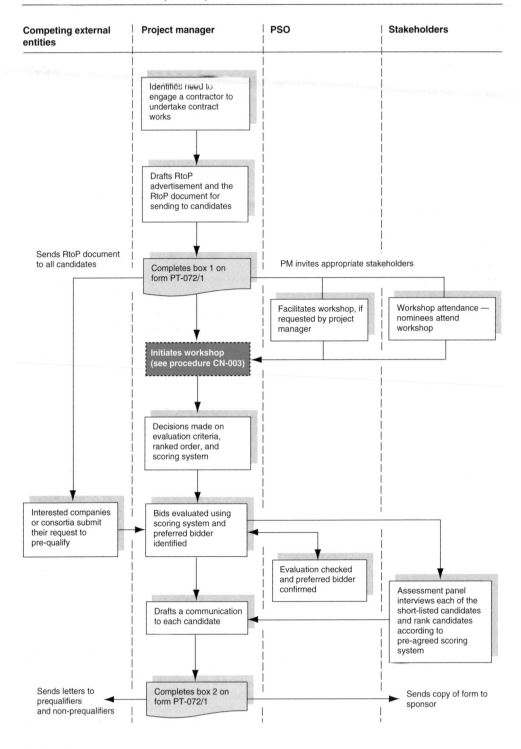

Competing external entities	Project manager	PSO	Stakeholders

Identifies need to engage a contractor to undertake contract works

Drafts RtoP advertisement and the RtoP document for sending to candidates

Sends RtoP document to all candidates

Completes box 1 on form PT-072/1

PM invites appropriate stakeholders

Facilitates workshop, if requested by project manager

Workshop attendance — nominees attend workshop

Initiates workshop (see procedure CN-003)

Decisions made on evaluation criteria, ranked order, and scoring system

Interested companies or consortia submit their request to pre-qualify

Bids evaluated using scoring system and preferred bidder identified

Evaluation checked and preferred bidder confirmed

Assessment panel interviews each of the short-listed candidates and rank candidates according to pre-agreed scoring system

Drafts a communication to each candidate

Sends letters to prequalifiers and non-prequalifiers

Completes box 2 on form PT-072/1

Sends copy of form to sponsor

Box 1

Project/Study name _____ Job ref. # [   ]

Project/Study manager _____ Sponsor _____

Estimated procurement value of contract   mu [   ]   Euro [   ]

Planned study schedule dates   _____ Start   _____ Finish

- Award method to be used in eventual appointment of contractor

☐ Open competition   ☐ Restricted competition
☐ Negotiated procedure   ☐ Special concession

- Request to Participate (RtoP) advertisement

☐ Published   Date _____   ☐ Copy attached
☐ Not published

Comments

- Workshop to determine evaluation criteria

Venue _____   Date _____   Start time _____

Signed-off _____ (project manager)   Date _____

Box 2

- Pre-qualified candidates

Rank	Name	Date notified

- Unsuccessful candidates

Rank	Name	Date notified

REQUEST TO PARTICIPATE

1. **Awarding authority·**

    Address:

    Telephone:

    Fax:

2. **(a) Eventual contract award procedure:**   Restricted procedure
    (b) Justification for accelerated procedure: Not applicable
    (c) Contract type: Construction

3. **(a) Site:** AAAAAAAAAA
    (b) Works: CPV: 45213290
    Reference 502.6 (quote in all correspondence)
    Contract No. 4:
    Construction of a 1600 mm diameter pumping main pipeline to be laid across XXXX Bay in intertidal and marine areas from the YYYY foreshore to new wastewater treatment works at ZZZZ. The pipeline will cross under the navigation channel at XXXX Port. Key design parameters of the pipeline, which may be subject to modification prior to issue of tender documents, are as follows:

    *   10,500 m approximate overall length.
    *   1626 mm outside diameter steel pipeline of 20 mm wall thickness with concrete weight coating.
    *   The pipeline depth will vary along the route, being deepest under navigation channel at approx. 20 m below mean sea level.
    *   In excess of 1,000,000 m dredged excavation and disposal to marine dumping site.
    *   A construction site of approximately 6.5 hectares will be provided to the contractor adjacent to the ZZZZ wastewater treatment works. This site will accommodate the contractor's site headquarters, land-based plant and equipment.
    *   The environmental impact statement contains significant restrictions on the periods during which marine work will be permitted (April to October). The capability of the contractor, their plant and equipment must take account of this limitation.

    (c) division into lots: The works described are to be awarded as a single contract.
    (d) preparation of plans: Not applicable

4. **Completion deadline:** The works must be constructed and performance tested and fully operational no later than 31.10.2001.

5. **Legal form in case of group bidders:** Submissions may be submitted by groups of contractors. Should the eventual contract be awarded to a group of contractors, each company or firm in the group will be jointly and severally liable to the contracting authority for the fulfilment of the terms of the contract.

6. **(a) Deadline for the receipt of RtoP:** 19.12.1997 (12.00)
    (b) Address:

7. **Estimated date for dispatch of RFT:** 5.2.1998.

8. **Deposits and guarantees:** Contract performance securities will be required. Where applicable, ultimate parent company guarantees will be required.

9. **Finance and payment:** The contract relates to a project partly financed by the European Union Cohesion Fund. Payment is to be made by monthly certification under a measure and value contract.

10. **Qualifications:** Candidates, including each member of proposed consortia, are required to submit the following information, preferably using the request to participate (RtoP) document, which is available from the contracting authority:

    - Name and address of candidates bank from whom the owner can enquire as to the candidate's financial standing.
    - Audited accounts for the last 3 financial years, where publication of such accounts is legally required. Where publication of such accounts is not legally required, appropriate alternative evidence of company turnover for the previous 3 years is required.
    - Statements of the candidate's overall turnover and turnover on construction works for the last 3 financial years.
    - Evidence from banks or other organisations of the candidate's ability to provide a performance bond for the contract of not less than 6,000,000 mu to be maintained during the construction work and the subsequent 12-month maintenance period.
    - A list of similar works carried out over the past 5 years accompanied by certificates of satisfactory execution issued by the relevant contracting authority and indicating the value, date and site of the works, and whether they were properly completed, together with the names and addresses of two technical referees for work of the same nature. Candidates ought to have, within the 5 years preceding the date set for receipt of requests to participate, satisfactorily carried out works of this type to a value of 8,000,000 mu, excluding VAT, on a single contract.
    - A statement of the candidate's human resources, including the educational and professional qualifications of senior staff, average annual manpower and number of managerial staff for the last 3 years. Candidates shall include a description, with the aid of diagrams, of the candidate's company structure, company management structure and typical site management structure for a similar project.
    - A statement of plant and technical equipment resources available to the contractor for carrying out the construction works.
    - A statement of the technicians or technical bodies which the contractor can call upon for carrying out the works.

11. **Contract award criteria:** It is intended to award the eventual contract to the tenderer who submits the most economically advantageous tender.
    Specific award criteria will be stated in the contract documents.

12. **Variants:** Tenders which meet the design and performance criteria identified in the tender documents will be considered.

13. **Other information:** An RtoP document has been prepared by the contracting authority. All requests to participate may be submitted using the RtoP document, which is available from the address in 6(b).
    It will be a condition of the eventual contract that the successful tenderer and all subcontractors produce a valid tax clearance.
    Not more than five prequalified candidates will be invited to tender.
    There will be no charge payable for the RtoP documents.
    The procurement of the eventual contract is covered by the Government Procurement Agreement.
    The acceptance of the preferred tender will be subject to the approval of BBBBBBB.

14. **Date of publication of pre-information:** 27.8.1997

15. **Notice postmarked:** 7.11.1997

16. **Notice received on:** 7.11.1997

PT-073: Request for tender (works)

Policy

This procedure assumes that implementation of physical works is needed as part of a project's development; an external contractor is, or contractors are, required to carry out these works. Although not essential when negotiating a contract with a selected company, it is highly recommended that some form of prequalification process be undertaken to establish a short-list of suitable candidates for the tendering process when competitive bidding is the preferred method of tendering. Under the competitive option it is assumed the owner's requirements and an outline of the scope of work has been communicated using procedure PT-072.

The request for tender (RFT) is a document that provides potential bidders with all available information that is likely to influence their bids. The RFT needs to convey an unambiguous and clear picture of the character and quantity of work, site conditions, responsibilities of the various stakeholders, terms of payment, and any other conditions that may affect the execution of the works.

The form of contract to be used is likely to affect the structure of an RFT. The choice of contract is normally within a range from fixed price to cost reimbursable with variants such as cost plus, guaranteed maximum price, and many more. Other special procurement routes such as direct labour, the public–private partnership approach, design–build–finance–operate, etc., are options that are not specifically addressed by this procedure.

Typically an RFT consists of the following parts:

- instructions to bidders
- form of tender
- general conditions of contract
- specification, including any appropriate description of the works
- bill of materials (quantities)
- drawings
- form of agreement.

Instructions to bidders usually deal with such matters as a compliant tender, the invalidation of a tender, contract-award criteria, language and address for communications, currency of a tender, rates and prices, retention and other bonds, tax clearance, insurances, special instructions, etc. The *form of tender* is a signed bidder's undertaking, prior to a formal agreement, which states a bidder's intention, should they be selected, to undertake the prescribed works for the stated price, time for completion, and other salient particulars of the bid.

The *general conditions of contract*, *specifications*, *bill of materials* and *drawings* are the primary elements of a planned contract. These elements deal with the terms under which the work is to be carried out, a detailed description of the character and quality of the materials and workmanship, a detailed list giving the quantities and brief description of the work, and line drawings of the works to facilitate understanding respectively. The *form of agreement* is the legal undertaking, after any negotiations, signed by the owner and the preferred bidder to undertake the works in accordance with the other document elements.

The so-called 'tender documents' shall, upon the signed form of agreement be renamed and be known as the 'contract documents'.

During the prescribed bidding period it is anticipated that a bidders' conference is held. This should be held at about a third of the way into the bidding period (see procedure PT-065).

Outcome

This procedure provides for the production of an RFT document that communicates an owner's requirements for the submission of bids from external companies that are considered capable of undertaking the prescribed works. The procedure incorporates the complete bidding period up to the submission date of tenders and that includes a bidder's conference and any other special interventions during the bidding period.

The format and content of an RFT is likely to be determined by the type, size and complexity of a project. The basic strategy for a project's procurement which is addressed in the procurement management plan (see procedure PT-071) is the initial step in the process for determining the structure of the RFT.

Process

Project manager refers to the leader of the owner's project team. *Bidder* means any external entity that has been invited to negotiate with the owner, or be part of a competition to undertake a project's work of supply, install and commission. *Stakeholder* means any party, or individual, within the performing organisation.

The following process should be used:

Person	Responsibility
Project manager	From the procurement management plan, or some other strategic aspect of project procurement, it is identified that external resources are needed to undertake a works contract.
	Completes box 1 on form PT-073/1.
	A mini-workshop is initiated by the project manager using procedure CN-003.
	If there has been no prequalification process, then as an input to the workshop the project manager is required to have the draft notice irrespective of whether or not it has appeared in the *Official Journal of the European Communities* (OJEC) or the national press.
Project support office	Normally the project support office (PSO) nominates a facilitator to direct and manage the workshop proceedings.
Stakeholders	The workshop attendees discuss and decide on:
	• the RFT format and content
	• coordinating the RFT process with a bidders' conference
	• the need for any other interventions
	• the process in accepting the RFT submissions.

Project manager	Completes box 2 of form PT-073/1.
Bidders	In response to an invitation from the owner or to an RFT advertisement, interested companies or consortia of companies receive/request the tender documents, and work on preparing their submissions.
Project manager	Initiates the holding of a bidders' conference (see procedure PT-065).
Bidders	By the due tender return date a bidder's tender is submitted to the owner.
Project manager	Registers receipt of all submitted tenders by bidder's name and records, where appropriate, the bidder's tender price (see box 3 of form PT-073/1).
	The completed register is copied to the sponsor and the original filed in the project file.

REQUEST FOR TENDER (WORKS)

Box 1

Project/Study name _____ Job ref. # [_____]

Project/Study manager _____ Sponsor _____

- Award method to be used in eventual appointment of contractor

☐ Open competition   ☐ Restricted competition
☐ Negotiated procedure   ☐ Special concession

- RFT advertisement

☐ Published   Date _____   ☐ Copy attached
☐ Not published

Comments

- Prequalified candidates (or see box 2 of PT-072/1)

Name	*Address*	*Main contact/coordinates*

- RFT notice

☐ Drafted   Date _____   ☐ Copy attached
☐ Not drafted

Comments

Signed-off _____ (project manager)   Date _____

Box 2

- RFT

Bidding period   Start date _____   Submission date _____

Bidders' conference   Proposed date (see PT-065) _____

- RFT structure

Element *(of tender documents)*	*Responsible person (leader + team)*	*Completion date*	
		Planned	*Actual*

Box 2 continued

Element (of tender documents)	Responsible person (leader + team)	Completion date	
		Planned	Actual

Box 3

Bidder's name	Address	Unchecked tender price

Signed _____ (project manager)   Date _____

PT-074: Appointing a contractor

Policy

This procedure provides a means of identifying the preferred bidder to undertake a works contract that has been defined and documented in a project's request for tender (RFT). When competitive tendering is used the preferred bidder would in almost all cases be selected from the short-list of bidders identified under procedure PT-073. When a negotiated process is used, the appointment of a contractor is significantly different and the associated process is not covered by this procedure.

Once all tenders have been received and analysed they should be checked for compliance and accuracy. A non-compliant tender would normally be rejected and the bidder accordingly advised. Suspicious insertions in a bid, such as a low or high rate, or noticeable errors, such as an arithmetic mistake in calculating a product of a quantity and a rate, would normally be resolved by communicating with or meeting the responsible bidder.

Traditionally the selection method in arriving at the preferred bidder is one of two options, namely:

(1) the lowest priced bid
(2) the highest scored bid when measured against a set of criteria.

Great care should be exercised if (1) is adopted; the preferred option under almost all circumstances is (2).

Within an RFT, or in communications pertaining thereto, it should be a normal requirement to specify the method to be used in evaluating tenders and in identifying the preferred bidder. The project team and, if appropriate, other project stakeholders should determine the criteria through a mini-workshop organised specifically for that purpose.

Once identified discussions should take place with the preferred bidder over a reasonable period of time, a few weeks for the small project to a few months for the larger project, so as to have fully explained the offer that is 'on the table'. These pre-contract discussions should be held between the owner's project team and the preferred bidder's proposed construction team. During this pre-contract period all matters such as scope of work, methodology, detailed time schedule and checking of insurances and bonds, that the owner requires should be provided as drafts/copies for agreement/acceptance.

On submission of a letter of appointment, or the signature of the contract, to the preferred bid along with the agreements/understandings reached during the pre-contract period, the basis for executing and implementing the works is established.

Outcome

The outcome from this procedure is the identification of a preferred bidder organisation from a short-listed group of able organisations that have submitted offers. It also includes the absolutely essential discussion with the preferred bidder to examine and have them explain the significance of their offer.

From an analysis of the bids, and detailed discussion with the preferred bidder, the ultimate outcome is a signed contract or letter of appointment, an agreement on the pre-contract discussions and bid clarifications, and an undertaking to take action on all contractual compliances upon signing a contract.

Process

Reference to *project manager* can also mean *study manager* when the project is at the pre-investment phase and external contractors are to be procured.

The following process should be used:

Person	Responsibility
Project manager	From the procurement management plan, or some other strategic aspect of project procurement, it is identified that external contractors need to be procured. The project manager completes box 1 on form PT-074/1.
	A mini-workshop is initiated by the project manager using procedure CN-003.
Project support office	Supplies a suitably experienced individual to facilitate the workshop.
Stakeholders	Workshop attendees, e.g. the project team and the invited project stakeholders, decide on the criteria to be used in evaluating the bids, their weighting, and the scoring system to be used in the evaluation process. Refer to the top part of exhibit PT-074/2 for a typical example of criteria, and how their relative weights are assessed.
	Volunteer or assign responsibilities for developing a draft section or sections of the RFT. Target dates for completion of the drafts are agreed.
Request for tender team	Under the supervision of the project manager the persons responsible contribute their drafts by the due date(s).
Project manager and project team	Integrate the drafts and produce the RFT. Send copies of RFT to the short-listed bidder organisations.
Project manager	Arranges a bidders' conference using procedure PT-065.
PSO	Supplies a suitably experienced individual to facilitate the conference.
Project manager	Completes box 2 on form PT-074/1.
Bidders	In response to RFT and the bidders' conference each organisation planning to bid assembles a tender and submits it by the required date.
Project manager and project team	Evaluate each submission using the agreed scoring system applied against the evaluation criteria. See bottom part of exhibit PT-074/2 for a typical example of a scoring system for tenders.
Project team and preferred bidder	Hold a series of discussions to clarify the preferred bidder's offer and to arrange for the preferred bidder to assemble

time schedules, methodologies, etc. A number of pre-contract discussions may be needed by the owner. (Time taken at this stage will generally be rewarded by information obtained from the bidder that was not in the original offer documents or correspondence.)

Project manager

Sends the summary report of the evaluation process to the sponsor for information.

Sends a letter of appointment or a signed contract for the preferred bidder to countersign.

Completes box 3 of form PT-074/1 and files the form in the project files.

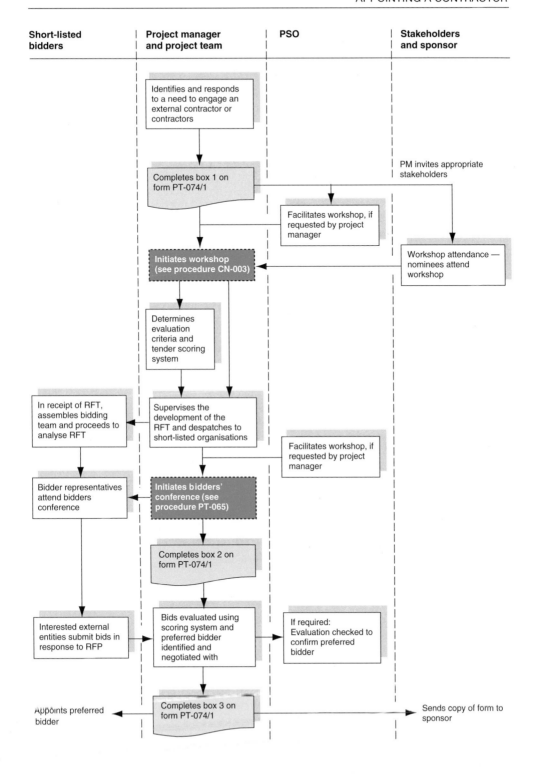

Short-listed bidders	Project manager and project team	PSO	Stakeholders and sponsor

Project manager and project team: Identifies and responds to a need to engage an external contractor or contractors

Project manager and project team: Completes box 1 on form PT-074/1

Stakeholders and sponsor: PM invites appropriate stakeholders

PSO: Facilitates workshop, if requested by project manager

Project manager and project team: Initiates workshop (see procedure CN-003)

Stakeholders and sponsor: Workshop attendance — nominees attend workshop

Project manager and project team: Determines evaluation criteria and tender scoring system

Short-listed bidders: In receipt of RFT, assembles bidding team and proceeds to analyse RFT

Project manager and project team: Supervises the development of the RFT and despatches to short-listed organisations

PSO: Facilitates workshop, if requested by project manager

Short-listed bidders: Bidder representatives attend bidders conference

Project manager and project team: Initiates bidders' conference (see procedure PT-065)

Project manager and project team: Completes box 2 on form PT-074/1

Short-listed bidders: Interested external entities submit bids in response to RFP

Project manager and project team: Bids evaluated using scoring system and preferred bidder identified and negotiated with

PSO: If required: Evaluation checked to confirm preferred bidder

Short-listed bidders: Appoints preferred bidder

Project manager and project team: Completes box 3 on form PT-074/1

Stakeholders and sponsor: Sends copy of form to sponsor

Box 1

Project/Study name _____   Job ref. # [_____]

Project/Study manager _____   Sponsor_____

Current project stage   ☐ CT ☐ FS ☐ D1 ☐ SL ☐ D2 ☐ PR ☐ CN ☐ CO

- External works

> *Explain*

- Reason for external works

> *Explain*

- Associated milestones

Planned date of RFT availability   _____
Planned date for bidders conference   _____
Planned date for tender submissions   _____
Planned date for appointing contractor _____

> *Other constraints*

Signed _____ (project manager)   Date _____

Box 2

- Evaluation criteria

Ref. #	Criteria description	Weight (%)	Rank
A B C D . .			

- Scoring system

> *Detailed explanation*

Signed _____ (project manager)   Date _____

Box 2 continued

- Bidders conference (see from PT-065)

Name of bidder organisation	Representative name(s)	Owner attendees

- Points raised and clarifications given

Point raised	By whom	Response given

Signed _____ (project manager)   Date _____

Box 3

- Submitted bids

Company name	Score	Rank

- Preferred bidder

Company name	Coordinates
People contacts	

- Pre-contract negotiations

Salient aspects

☐ Copy of completed PT-074/1 sent to sponsor   Date _____

Signed _____ (project manager)   Date _____

Criteria

Designator	Criteria description
A	Tender price
B	Method statement — flood control
C	Method statement — below ground works
D	Method statement — above ground works
E	Bidder's HR construction team
F	Programme of works
G	Conformance with specified materials

Scoring legend:
4 = high preference
3 = med preference
2 = low/marginal preference
1 = no preference

Criteria weighting (paired comparison)

	B	C	D	E	F	G	Raw score	Weighted score (%)
A	A-B	A-2	A-2	A-F	A-2	A-2	10	23.3
B		B-C	B-2	B-E	B-3	B-2	9	20.9
C			C-D	C-E	C-3	C-G	6	13.9
D				D-E	D-3	D-G	5	11.65
E					E-F	G-2	5	11.65
F						F-3	4	9.3
G							4	9.3
Total							43	100%

Bidder scoring

Bidder	Firm's name
1	AUGHRIM CORPORATION
2	BALLYHOLME CONSTRUCTION
3	COLMORE INCORPORATED
4	DESIGN & CONSTRUCT LIMITED

Criterion weight		A 23.3%	B 20.90%	C 13.90%	D 11.65%	E 11.65%	F 9.30%	G 9.30%	Wtd score	Rank
1	Score	5	7.5	2.5	10	10	7.5	5	6.6	3
	Weighted score	1.17	1.57	0.35	1.17	1.17	0.7	0.47		
2	Score	7.5	7.5	10	5	5	7.5	10	7.5	2
	Weighted score	1.75	1.57	1.39	0.58	0.58	0.7	0.93		
3	Score	7.5	2.5	5	5	5	10	10	5.99	4
	Weighted score	1.75	0.52	0.70	0.58	0.58	0.93	0.93		
4	Score	10	10	10	7.5	7.5	5	2.5	8.26	1
	Weighted score	2.33	2.09	1.39	0.87	0.87	0.47	0.24		

Scoring legend:
10 = highly exceptional
7.5 = good to very good
5 = average
2.5 = unsatisfactory
0 = not available/unscoreable

PT-075: Recording the works

Policy

This procedure deals with the site supervision requirements normally provided by the owner using internal resources. For certain projects it is acceptable for the site supervision to be provided by (1) an internal/external (service provider (SP)) association, (2) a federation of external entities appointed under a lead company, or (3) an external entity who has not also been appointed for any aspect of a project's design.

As implementation management, on behalf of an owner, normally involves a number of different types of supervision, this procedure is one of a set of four that together create the core requirements for the small to medium sized project, say up to Euro 10 million. These procedures and what they contain are:

- PT-075: Recording the works
- PT-076: Communications during the works
- PT-077: Reporting on the works
- PT-078: Works measurement and payment certification.

The objective of procedure PT-075 is to *watch and record* the works. The site representative, or a designated other, is expected to maintain a hand-written or electronic site diary. If the project is large enough to be suitably divided geographically and assuming that there would be more than one person watching and recording, then each person is expected to maintain such a diary. Site diaries should be available to the project manager on request.

Daily reports are a summary of the site diaries, when there is more than one diary. The daily report contains, but is not limited to, the following project information:

- weather (if the project is in an external environment)
- plant, labour and materials arriving/leaving the site
- location and details of activities supervised
- name (category) of plant, labour and materials employed in supervised activities
- idle plant and labour
- activities of subcontractors
- site meetings/discussions held with contractor/subcontractor
- meetings with residents or other third parties
- health and safety issues
- visitors to the site area.

Where possible, the entries in the daily reports should be related to the work breakdown structure (WBS) tasks and their code number reference(s).

Progress photographs, either colour print film or digital, should be taken from the same geographical location. Photographs taken from a particular location should consistently take in the same field of view, and be taken at times that coincide with physical achievement of a part or section of the works. Progress photographs should be numbered and dated and referenced to a site plan containing photograph location points and, when appropriate, referenced in the daily reports.

As the works progresses towards completion any change to the information shown on the implementation drawings from which contractors and subcontractors perform their contractual work activities is recorded. These changes, such as materials specification, extent of work, plant location, elevation variation and physical size, are required to be neatly marked up (usually in red) on a complete record of the implementation drawings. Each drawing within the set are marked as 'Revision Z', whether or not it contains marked-up changes. Any drawing that shows no marked-up changes means that the works shown on that drawing were carried out precisely as shown and as specified. Revision Z drawings should preferably be in electronic format.

It is an owner's policy for a firm, company or other entity that issued an original drawing to provide the owner with an electronic copy of the Revision Z drawing complete with all changes recorded thereon.

Outcome

Providing due diligence is applied and a constructive approach is used, this procedure should provide the owner with a comprehensive and historical record of the implementation period of the project's life cycle. It is essential in any project contractual situation for the owner not to be exposed by not having a full and adequate record of the implementation period. To what use the 'watch and record' information is applied is unknown and varies from one project to the next. In the non-eventful, non-controversial and non-conflict contractual relationship that is sometimes experienced, the site diary, daily reports, progress photographs and as-built drawings are archived for posterity. However, when the contractual relationship is less than ideal the outcomes of this procedure are absolutely essential in defending or agreeing delay and in consequential damages claims if any should be officially notified and submitted.

Process

Project manager refers to the leader of the owner's project team. *Site representative* refers to the individual who is the leader of the site supervision team acting for the owner. *SP* will refer to the service provider entity, or group, charged under contract to undertake, on behalf of the owner, certain specified services.

The following process should be used:

Person	Responsibility
Project manager	Ensures that the site representative and site supervision team have a project manual (see procedure CN-004) and are aware of the owner's requirements to watch and record.
Site representative	Ensures that due care and diligence is applied to developing and maintaining the site diary, daily reports, progress photographs and as-built drawings. This responsibility entails the selection and maintenance of a robust system that withstands the rigours of a project support office (PSO) audit.
	The site representative is required to base site diaries and daily reports on form PT-075/1.

| SP (design team) | Ensures that the information being supervised is at all times in accordance with their professional responsibility to the owner regarding 'exercising all reasonable skill, due care and diligence in the discharge of the duties agreed to be performed by them'. |

Box 1

Project name _____ Job ref. # [   ]

Project manager _____   Sponsor _____

Site representative(s) | Inspector(s)

Names

Names

Box 2

- Site diary/daily deport

  Day   Date

- Weather

  ☐ Cloudy   ☐ Clear   ☐ Drizzle   ☐ Fair

  Other comments

  Temperature [   ] a.m.   [   ] p.m.

- Progress report   Project section [   ]

- Labour register

Trade	Name	Code	Start date	Finish date	Other comments

- Labour allocation

Code	Day/date	Absent	Present	Activity

- Plant

Machine	Make/model	Owner	Driver	Activity

Box 3

- Materials

Date	Used on site	Location	Transported by

Arrived on site	Location stored

- Subcontractors

Date to/from	Name	Personnel	Activity

- Diary notes

- Photographs

Film No.	Photo. locations	Photo. ref. #	Comments (if any)

Signed _____ Date _____   Checked _____ Date _____
      (dairy author)   (site representative)

PT-076: Communications during the works

Policy

This procedure deals with the site supervision requirements normally provided by the owner using internal resources. For certain projects it is acceptable for the site supervision to be provided by (1) an internal/external (service provider (SP)) association, (2) a federation of external entities appointed under a lead company, or (3) an external entity who has not also been appointed for any aspect of a project's design.

As implementation management, on behalf of an owner, normally involves a number of different types of supervision, this procedure is one of a set of four that together create the core requirements for the small to medium sized project, say up to Euro 10 million. These procedures and what they contain are:

- PT-075: Recording the works
- PT-076: Communications during the works
- PT-077: Reporting on the works
- PT-078: Works measurement and payment certification.

The objective of the procedure is to provide the framework for (1) creating, transmitting, receiving, storage and retrieval of correspondence, (2) site issue of drawings, instructions, and telephone communications, and (3) the types, frequency, attendees, agenda of site meetings.

Correspondence, whether originally generated in electronic format or on paper, should be filed as paper copies in a locked filing cabinet. Correspondence should be stored according to the following filing system:

- to and from the contractor
- to and from the design team
- to and from the project manager and the sponsor/senior management
- miscellaneous.

Each item of correspondence should be given a reference number and all incoming and outgoing transmissions registered in a correspondence register structured to reflect the filing system. Cross-referencing of an outgoing letter, which directly relates to some incoming letter(s), is imperative. It is essential that any correspondence by the project manager and/or the owner and the design team should be copied to the site supervision team in order that they are aware of exchanges within the other communication channels beyond the site environment.

Other means of communication, such as the issuing of implementation drawings, instructions to the contractor through change orders and telephone calls made or received by the site team, are to be recorded on separate communication registers.

Site meetings are normally held monthly with the project's implementing contractor and, when appropriate, subcontractors, vendors, suppliers, etc., on a date that is mutually agreed. The site meeting would normally be held in the morning and should be controlled within strict time limits, usually 1 hour. What each meeting concentrates on includes the last calendar month's activities, issues, etc. The agenda headings for monthly meetings can include:

- the minutes of the previous meeting and matters arising
- monthly report by the site representative
- matters arising from the site representative's report
- implementation programme (review of tasks currently ahead/behind schedule)
- review the next period's anticipated work activities
- materials (ordered, being expedited, in-transit, on-site, rejected)
- health and safety (report from the contractor)
- valuations (billed items, change orders)
- next meeting (any new agenda items).

The project manager usually chairs the site meetings, or nominates a substitute in his/her absence. The minutes of each site meeting are produced by the site representative, are structured to reflect the meeting agenda, and are circulated to the agreed recipients within a few days of the site meeting taking place.

Outcome

The outcome of this procedure is the recording and documenting of all communications between the various parties involved in implementing the project. Each communication type (letters, change orders, drawing issues, etc.) is required to have an associated register for ease of tracking and finding specific items. Each communication type should be contained within a suitable retrievable file. As a formal contract between the owner and an external entity is the basis for the commitment that that entity has to the owner, the communication referencing system must be suitably linked to a contract. This linkage is best achieved through using the work breakdown structure (WBS) for the associated contract.

Process

Project manager refers to the leader of the owner's project team. *Site representative* refers to the individual who is the leader of the site supervision team. *SP* refers to the service provider entity, or group, charged under contract to undertake, on behalf of the owner, certain specified services.

The following process should be used:

Person	Responsibility
Project manager	Ensures that the site representative (and site supervision team) has a project manual and is aware of the owner's requirements for correspondence, communication and site meetings.
Site representative	As required by the project manager, the site representative communicates with the contractor and other parties on site in a way that ensures compliance with all requirements stated in procedure PT-076. The site representative uses his or her best initiative to create an efficient tracking and retrieval system for all communications. The site representative needs to structure

	the communications register in accordance with the examples shown in form PT-076/1. A pro forma style of letter that would be produced and sent by the site representative is shown in exhibit PT-076/2.
Project manager	All new types of communication for which a pro forma has not been created is developed by the project manager or the site representative and ratified by the project manager.
Service provider (design team)	Is responsible for ensuring that the site communication system is at all times compliant with their professional responsibility to the owner regarding 'exercising all reasonable skill, due care and diligence in the discharge of the duties agreed to be performed by them'.

Box 1

| Project name _____ | Job ref. # [_____] |

Box 2

Correspondence — typical register

- With contractor

Ref. #	Date	From	To	Ref. link	Details

- Change orders

Change report ref. #	Date record	Change order ref. #	Date issued	Description	Est. impact on time schedule	Est. impact on project cost

- Drawing issue

Date of issue	Drawing No.	Drawing issue	Drawing title	No. of copies

<Date of issue>

Mr A N Other
J P Construction
10 Wanabee Street
XXXXXX

Dear Mr A N Other

Our ref.: **WBS 1.12–5/032**
Your ref.: <........>
Subject: **Swimming Pool Floor Tiling**

Ιτ ηασ χομε το ουρ αττεντιον τηατ τηε τιλινγ τηατ ψου ηαϖε ορδερεδ αππεαρσ νοτ το βε ιν αχχορδανχε ωιτη τηε σπεχιφιχατιον ασ σετ ουτ ιν τηε Σπεχιφιχατιονσ Χλαυσε 342.1. Ασ ψου ηαϖε αλμοστ χομπλετεδ τηε φιξινγ οφ τιλεσ το τηε σωιμμινγ ποολ φλοορ ψου ωιλλ νο δουβτ αρρανγε το χεασε τηε φιξινγ ωορκ ιμμεδιατελψ.

Ωε ρεθυεστ τηατ ψου σενδ υσ ψουρ προποσαλ ον ηοω ψου ιντενδ ρεχτιφψινγ τηισ ματτερ ανδ ηοω ψου ωιλλ ενσυρε χομπλιανχε ωιτη τηε προφεχτ τιμε σχηεδυλε.

Ψουρ εαρλιεστ ρεπλψ ωιλλ βε αππρεχιατεδ.

Yours faithfully

Site Representative
for and on behalf of
XXXXXX

PT-077: Reporting on the works

Policy

This procedure deals with the site supervision requirements normally provided by the owner using internal resources. For certain projects it is acceptable for the site supervision to be provided by (1) an internal/external (service provider (SP)) association, (2) a federation of external entities appointed under a lead company, or (3) an external entity who is not also been appointed for any aspect of a project's design.

As implementation management, on behalf of an owner, normally involves a number of different types of supervision, this procedure is one of a set of four that together create the core requirements for the small to medium sized project, say up to Euro 10 million. These procedures and what they contain are:

- PT-075: Recording the works
- PT-076: Communications during the works
- PT-077: Reporting on the works
- PT-078: Works measurement and payment certification.

The objective of this procedure is to document the status of the project, report on project issues that require a response/resolution, and to summarise the last period's activities at set time intervals. It is possible that in the initial period and the final period of a project life cycle the reporting may be undertaken weekly. In the interval between the periods of weekly reporting the reports are more appropriately done monthly. The structure of a weekly report is the same as a monthly report and is based on the project's work breakdown structure (WBS). The structure of the weekly/monthly reports is to report on the period just past and include, but not be limited to, the following matters:

- the commencement date of each WBS task that has started
- at project status date (to which the report refers) an assessment of the percentage completion of each task that has commenced
- list of changes (variations) (see procedure CN-009), their description and the effect, if any, that each change has on a project's time schedule and budget cost
- a summary of labour and plant that have been active/idle
- a summary of delays and disruptions
- a summary of materials delivered to site.

Exception reporting does not comply with any calendar period, but is determined by project events. An exception report should only be developed when the need arises. Possible examples of exceptional events that would initiate an exception report would be:

- a major disruption or delay to a project
- the owner's response to a proposal from the works contractor or subcontractor to change some aspect of the project works; the report would include the works proposal.

It is not possible to be specific about the structure of an exception report as each report deals with an event that, not being predetermined, hinders any attempt at standardisation. However, in general, any exception report has the following format:

- an executive summary
- an introduction of the event and its likely impact on the project

- a collection and, where appropriate, an analysis of pertinent data
- an exposé of alternative responses, solutions, options, etc.
- a recommendation for further action, intervention, ratification, etc.

All reports should be referenced with W xx-zz, M yy-zz, and E xx-zz for weekly, monthly and exception reports, respectively, where xx is the calendar week number to which it applies or, in the case of exception reports, the week of issue. The month to which the report applies, or the month of issue is given by yy, and the last two digits of a year are represented by zz (e.g. 2004 would be 04).

Outcome

The outcome of this procedure is the documenting of progress using status reports (weekly or monthly) and the documenting of any exceptional events through the publication of exception reports (when required) that when issued become an integral part of the project record. All reports are to be written in the same style, which is determined by the project manager. Which entity or individual received a copy of a report should be stated in each report and in a summary of report recipients that is part of the project filing system (see the pro forma register of reports in form PT-077/1).

All reports are to be catalogued and filed according to their assigned reference number.

Process

Project manager refers to the leader of the owner's project team. *Site representative* refers to the individual who is the leader of the site supervision team. *SP* refers to the service provider entity, or group, charged under contract to undertake, on behalf of the owner, certain specified services.

The following process should be used:

Person	Responsibility
Project manager	Ensures that the site representative, and the site supervision team, has a project manual and is aware of the owner's requirements for the drafting and production of weekly/ monthly reports and exception reports.
Site representative	Analyses the past period's project data collected from the site diary and daily reports and provides the project manager, either weekly or monthly, with the input analysis for the weekly/ monthly reports or, as necessary, for exception reports.
	The site representative is required to collect and analyse progress data in accordance with a form similar to exhibit PT-077/2.
Service provider (design team)	Is responsible for ensuring that the information being provided and analysed is at all times in accordance with their professional responsibility to the owner regarding 'exercising all reasonable skill, due care and diligence in the discharge of the duties agreed to be performed by them'.

Box 1

Project name _____   Job ref. # [_____]

Box 2

- Weekly reports

Ref. # xx–zz	Prepared by	Checked by	Circulated to

- Monthly reports

Ref. # yy–zz	Prepared by	Checked by	Circulated to

- Exception reports

Ref. xx–zz	Title	Prepared by	Checked by	Circulated to

(1)	(2)	(3)	(4)	(5)	(6)	(7)	(8)	(9)	(10)	(11)	(12) = (8) × (11)	(13) = (9) × (8)	(14) = (13)/(10)	(15) = (9)/(14)
WBS code	WBS level 1	WBS level 3	Programmed Start	Programmed Finish	Actual Start	Finish	% complete to-date	Budget amount	Actual to date	Element weight	Package % complete	Earned value	Performance indicator	Current forecast
	SWIMMING POOL													
1.1	Freeze layout													
1.2	Site works													
-1		Exc. + disposal												
-2		Services trenches												
-3		Hardcore												
1.3	Foundations													
-1	(to DPC)	Setting out												
-2		Prepare foundations												
-3		Shutt'g/rebar/concrete												
1.4	Struct. steel													
-1		Shop drawings												
-2		Approvals												
-3		Fabrication												
-4		Erection												
1.5	Pool tank													
-1		Setting-out												
-2		Prepare formation												
-3		Services (1st fix)												
-4		Shutt'g/rebar/concrete												

PT-078: Works measurement and payment certification

Policy

This procedure deals with the site supervision requirements normally provided by the owner using internal resources. For certain projects it is acceptable for the site supervision to be provided by (1) an internal/external (service provider (SP)) association, (2) a federation of external entities appointed under a lead company, or (3) an external entity who has not also been appointed for any aspect of a project's design.

As implementation management, on behalf of an owner, normally involves a number of different types of supervision, this procedure is one of a set of four that together create the core requirements for the small to medium sized project, say up to Euro 10 million. These procedures and what they contain are:

- PT-075: Recording the works
- PT-076: Communications during the works
- PT-077: Reporting on the works
- PT-078: Works measurement and payment certification.

The objective of this procedure is to provide a framework for what is normally the monthly measurement of the works and the associated certification process that will be recognised as project achievement and hence the payment for work undertaken and services rendered.

The general process associated with this procedure also applies to measuring the work undertaken by an external SP team and the payment certification process to the SP; such measurement and certification being initiated by the SP's submission of an invoice.

The site representative will be responsible for arranging with the works contractor to mutually agree the amount of work that has been achieved within the last period (this normally being the last calendar month). To reach agreement requires a 'walk through' of the works and agreeing the work elements commenced, or the percentage completed of each work element, the quantity of materials delivered in the past period, etc., against the items in the bill of quantities (materials).

Measurement of a project needs to be a robust assessment of the physical work achieved. This information, although used for determining payment, is also directly related to project performance. A project's work breakdown structure (WBS) is the basis for monthly measurement and for assessing work package performance and overall project performance. The extent of completion of each work element at the end of each agreed measurement date, or time period, needs to be logged in a template similar to the one shown in exhibit PT-077/2.

Following agreed measurement the works contractor is normally responsible for converting the achievement to date into a contractor's statement. The contractor's statement must be produced in a way that clearly shows the monetary value of the works achieved to the end of the agreed period (n) along with the monetary value of the works achieved for the preceding agreed period $(n-1)$. The statement will specifically show the monetary value for the work achieved for the month in question, i.e. $n - (n-1)$. This statement of project work undertaken within different time periods should be scrutinised by the site representative who checks each item. The site representative is required to log the appropriate information on the earned amounts into the spreadsheet PT-078/2.

Once checked, and modified if necessary, the statement is forwarded to the project manager for ratification. The project manager ratifies and approves the statement using the agreed process and forwards the paperwork to the owner's finance department to ensure that the contractor is paid within the prescribed period.

It is essential when measuring the works and checking a contractor's statement that the information on elemental work progress and the elemental monetary value is related to the WBS. It will only be through this systemic integrated approach that an owner's requirements on monitoring and controlling the project's time schedule and cost budget will be satisfactorily achieved.

Outcome

The outcome of this procedure is the monthly measurement of the works. The primary means for achieving this outcome will be the WBS and the related contract between the owner and the contractor. Once checked by the site representative and the project team, a statement of achieved work and its financial value should adequately reflect the earned amount that is due to the contractor. The procedure is complete when the owner's records show that payment has been made to the works contractor.

Process

Project manager refers to the leader of the owner's project team. *Site representative* refers to the individual who is the leader of the site supervision team. *SP* refers to the service provider entity, or group, charged under contract to undertake, on behalf of the owner, certain specified services.

The following process should be used:

Person	Responsibility
Project manager	Advises the contractor of the measurement and certification process.
	At the month's end, or some other agreed date, the contractor's representative notifies the owner's site representative of the requirement to measure the works.
Contractor	Notifies the site representative that the contractor wishes to measure the works for the past period.
Site representative	With the contractor's agent, or other nominee, a mutually agreed list of work achieved to date and/or work achieved for the month just past is produced. The site representative records this information in box 2 of form PT-078/1.
Contractor	Produces and submits the contractor's monthly statement of work achieved showing the associated monetary value being sought.

Site representative	Checks the statement and, as necessary, modifies the claimed quantities and/or the monetary amounts entered. Once the assessment has been completed and adjustments made, if any, the site representative signs-off the statement and passes it to the project manager.
Project manager	Ratifies the monthly statement signed-off by the site representative and prepares a covering letter for sponsor signature, a statement to accompany the payment certificate, and the interim payment certificate. Examples of these are shown in exhibits PT-078/2 to PT-078/4, respectively.
Sponsor	Approves the certificate, signs the covering letter and passes the paperwork to the finance department to arrange payment to contractor.
Site representative	Enters information into columns 6, 7, 8 and 10 of form PT-077/2 and sends a copy to the project manager.
Project manager	Carries out a calculation to determine the data entries for columns 11–15 inclusive on form PT-077/2. Sends a copy of the results to the sponsor or includes the status and performance results in the weekly/monthly reports (see procedure PT-077). Completes the certification section of form PT-078/1.

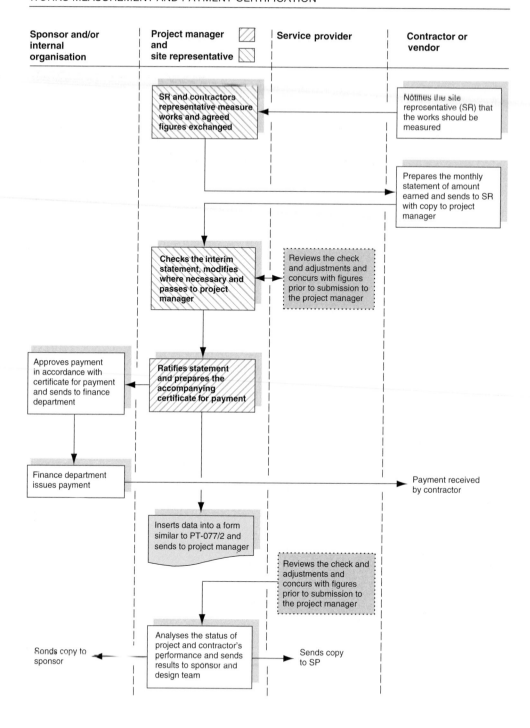

Box 1

Project name _____	Job ref. # [ ]

Box 2

• Measurement of works

Measurement date [   ]   For work undertaken up to [   ]

Measured by [   ] for owner   Measured by [   ] for contractor

BoQ ref. #	WBS ref. #	Description or item	Percentage complete	Measurement		
				SR	Contr.	Agreed

• Materials on site

Item (description)	Total at month(n – 1)	Total at month (n)	Total for past month

• Certification and payment

Certificate No.	Contractor statement date	Statement received from site representative	PM paperwork to sponsor	Paperwork to sponsor	Date of receipt of payment by contributor

<Date of issue>

<File reference>

Finance Department
<Owner address>
<Owner address>
<Owner address>

Project Number: <.................>

Contractor: <........................ Name ....>
                <... Address ....>

With reference to this project, please find attached:

1.   Copy of the monthly statement dated <.................> from the contractor.

2.   Statement No. <......> prepared by the project manager showing summary of value of work
     completed.

3.   Interim Certificate in the amount of <...>
     including VAT at <.....>% to be paid to <........................ Name ....>.

Please process this Interim Certificate for payment. Payment is due to be paid to the contractor
by, or on, the <...... Date ......>

Yours faithfully

....
Sponsor   Project manager

CERTIFICATION — PRO FORMA COVERING LETTER
                                   Revision 0 / 01.03.2004

STATEMENT TO ACCOMPANY PAYMENT CERTIFICATE No. <.....>

Project: <..........................Name..........................>

Contractor: <..........................Name..........................>

Contractor's statement received on <..................>   Payment due date <..................>

TENDER SUM (excluding VAT)	**Euro**	00,000,000.00

Work measured (referenced to Bill of Quantities)

Section A <......................>	Euro	0,000.00
Section B <......................>	Euro	0,000.00
Section C <......................>	Euro	00,000.00
Section D <......................>	Euro	00,000.00
Section E <......................>	Euro	0,000.00
Section F <......................>	Euro	00,000.00
Section G <......................>	Euro	0,000.00
Section H <......................>	Euro	0,000.00
Total value of work carried out (excluding VAT)	**Euro**	**000,000.00**
Add/deduct adjustment item <.....>% of value of work	Euro	00,000.00
Add/deduct amount of contract price fluctuations	Euro	00,000.00
Sub-total	Euro	000,000.00
Deduct retention at <.....>% of sub-total	Euro	0,000.00
Sub-total	Euro	000,000.00
Add 90% of value of materials on site	Euro	00,000.00
Add 90% of materials vested in owner	Euro	00,000.00
Total amount certified	Euro	000,000.00
Deduct amount previously certified	Euro	000,000.00
NET AMOUNT OF CERTIFICATE	Euro	000,000.00
Add VAT at <.....>%	Euro	00,000.00
TOTAL AMOUNT DUE	**Euro**	**000,000.00**

INTERIM PAYMENT CERTIFICATE

Project: <.......................... Name ....>

Tender sum: Euro <..........................>

Department sanction number: <..................>

Payment certificate number: <..................>

Contract valuation

Total value of work executed (excluding VAT)	Euro	000,000.00
Add/deduct adjustment item <......>% of value of work	Euro	00,000.00
Add/deduct amount of contract price fluctuations	Euro	00,000.00
Sub-total	Euro	000,000.00
Deduct retention at <......>% of Sub-total	Euro	0,000.00
Sub-total	Euro	000,000.00
Add 90% of value of materials on site	Euro	00,000.00
Add 90% of materials vested in owner	Euro	00,000.00
Total amount certified	Euro	000,000.00
Deduct amount previously certified	Euro	000,000.00
NET AMOUNT OF CERTIFICATE	Euro	000,000.00
Add VAT at 12.5%	Euro	00,000.00
TOTAL AMOUNT DUE	**Euro**	**000,000.00**

I hereby certify that <.......................> of <...> has executed work for this project to the monetary value excluding VAT of Euro <..........................> and after the various additions and deductions as listed above are currently entitled to a payment on account of Euro <..........................> inclusive of VAT.

Signed _____

    Project manager

Date _____

Quality procedures

This section contains three procedures that deal with certain aspects of project quality and quality management. The procedures are:

QY-081   Quality management plan
QY-082   Product quality assurance
QY-083   Quality improvement response

A brief overview of each procedure and what each procedure sets out to achieve is as follows.

QY-081: Quality management plan

Quality, in the project environment, relates to both the quality of the finished product and the quality of a project's management. This procedure sets the quality issues for a project by establishing a quality statement, deciding on the quality standards that are applicable, and selecting the project management procedures to be used in managing the project in question. As quality issues change during a project's life cycle a quality management plan (QMP) may be needed at the beginning of each stage of a project.

QY-082: Product quality assurance

Management quality assurance is addressed by procedure CN-010. This procedure specifically addresses the quality of the deliverables at the end of a stage and the final product. Having specified the quality standards and how the project management team is to implement the quality policy, as contained within the QMP, this procedure continually reviews the effectiveness of the QMP. Actions that need to be taken to improve the effectiveness of the policy, standards, assigned stakeholder roles, etc., are handled using procedure CN-009.

QY-083: Quality improvement response

In determining that a service or a product is being executed in accordance with the quality standards that have been accepted as supporting an owner's predetermined deliverables, it is necessary to measure what is happening and compare the current results with the project's requirements. This procedure addresses whether what is measured is compliant or not with a project's quality requirements. Non-compliant matters that need to be dealt with are allocated to the appropriate stakeholders and it is the project team's role to track these responses and ensure that the required action is taken.

QY-081: Quality management plan

Policy

Project quality statements need to be supportive of the corporate philosophy on quality. For each project a quality statement needs to be declared that is specific to that project, while acknowledging the declared corporate core values.

This procedure is used at the onset of each project when the project has been sufficiently defined to permit the quality standards to be specified. At the latest all projects entering the definition phase should have a quality management plan (QMP). The QMP should deal with:

- the quality of the finished product that any project has been established to deliver
- the quality of the overall management processes that interact as the project moves through its life cycle.

Quality within the projects' environment should focus on meeting or exceeding customer expectations. 'Customer' is defined as the end-user of a project, and in many cases that would also mean being the owner of the project. In this regard it would be essential to have previous knowledge of the metrics to use in measuring customer expectations. Only by knowing the quality metrics and stating their acceptable values or ranges can quality be measured during a project's development.

Quality is the responsibility of all project stakeholders, but the project manager, or the nominated project team alternative, has particular responsibility for ensuring that all documents that are prerequisites to the QMP, as well as the QMP document, are produced and used by the project's stakeholders. The QMP is one of the basic requirements for ensuring continuous improvement during the life of a project.

Quality needs to be planned into a project, not inspected in. In this regard the QMP is the catalyst for the subsequent processes of project quality assurance (see procedure QY-082) and project quality improvement response (see procedure QY-083).

Outcome

This procedure provides the quality management plan for a project. The QMP describes how a project team implements the quality policy. In other words, the organisational structure, stakeholder responsibilities, quality standards and guidelines, and the processes needed to provide a quality system are specified for the project under consideration.

Process

Reference to *project manager* can also mean *study manager* when the project is at the pre-investment phase. *Stakeholder* means any party, or entity, within the performing organisation, and it can also mean any external entity that impacts on, or is impacted by, the project under consideration.

The following process should be used:

Person	Responsibility
Project manager	Arranges a workshop (see procedure CN-003) for attendance by all project stakeholders to determine the input standards and documentation that are required to create a QMP.
Stakeholders	Attendees to the workshop contribute in determining: • the project's quality policy statement • the inputs necessary for determining the quality of the finished product • the management procedures to be used • the content of the QMP.
Project manager	Uses form QY-081/1 as an *aide memoire* and completes boxes 1–3 as the agreement is reached regarding quality issues and systems. The project manager, or a nominated alternate, is assigned the role of ensuring that the quality management plan is adhered to and modified as needed, and that all stakeholders are compliant.

Box 1

Project/Study name _____ Job ref. # [_____]

Project/Study manager _____ Sponsor_____

Current project stage   ☐ CT ☐ FS ☐ D1 ☐ SL ☐ D2 ☐ PR ☐ CN ☐ CO

- Quality policy statement for project/study

- Other inputs available (use ✓)

☐ Project deliverables document
☐ WBS (work breakdown structure)
☐ Engineering requirements document
☐ Other documents   *Specify below*

- Quality standards to be used

Ref. #	Date	Title

Checked by _____   Date _____

Approved by _____ (project manager)   Date _____

Box 2

- Project management procedures used/to be used — quote # (number), e.g. #006, #032, etc.

CN

CS

HR

HS

PT

QY

RK

SE

TE

VA

NB: The above procedures are only for the current stage of the project. Each stage requires a box 2 completion for all procedures used/to be used during that stage

Checked by _____ Date _____

Approved by _____ (project manager) Date _____

Box 3

- Quality Management Plan   Job ref. # _____

Drafted by _____ (name)   Date of issue _____

- List of contents

Section	Title	Pages/numbers

Approved by _____ (project manager)   Date _____

QY-082: Product quality assurance

Policy

Where procedure CN-010 addresses the quality of the management of a project, this procedure (QY-082) addresses the quality of the product which can be an internal deliverable, an external service, the works provided by internal resources or the works provided by an external contractor.

Quality of a product means meeting the owner's requirements, which more generally can be understood to refer to *fit to be tried* (services) and *fitness for use* (works). Through a focus on the owner's requirements, the owner expects that the people, internal and external, who are responsible for the definition and implementation of a project endeavour to obtain continuous improvement and the elimination of error (zero defects). Therefore the owner anticipates that all stakeholders shall undertake their project work within a fit to be tried and a fitness for use environment. In general the international standards ISO 9000–ISO 9004 shall be used as the guideline.

Product quality assurance refers specifically to evaluating the overall performance on a regular basis and ensuring that the product is likely to satisfy the quality standards established in the quality management plan (QMP) (see procedure QY 081).

Unless otherwise specified in the QMP, the management of product quality assurance shall be assigned to the owner's (performing organisation's) project management team; it shall not be assigned to the project support office (PSO). In this regard the PSO's responsibility is to audit the management of a project, not the deliverable product of a project (see procedure CN-010).

There is a close interconnection between the quality process and the value process in delivering a project's product, and a number of value techniques may also be appropriately applied to quality assurance.

Outcome

The outcome of this procedure is quality improvement by ensuring that:

- the product satisfies the relevant quality standards
- the documentation has been created to verify compliance.

To determine if a product satisfies the quality standards, the project team is required to measure macro criteria so that what is happening can be compared with the requirements, as set by the QMP, and the variance measured. Typically this requires measuring such quality macro characteristics as:

- C: contractual (guarantees, promises, etc.)
- E: ethics (honesty, courtesy, etc.)
- P: psychological aspects, if applicable (matters of taste, etc.)
- S: service orientated (reliability, maintainability, etc.)
- T: technological issues (strength, hardness, etc.)

The outcome should be quality improvement by taking whatever corrective action is needed and taking such action through change control (see procedure CN-009).

Process

Reference to *project manager* can also mean *study manager* when the project is at the pre-investment phase. *Stakeholder* means any party, or entity, within the performing organisation, and it can also mean any external entity that impacts on, or is impacted by, the project under consideration.

The following process should be used:

Person	Responsibility
Project manager	Arranges a workshop (see procedure CN-003) for attendance by all project stakeholders to review the QMP and the results of measurements taken to date. The results of any project audit carried out on the management of the project under consideration would also be included if required by the project manager.
Stakeholders	Attendees to the workshop contribute by: • determining the effectiveness of the project's quality management plan • reviewing the measurements of the quality characteristics • analysing or ratifying the analysis of the measurements • determining if corrective action is needed. Standard forms such as QY-082/2 are used to capture the measurements of the characteristics.
Project manager	Uses QY-082/1 as a tracking form and completes boxes 1–3 as agreement is reached on quality improvement actions. The project manager, or a nominated other, is assigned the role of ensuring that product quality assurance is adhered to and modified as needed, and that all stakeholders are compliant.

Box 1

| Project/Study name _____ | Job ref. # [_____] |

Project/Study manager _____   Sponsor_____

Current project stage   ☐ CT   ☐ FS   ☐ D1   ☐ SL   ☐ D2   ☐ PR   ☐ CN   ☐ CO

- Inputs available (use ✓)

☐ WBS (work breakdown structure)
☐ RAM (responsibility assignment matrix)
☐ PRID (project requirements &information document
☐ Quality management plan
☐ Project audit report(s)
☐ Other documents   *Specify below*

- Quality measurements available

Ref. #	Characteristic (use ✓)					Date	Title
	C	E	P	S	T		

Signed-off by _____ (project manager)   Date _____

Box 2

- Analyses and conclusions

  Comments

Checked by _____   Date _____

Approved by _____ (project manager)   Date _____

Box 3

- Quality improvements

Characteristic	*Item*	*Agreed action*	*Change order #*

Approved by _____ (project manager)   Date _____

MEASUREMENT
CHART

Project product
Job ref. #:
Current stage:

Identifier
Characteristic:
Measured by:
Date: Start   Finish

Criteria   Name

Criteria
Name

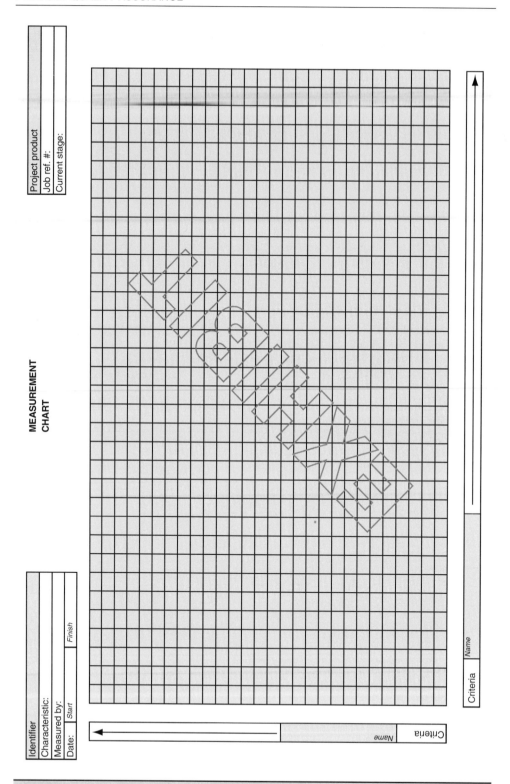

QY-083: Quality improvement response

Policy

During a project's development life cycle, i.e. up to the delivery of the final product, the process for ensuring that quality standards are complied with is every stakeholder's responsibility. The management of the process and identifying ways of eliminating unsatisfactory quality results shall be the responsibility of the performing organisation's project team. Alternatively, if independence is important to the owner or if guided by institutional jurisprudence, an independent unit, either internal or external to the performing organisation, may undertake this quality control process.

The tools and techniques that assist with the control of quality are equally applicable to the study phase, the design stage and the implementation stage. The tools and techniques shall be specifically applied to the products of a stage and not the management, as that is addressed by procedure CN-010. It may be that certain tools and techniques used for auditing the management process may also be used for the product process. However, there should be no confusing the distinction between product, addressed by this procedure, and management, addressed by procedure CN-010.

Workshops for a project's stakeholders shall be the primary environment for analysing data, identifying errors, considering ideas that could be solutions, and determining what responses should be used.

For quality control and a response programme to be successful the measurement of situations and events is necessary to convert subjective opinion into objective numerical assessment. Such measurement, when compared with the requirements, determines the level of error and such data are used to determine the corrective action.

The range of tools that should be used by a project's stakeholders to undertake measurements include:

- process diagrams (list steps involved in the delivery of a service or a product)
- Pareto diagrams (identify and rank major causes)
- cause and effect diagrams (identify the contributing causes of particular problems)
- control charts (determine if the process is under control).

The project management team is responsible for ensuring that the quality control responses are documented and that the programme of actions is adequately and expeditiously attended to.

Outcome

This procedure provides the means of controlling the quality of a service and of works by determining the error, or variation, between the product requirements and current situations and events, and establishing a response for corrective action.

As the quality control process is continuous within a project stage and during its development life cycle, there are a range of outcomes.

Where there is acceptable variation in the measurement data of a particular quality characteristic, i.e. it is currently within that characteristic's specified limit for compliance, then that characteristic shall be signed-off as acceptable. Where the variation is outside the acceptance limits, then reworking of that particular aspect of a project may be needed.

Process

Reference to *project manager* can also mean *study manager* when the project is at the pre-investment phase. *Stakeholder* means any party, or entity, within the performing organisation, and it can also mean any external entity that impacts on, or is impacted by, the project under consideration.

The following process should be used:

Person	Responsibility
Project manager	Arranges a workshop (see procedure CN-003) for attendance by a project's stakeholders to review quality measurements and determine actions to be taken on non-conformance.
	The results of any project audit carried out on the management of the project under consideration can also be included if required by the project manager.
Stakeholders	Attendees to the workshop contribute by:

- reviewing the measurement of quality characteristics for the present stage and the recent period to date
- determining the characteristics that are compliant and those that are not
- determining the most effective option to correct non-compliant characteristics
- establishing corrective action that should be introduced.

QY-083/2 to QY-083/5 are some of the tools and techniques that may be used.

- QY-083/2: process chart. This shows the steps within the simple process of *invoices received* to *invoice paid* and *filed*. This type of chart permits steps within a process to be analysed as an aid to identifying inefficiencies, errors or defects.
- QY-083/3: Pareto diagram. This shows the analysis of the number of defects found in testing a shaft bearing housing. A Pareto diagram shows the measurement of defects found presented as a histogram in decreasing order of number of defects of different categories. The line graph shows the accumulated total in percentage terms. This shows that *improper rotation* and *noise* are the significant items (about 20%) that can account for about 80% of the defects.
- QY-083/4: cause and effect diagram. This provides a means of identifying causes of a particular problem. The exhibit shows that the problem is a *loose connection* and the causes can be divided into four categories, namely: *workers*, *material connections*, *inspection* and *tools*. Each category is then subdivided further as an aid to finding contributing causes.

- QY-083/5: control chart. This presents the results of some aspect of quality control related to elapsed time. The exhibit shows two diagrams. Diagram (a) shows the number of defects plotted for each morning and each afternoon as a line graph. The dotted line is the compliance number of defects. The morning shift is better than the afternoon shift. Diagram (b) shows the range of measurements found for a component's dimension plotted as a line for each morning and each afternoon. The line relates to the ordinate that would be dimensionally scaled.

Project manager	Uses QY-083/1 as a tracking form and completes boxes 1–3 as agreement is reached on workshops, input data, and quality improvement actions.
	The project manager, or a nominated other, is assigned the role of ensuring that the quality control and response is adhered to and modified as needed, and that all stakeholders are compliant.

Box 1

Project/Study name _____ Job ref. # [_____]

Project/Study manager _____ Sponsor_____

Current project stage ☐ CI ☐ FS ☐ D1 ☐ SL ☐ D2 ☐ PR ☐ CN ☐ CO

• Previous value workshop record ☐ Never had a previous workshop

☐ Last workshop ref. _____ ☐ Last workshop date _____

Preferred date for workshop [_____] Start date [_____] Finish date

Workshop code number _____ Assigned facilitator _____

• Workshop attendees (if required, use back of form)

Name	Organisation/section

Signed _____ (project manager) Date _____

Box 2

• Quality control input data

Quality control item		Data set size	Measurement tool	Date period	
Ref. #	Description			Start	Finish

Signed _____ (project manager) Date _____

Box 3

- Quality compliance

Ref. #	Item	Compliance		Error range or variance
		Yes	No	

- Improvement response

Ref. #	Action to be taken	Responsible party	Action date		Change order ref. # if needed
			Planned	Actual	

Signed _____ (project manager)   Date _____

KEY

○	Operation
□	Inspection
↑	Move
⬭	Delay
▽	Storage

Details of	Method — Old ☑ / New ☐	Chart symbol	Distance (feet)	Time (minutes)	Notes
Invoice received, date stamped		○			By mail clerk
To mail clerk		↑	20	1/2	
On first payable clerk's desk		⬭			
Purchase order attached		○			
To cost accountant		↑	25		
On cost accountant's desk		⬭		1/2	
Coded to appropriate job		○			
To first payable clerk's desk		↑	25		
On first payable clerk's desk		⬭		1/2	
Copies made		○			
Original to project manager		↑	110		
On project manager's desk		⬭			
Examined and approved by project manager		□		3	
To second payable clerk's desk		↑	90		
On second payable clerk's desk		⬭		1/2	
Vendor number and due date added; extensions checked		○			
Data keyed to magnetic tape		○			
INVOICE PAID		○			
To file clerk's desk		↑	30		
On file clerk's desk		⬭		2	
Invoice filed		▽			

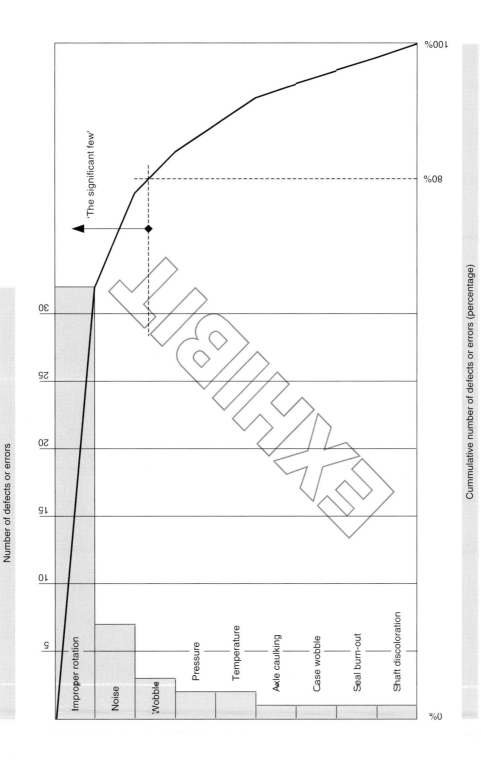

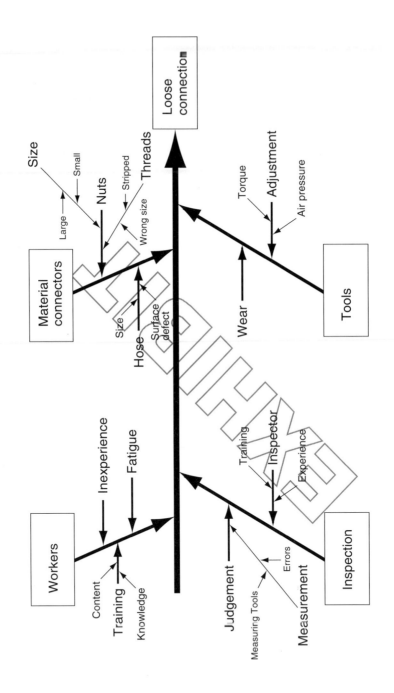

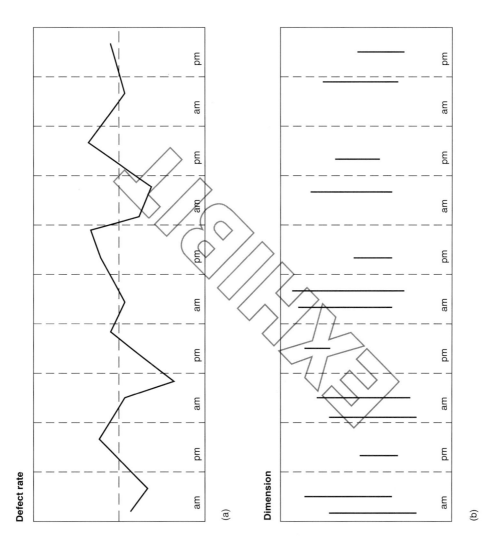

Defect rate

(a)

Dimension

(b)

Risk procedures

This section contains four procedures that deal with certain aspects of project risk and risk management. The procedures are:

RK-101   Risk management plan
RK-102   Identify and qualify risk sources
RK-103   Quantitative risk assessment
RK-104   Risk response plan

A brief overview of each procedure and what each procedure sets out to achieve is as follows.

RK-101: Risk management plan

A risk management plan is a document that establishes the approach to be used in the management of project risk. A risk management plan documents how risks are to be classified, which stakeholder will be responsible for each of the different types of risk, how each risk type is to be responded to, when responses are to be made, and so on. The plan also deals with the initiation of project risk management by ensuring an appropriate contractual clause is included in the request for proposal (RFP)/request for tender (RFT).

RK-102: Identify and qualify risk sources

Procedures RK-102 and RK-101 are the minimum risk procedures that should be used on all projects. The discipline of establishing a risk plan and arranging to qualify the risk events in a project is basic and should not be bypassed. Qualifying risk events provides the owner and the project's stakeholders with an overview of those project activities and tasks that are a risk, and classifies the risks into three groups: high, medium and low. Simply by knowing which are risk events and whether an event is classified as high, medium or low risk means that those involved in a project's management have more than an opinion on risk.

RK-103: Quantitative risk assessment

The next step in the management of risk is to undertake a detailed assessment of the probability and the impact of each risk event. By engaging project stakeholders, who have an assigned role in a project and are highly skilled in their discipline, in a risk workshop the probability and the impact range of the risk events can be determined. By using, for example, the central limit theorem a prediction can be made on a range of project (or project package) costs allied to the probability of not being exceeded. (See procedure TE-144 for the same approach applied to a project's time schedule.)

RK-104: Risk response plan

Classically there are four responses that can be made on any risk event or a group of risk events. The four responses are avoid, transfer, mitigate and accept. Having taken the preceding steps of identifying risk events, qualifying them and quantifying them, the subsequent step is to determine what response to take for each event. This procedure provides a template to facilitate the determination of risk response.

RK-101: Risk management plan

Policy

It is a requirement for all projects, irrespective of size or complexity, to have a risk management plan established as early in a project's life cycle as is practically possible. The risk management plan should be commenced and established during the concept stage or the feasibility stage and, if necessary, refined during the subsequent design and implementation stage(s). The risk management plan of a project is a document developed by the project manager with assistance from the project team and inputs from other project stakeholders. If required, the project manager can use support services from the project support office (PSO).

It is normal for a risk management plan to be created from the results and outcomes of a risk planning workshop or series of workshops. The project manager shall initiate the need for workshops. The PSO is normally required to facilitate such events. The project manager, with assistance from the PSO if needed, shall compile a document for the start of the workshop that is sent to all potential attendees during, say, the week preceding the workshop's selected date.

Outcome

The deliverable from this procedure is the document referred to as the risk management plan that describes how project risks are to be identified, qualified and quantified during the life of the project under consideration.

The content of a project's risk management plan is likely to be related to the size and complexity of the project and whether there are special extenuating owner policies or circumstances associated with the identification and assessment of risk that need to be considered. Although it is not possible to be prescriptive, the risk management plan is likely to include:

- the approach to be used in identifying risk
- how the risks are to be classified
- how the risks are to be assessed
- who is responsible for the risk planning tasks of identification, classification and assessment
- when risk management actions are to be taken
- the means to be used in documenting and communicating the actions identified and stated in the risk management plan.

The risk management plan document is likely to include such inputs as the:

- project charter
- owner's risk management policies
- project's work breakdown structure (WBS)
- project's responsibility assignment matrix (RAM)
- project's time-related schedule.

Should either the WBS or the schedule be unavailable, then action needs to be taken to produce both these items before commencing the risk planning workshop.

Specifically excluded from the risk management plan are the range of responses that are the result of risk items being identified. These actions should be set out and described in the project management working practices risk response plan, which is contained in procedure RK-104.

Process

Reference to *project manager* can also mean *study manager* when the project is at the pre-investment phase. *Stakeholder* means any party, or entity, within the performing organisation, and it can also mean any external entity that impacts on, or is impacted by, the project under consideration.

The following process should be used:

Person	Responsibility
Project manager	Is required to arrange a workshop of all appropriate stakeholders to examine the approach that should be adopted for determining the content of the risk management plan. In this regard the project manager is required to consult and use procedure RK-101.
Stakeholders	Each entity invited to attend a risk planning workshop nominates the attendee to represent them and informs the project manager accordingly. Each attendee is required to make a positive contribution to the outcomes and goals of the prearranged workshop.
Project manager	Upon initiation of the risk planning workshop the project manager completes boxes 1 and 2 of form RK-101/1. As a direct result of the workshop outcomes and/or through independent actions, the project manager completes box 3.
	Is responsible for sign-off to the content of RK-101/1, which along with any other associated and detailed information constitutes the project's risk management plan.
	Is responsible for circulating a copy of the completed 'Risk management plan — overview' to the appropriate and associated stakeholders.

Box 1

- Project and workshop data

Project/Study name _____ Job ref. # [_____]

Current project stage ☐ CT ☐ FS ☐ D1 ☐ SL ☐ D2 ☐ PR ☐ CN ☐ CO

Previous risk workshop record ☐ Never had a previous workshop

☐ Last workshop ref. _____ Last workshop date _____

Preferred date for workshop [_____] Start date [_____] Finish date

Workshop code number _____ Assigned facilitator _____

- Invited attendees (if required use back of form)

Name	Organisation/section

Signed _____ (project manager) Date _____

Box 2

- Input documents to the initial risk planning workshop

Document	Availability		Why?
	Yes	No	
• Project charter	☐	☐	_____
• Owner's risk management policies	☐	☐	_____
• The project's WBS	☐	☐	_____
• The project's RAM	☐	☐	_____
• The project's time-related schedule	☐	☐	_____

Comments

- Pre-workshop document

Comments

☐ Drafted   Signed-off by _____   Date _____

☐ Checked   Signed-off by _____   Date _____

☐ Despatched   Signed-off by _____   Date _____

Signed _____ (project manager)   Date _____

Box 3

- Risk strategy

  Explanation of approach

- Risk classifications

Low   Define [   ]
Medium   Define [   ]
High   Define [   ]

  Explanation of approach

- Responsibility for risk tasks

  Explanation of approach

- Documenting and communicating risks

  Explanation of approach

- Draft risk clause for inclusion within RFP/RFT

Signed _____ (project manager)   Date _____

RK-102: Identify and qualify risk sources

Policy

This procedure should be used as early in the life cycle of a project as possible. It should be applied on an on going basis as often as the project manager deems it necessary.

The identification and qualification of project risk items should be undertaken using cross-discipline workshops; at least one workshop per life cycle stage would be normal. Internal and external stakeholders are the usual attendees at risk workshops. The nominated attendees should be individuals who have specific and detailed knowledge of the project and/or the type of project under consideration.

The backdrop for identifying risks is normally a project's work breakdown structure (WBS), and therefore a current WBS is a prerequisite to risk identification. The extent and comprehensiveness of a project's WBS usually depends on the current stage of life cycle development. Earlier stages are more likely to offer a less detailed WBS than later stages. For convenience of use and application, a WBS, at any stage in a project, should be in the format of a computerised spreadsheet.

All risks identified should, in the first instance, be assessed using two criteria. The criteria for each risk event are:

- the *probability* of a risk event happening
- if the risk event was to happen what the *consequence* would be to the project.

A technique referred to as 'mini-risk' should be used to classify each identified risk event as high (H), medium (M) or low (L) risk using the assessed values of the two criteria (probability and consequence). At this point in the process each identified risk event has been classified as an H, M or L risk; this is what is meant by qualifying (classifying) risk events.

The next steps in the management of project risk are risk quantification, risk response and risk control; these are all subsequent processes within the system. However if, for whatever reason, the subsequent processes are not used on a project, it is a fundamental requirement that the risk events in a project be identified and classified.

It is the project manager's responsibility to ensure that risk workshops are held as required, that all appropriate stakeholders are engaged, and that the outcomes of this procedure are achieved. Alternatively, the project manager may nominate another person from the project team to be assigned the responsibility of overseeing the management of project risk.

Outcome

The outcome of this procedure is a list of WBS-related tasks that have been identified as being a potential risk to one or more of a project's success factors. A project's success factors include, but are not be limited to: meeting the owner's requirements, completing the works on time, satisfying the customer's expectations, being within the cost budget, and satisfying predetermined technical performance requirements.

Through application of this project management procedure, all risk events are identified and classified in accordance with a classification system that can be used directly for decision-making or can be used as input into subsequent risk processes and/or workshops.

Process

Reference to *project manager* can also mean *study manager* when the project is at the pre-investment phase. *Stakeholder* means any party, or entity, within the performing organisation, and it can also mean any external entity that impacts on, or is impacted by, the project under consideration.

The following process should be used:

Person	Responsibility
Project manager	Decides to undertake risk identification and qualification, liases with the project support office (PSO) on a suitable date for a workshop and to nominate a facilitator.
	Completes box 1 on form RK-102/1 and sends a copy to the PSO.
Project support office	The assigned facilitator reviews with the project manager the status of risk management on the study/project under consideration, the input documentation for the next workshop, the proposed attendees, and a suitable venue and date for the next workshop exercise.
Project manager	Books the venue and arranges equipment, refreshments, etc. Sends invitations to the cross-discipline stakeholder organisations and individuals, along with any documentation needed to brief the attendees.
Stakeholders	Nominee(s) is/are assigned to attend the workshop and the project manager is informed.
Attendees	Contribute to the workshop proceedings and are assigned roles during the workshop to provide information/produce analyses of relevant WBS items and risk events. The normal workshop process to be followed is shown sequentially in the left column of the flow diagram.
	The mini-risk exhibit classifying risk events into high, medium and low is shown in RK-102/2. What is shown is for demonstration purposes only. Determining the classification of what is in each cell (H, M or L) is derived by the project stakeholders through the workshop process.
Project manager	Prepares a report that summarises the workshop outcomes and lists the actions to be taken by each stakeholder. Sends a copy of this report to each attendee.
Project support office	Within a reasonable time period after the workshop the PSO audits the project to determine the status of the actions on specific risk events. A summary report of audit findings is prepared by the PSO and a copy sent to the project manager. The audit report indicates one of three results on each risk event:

	• the action is satisfactorily completed • the action is satisfactorily on going and has been given an estimated completion date by the responsible stakeholder • the required action has not been taken.
Project manager	Is required to decide on further actions to be taken, by whom and by what date on any and all risk events that are of type 3. Completes box 2 on form RK-102/1 and places the completed form in the project files for future and on going reference. (Descisions on responses at this stage are necessary in the event that procedure RK-103 is not applied.)

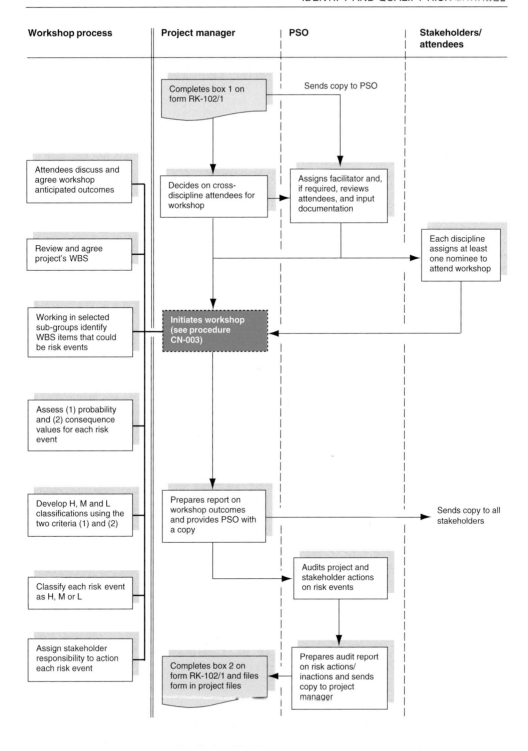

Workshop process	Project manager	PSO	Stakeholders/attendees

Completes box 1 on form RK-102/1

Sends copy to PSO

Attendees discuss and agree workshop anticipated outcomes

Decides on cross-discipline attendees for workshop

Assigns facilitator and, if required, reviews attendees, and input documentation

Each discipline assigns at least one nominee to attend workshop

Review and agree project's WBS

Working in selected sub-groups identify WBS items that could be risk events

Initiates workshop (see procedure CN-003)

Assess (1) probability and (2) consequence values for each risk event

Develop H, M and L classifications using the two criteria (1) and (2)

Prepares report on workshop outcomes and provides PSO with a copy

Sends copy to all stakeholders

Classify each risk event as H, M or L

Audits project and stakeholder actions on risk events

Assign stakeholder responsibility to action each risk event

Completes box 2 on form RK-102/1 and files form in project files

Prepares audit report on risk actions/inactions and sends copy to project manager

Box 1

Project/Study name _____	Job ref. # [_____]

Current project stage ☐ CT ☐ FS ☐ D1 ☐ SL ☐ D2 ☐ PR ☐ CN ☐ CO

Risk workshop #1 ☐ ☐ ☐ ☐ ☐ ☐ ☐ ☐
　　　　　　　 #2 ☐ ☐ ☐ ☐ ☐ ☐ ☐ ☐
　　　　　　　 #3 ☐ ☐ ☐ ☐ ☐ ☐ ☐ ☐

Next workshop [_____] Date [_____] Start time [_____] Venue

Workshop code _____ (e.g. FS#2)　　　Assigned facilitator _____

• Invited attendees (if required use back of form)

Name	Organisation/section

Signed _____ (project manager)　　Date _____

Box 2

• Workshop outcomes report

Report code _____ (e.g. FS#2-OR)　　Date filed _____　　Date to PSO _____

Checked by _____　　Signed-off _____ (project manager)

No. of risk items	Low	Medium	High
Project section/structure			
A			
B			
C			
D			
E			
etc.			

• PSO audit report

Report code _____ (e.g. FS#2-PSO-AO)　　Date filed _____　　Date to PM_____

Action assigned on outstanding risk events　Yes ☐　No ☐　　See attached document ref. _____

Checked by _____　　Signed-off _____ (project manager)

PROJECT RISK EVENTS — TRACKING FORM
Revision 0 / 01.03.2004

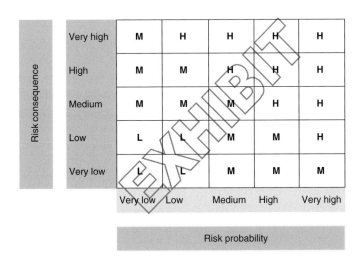

The vertical scale is the criteria 'risk consequence', i.e. the effect on the project if a risk event were to happen. The horizontal scale is the 'risk probability', i.e. the chance of a risk event happening.

A classification of risk events is normally minimised to:

L   Low
M   Medium
H   High

By creating three classes of risk, the project team's response on how to deal with project risk events can be simplified.

A mini-risk 5 × 5 matrix consisting of 25 cells is shown in the chart above. The class of risk shown in each cell is hypothetical.

The class of risk that should apply to each cell is not predetermined but is decided by a project's stakeholders, and the classification decided upon is often a feature of the size and complexity of the project under consideration.

RK-103: Quantitative risk assessment

Policy

This procedure is used in conjunction with the preparation of cost budgets and scheduling the plan of all significantly sized capital projects (say, greater than Euro 1 million) or when a project is considered to be 'a first' (of a type never undertaken before).

Risk quantification is applied as early as possible in a project's life cycle and is carried out at least once in each of the stages. This procedure provides a linkage between:

- the project time schedule and the probability of the time period not being exceeded
- the project cost budget and the probability of the cost budget not being exceeded.

Accordingly, this procedure is a companion to procedures TE-143, TE-144 and CS-022.

The basis for quantifying risk is the application of certain aspects of probability theory and includes the central limit theorem (CLT). It is necessary to use a range of time period and budget cost for each work element within a work breakdown structure (WBS). The exception is when an element's time period and/or budget cost are/is known with a high degree of certainty, i.e. a fixed time period and/or a fixed price for an element. These ranges are used to determine the 'expected' total project period and the overall budget cost along with the associated probability of not being exceeded.

The outputs of probability versus time period and probability versus budget cost should be tabulated and used as decision-making techniques by the project team to determine an acceptable time period and budget cost against which a project can be controlled. These outputs can be for a single stage or can be amalgamated for all stages to represent the complete project life cycle.

Outcome

The outcome of this procedure will be in two parts: time period and budget cost.

Time period

Using the outputs from TE-143 and TE-144 and applying the CLT, the time period versus probability can be calculated. By calculating the value Z the chance of it happening, or the probability, can be read from the table of probabilities shown in table RK-103/1. Using the CLT the following formula will provide the means to calculate Z:

$$Z = (T_x - T_e)/\sigma_e$$

where Z is the number of standard deviations from the mean, T_x is any chosen project time period, T_e is the project's critical path mean and σ_e is the standard deviation of the project's critical path.

The outcome is a range of time periods and their probability of achieving project completion within a stated time period for the project.

Budget cost

The budget cost outcome will be presented in the form of a range of costs and their associated chance (probability) of not being exceeded. To produce this range and associated probability the input data generated for each work element in the WBS will be monetary values (e.g. Euro, UK pounds, etc.) of the following variables:

- optimistic (best) cost (a)
- most likely cost (b)
- pessimistic (worst) cost (c).

In general, each work element has a value for a, b and c which will be different. From this range an expected cost, the standard deviation and the variance can be calculated for each work element using:

Expected cost $(E_c) = (a + 4b + c)/6$
Standard deviation $(\sigma) = (c - a)/6$
Variance $= \sigma^2$

A range of a project's overall cost and the associated probability (surety of staying below the quoted cost) can be obtained by summating the E_c values for all project work elements and by summating the variance (σ^2) for all work elements. The project cost and a probability range can be calculated using the CLT formula.

Form RK-103/2 provides the summation facility. By adding all the element values in column 6 of the table a total is obtained of a project's expected cost, and by adding all the element values in column 8 a total variance for the project's cost is determined. In the exhibit the total of column 6 is 1,438,883, a value that would be equivalent to the 50% probability of being exceeded. The total of column 8, the variance, is 36,100,243,445 and by taking the square root of this value the standard deviation of 190,000 is obtained.

The values for E_c and σ are then transferred to form RK-103/3. The form has been set-up showing the percentage chance of being exceeded (column 1) and its equivalent Z value (column 2). By using the formula for Z the project cost can be calculated from the following process steps:

- Step 1: insert the project's standard deviation value in column 3. In the exhibit this is 190,000.
- Step 2: taking account of the minus and plus signs, multiply the Z value (column 2) by the project's σ (column 3) and place result in column 4.
- Step 3: insert the project's expected cost in column 5. In the exhibit this is 1,438,883.
- Step 4: add the value in column 4 to the value in column 5 to obtain the range of project cost (uncertain items).
- Step 5: prepare a graph of values in column 1 versus values in column 6 which presents the percentage chance of being exceeded versus the project cost (uncertain items).

The exhibit on RK-103/3 shows the range of cost outcomes of the uncertain items in a project; to this range the cost of the certain items needs to be added.

Any quantitative risk assessment should be carried out initially in the earliest stage of a project, and then should be updated and re-evaluated as often as necessary, which will usually be determined by availability of more definitive information or by some exceptional event.

Process

Reference to *project manager* can also mean *study manager* when the project is at the pre-investment phase.

The following process should be used:

Person	Responsibility
Project manager	Undertakes the mathematical analysis of a project's logic diagram. The hand calculation method described in this procedure may be carried out by computer or time scheduling software model. In such circumstances the information to be recorded must be the same as required by this procedure.

The project manager is required to check all calculations to confirm acceptance of each scheduling analysis by signing-off on the mathematical analysis data sheets TE-144/1 and RK-103/2. The data is used as input to other processes. Once the information has been disseminated to other procedures and processes the data sheets are filed in the project files. |
| Project manager | Undertakes the mathematical analysis that will produce the project's out-turn cost and relate it to its associated probability of not being exceeded.

The project manager is required to check all calculations to confirm acceptance of the mathematical analysis. This will be undertaken using spreadsheets similar to that shown in exhibits RK-103/2 and RK-103/3. It is optional whether the project cost versus the percentage probability is documented as a tabulated set of results or as a line graph. A typical line graph is shown in RK-103/3. |

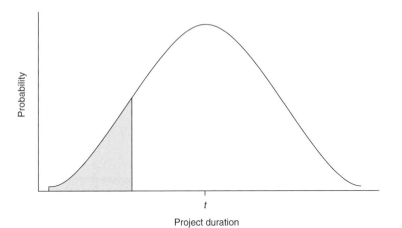

Project duration

z	0.00	0.01	0.02	0.03	0.04	0.05	0.06	0.07	0.08	0.09
0.0	0.500	0.504	0.508	0.512	0.516	0.519	0.523	0.527	0.531	0.535
0.1	0.539	0.543	0.547	0.551	0.555	0.559	0.563	0.567	0.571	0.575
0.2	0.579	0.583	0.587	0.591	0.594	0.598	0.602	0.606	0.610	0.614
0.3	0.617	0.621	0.625	0.629	0.633	0.636	0.640	0.644	0.648	0.651
0.4	0.655	0.659	0.662	0.666	0.670	0.673	0.677	0.680	0.684	0.687
0.5	0.691	0.695	0.698	0.701	0.705	0.708	0.712	0.715	0.719	0.722
0.6	0.725	0.729	0.732	0.735	0.738	0.742	0.745	0.748	0.751	0.754
0.7	0.758	0.761	0.764	0.767	0.770	0.773	0.776	0.779	0.782	0.785
0.8	0.788	0.791	0.793	0.796	0.799	0.802	0.805	0.807	0.810	0.813
0.9	0.818	0.818	0.821	0.823	0.926	0.828	0.831	0.834	0.836	0.838
1.0	0.841	0.843	0.848	0.848	0.850	0.853	0.855	0.857	0.859	0.882
1.1	0.864	0.866	0.868	0.870	0.872	0.874	0.877	0.879	0.881	0.883
1.2	0.884	0.886	0.888	0.890	0.892	0.894	0.896	0.898	0.899	0.901
1.3	0.903	0.904	0.906	0.908	0.909	0.911	0.913	0.914	0.916	0.917
1.4	0.919	0.920	0.922	0.923	0.925	0.926	0.927	0.929	0.930	0.931
1.5	0.933	0.934	0.935	0.937	0.938	0.939	0.940	0.941	0.942	0.944
1.6	0.945	0.946	0.947	0.948	0.949	0.950	0.951	0.952	0.953	0.954
1.7	0.955	0.956	0.957	0.958	0.959	0.959	0.960	0.961	0.962	0.963
1.8	0.964	0.964	0.965	0.966	0.967	0.967	0.968	0.969	0.969	0.970
1.9	0.971	0.971	0.972	0.973	0.973	0.974	0.975	0.975	0.976	0.976
2.0	0.977	0.977	0.978	0.978	0.979	0.979	0.980	0.980	0.981	0.981
2.1	0.982	0.982	0.983	0.983	0.983	0.984	0.984	0.985	0.985	0.985
2.2	0 986	0.986	0.986	0 987	0 987	0.987	0.988	0 988	0 988	0 989
2.3	0.989	0.989	0.989	0.990	0.990	0.990	0.991	0.991	0.991	0.991
2.4	0.991	0.992	0.992	0.992	0.992	0.992	0.993	0.993	0.993	0.993
2.5	0.993	0.994	0.994	0.994	0.994	0.994	0.994	0.994	0.995	0.995

(1) Risk ref. #	(2) Risk description	(3) Optimistic amount	(4) Most likely amount	(5) Pessimistic amount	(6) Expected value	(7) Standard deviation (σ)	(8) Variance (σ^2)
xxxx 00	Change in cast-*in-situ* piles scope	95,000	188,000	239,000	181,000	24,000	576,000,000
xxxx 01	Cast *in situ* piles	66,000					
xxxx 02	North-west pile group	80,000	350,000	434,000	333,333	44,667	1,995,140,389
xxxx 03	Standing time during de-watering	20,000					
yyyy 10	Delay and disruption	Nil	Nil	70,000	11,667	11,667	136,118,389
yyyy 11	Arch tubes	30,000	170,000	940,000	275,000	151,667	23,002,878,389
yyyy 12	Remove belly plates box girder 1 n/e	Nil	186,000	557,000	216,883	92,833	8,617,965,389
yyyy 13	Support framework for glass w/way	50,000	50,000	86,000	56,000	6,000	36,000,000
yyyy 14	Production test plates						
yyyy 15	Lower cable brackets (SI #0)						
yyyy 16	Duct sleeves (SI #1)	Nil	40,000	Nil	40,000	Nil	Nil
yyyy 17	Lamination checks (SI #2)						
yyyy 18	Additional ducts 10/-10 (SI #3)						
yyyy 19	Arch footing weld access (SI #4)						
zz 100	Variation in steel quantities	Nil	220,000	Nil	220,000	Nil	Nil
zz 101	Price variation clause	Nil	80,000	250,000	95,000	41,667	1,736,138,389
zz 102	COMADA ultrasonic test						
zz 103	COMADA lamination checks						
zz 104	Expansion joint in x Quay	Nil	10,000	Nil	10,000	Nil	Nil
zz 105	Car railing						
zz 106	Expansion joint in y Quay						
zz 107	Outer h/railing						
	Total				1,438,883		
	Total						36,100,243,44E
	Standard deviation						190,000

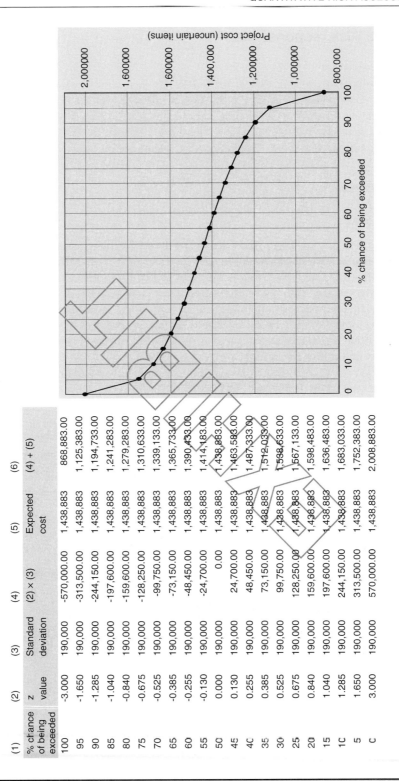

(1) % chance of being exceeded	(2) z value	(3) Standard deviation	(4) (2) × (3)	(5) Expected cost	(6) (4) + (5)
100	-3.000	190,000	-570,000.00	1,438,883	868,883.00
95	-1.650	190,000	-313,500.00	1,438,883	1,125,383.00
90	-1.285	190,000	-244,150.00	1,438,883	1,194,733.00
85	-1.040	190,000	-197,600.00	1,438,883	1,241,283.00
80	-0.840	190,000	-159,600.00	1,438,883	1,279,283.00
75	-0.675	190,000	-128,250.00	1,438,883	1,310,633.00
70	-0.525	190,000	-99,750.00	1,438,883	1,339,133.00
65	-0.385	190,000	-73,150.00	1,438,883	1,365,733.00
60	-0.255	190,000	-48,450.00	1,438,883	1,390,433.00
55	-0.130	190,000	-24,700.00	1,438,883	1,414,183.00
50	0.000	190,000	0.00	1,438,883	1,438,883.00
45	0.130	190,000	24,700.00	1,438,883	1,463,583.00
40	0.255	190,000	48,450.00	1,438,883	1,487,333.00
35	0.385	190,000	73,150.00	1,438,883	1,512,033.00
30	0.525	190,000	99,750.00	1,438,883	1,538,633.00
25	0.675	190,000	128,250.00	1,438,883	1,567,133.00
20	0.840	190,000	159,600.00	1,438,883	1,598,483.00
15	1.040	190,000	197,600.00	1,438,883	1,636,483.00
10	1.285	190,000	244,150.00	1,438,883	1,683,033.00
5	1.650	190,000	313,500.00	1,438,883	1,752,383.00
0	3.000	190,000	570,000.00	1,438,883	2,008,883.00

PROJECT COST VERSUS PROBABILITY
Revision 0 / 01.03.2004

RK-103/3
Page 6 of 6

RK-104: Risk response plan

Policy

The preceding risk procedures, RK-101 to RK-103, deal with the planning, identification, qualification and quantification of risk events within a project. This procedure deals with the subsequent process of developing response options and in determining the related actions to be taken.

The response to risk events should be to use one or other of the following options:

- avoidance
- transference
- mitigation
- acceptance.

Specific risks that are to be avoided should be the subject of a special study by the project team and/or other parties assigned by the project manager. The objective of risk management is to eliminate the identified risk event or to protect the project from any deleterious impact if the risk event cannot be eliminated.

Transferring risk does not eliminate risk but it shifts the consequence and ownership of the risk to some party who is considered most able to deal with it. Risk transfer can be achieved either through suitable insurance coverage or by using the most appropriate form of contract and contract conditions.

Mitigation refers to early action to reducing the likelihood and/or the consequence of some risk event. For risk events in which the decision is to mitigate it is necessary that (1) the acceptance threshold is determined, and (2) the potential costs of mitigation are evaluated.

Acceptance of any risk event by the project team requires that a plan for monitoring and controlling such events has been established. Such a plan needs to encompass the project's contingency allowance where appropriate project resources and their associated cost have been identified and budgeted for.

In developing a project's risk response plan the plan must reflect the potential for risk threats/opportunities and managing risk responses should have assigned ownership.

Outcome

The outcome of this procedure is a risk response plan. This plan is normally a significant document and is produced to a level of detail that permits risk event monitoring and control. The plan includes, but is not limited to, the following:

- work breakdown structure (WBS) showing the identified risks and their classification
- results of any quantification of risk event consequence and probability
- stakeholder ownership of risk events
- agreed risk response for each identified risk event
- specific actions to implement the chosen response strategy
- risk event contingency plans.

Exhibit RK-104/2 provides an example of a typical risk response plan. Columns 1–3 inclusive contain the task structure of a project (i.e. the WBS), and contain the code, the elements and the tasks respectively. Column 4 consists of as many columns as there are stakeholders having an impact or are impacted by the project. If a stakeholder has a design/administration/management role, this is identified in column 4 using the legend shown below the exhibit. Columns 1–4 taken together provide the project's responsibility assignment matrix (RAM). The data contained in columns 1–4 are an input to procedures RK-102, RK-103 and RK-104.

Risk events that were qualified in RK-102 are presented in column 5. The columns headed p, I and C relate to probability, impact (consequence) and risk classification, respectively. In qualifying risk events (see procedure RK-102) there is a need to classify each event as high (H), medium (M) or low (L) risk.

The response to each identified risk event will be either avoid, transfer, mitigate or accept. Column 6 is therefore used to indicate the response that is required to deal with each risk event. Column 7 should contain a commentary of the actions associated with the chosen response that is recommended for each risk event. Column 8 states what contingencies, if any, are to be established regarding the time schedule, cost budget or other resources required to complete the project successfully.

Some examples of each of the four risk responses are:

- *Avoidance*:
  - reduce the scope of the project to avoid high-risk tasks
  - add resources or available time
  - replace innovation with a familiar approach
  - do not use a particular supplier or contractor.

- *Transference*:
  - use a particular form of contract
  - increase the use of warranties and guarantees
  - examine the use of available insurance.

- *Mitigation*:
  - adopt a less complex technical process
  - undertake more testing
  - add resources or available time.

- *Acceptance*:
  - develop a contingency plan that will include amounts of money, time and resources to account for accepted risk events.

A further outcome of this procedure is for the project manager and project team continually to monitor and control the risk events, make constant reference to the response plan, and evaluate the effectiveness of actions taken in reducing risks. Any, and all, new risks identified and the modification of existing risks are to be included using procedures RK-101 to RK-104 on an on-going basis.

Process

Reference to *project manager* can also mean *study manager* when the project is at the pre-investment phase. *Stakeholder* means any party, or entity, within the performing organisation, and it can also mean any external entity that impacts on, or is impacted by, the project under consideration.

The following process should be used:

Person	Responsibility
Project manager	Arranges with the project stakeholders to assist in developing the risk response plan for the project under consideration. A workshop venue and date are arranged. The project manager completes box 1 on form RK-104/1 and accordingly informs the project support office (PSO) and the identified workshop attendees of the date and venue for the workshop.
Project support office	Assigns a facilitator who directs/manages the risk response workshop.
Stakeholders	The nominated persons attend the workshop and contribute to the creation of the project risk response plan. Determine the risk qualification classifications and the risk responses (see box 2 of form RK-104/1). Work through each risk event and agree what the response should be, and determine any contingency that needs to be added to the project time schedule, project cost or any other project resource.
Project manager	Produces the risk response plan as an active project document to be used for monitoring and controlling the project's risk events, and circulates a copy to each of the project's stakeholders. A risk response plan similar to exhibit RK-104/2 would normally be the layout that is used for the risk response plan.
	Completes box 2 of RK-104/1 and places the completed form in the project files.

Box 1

| Project/Study name _____ | Job ref. # [_____] |

Current project stage   ☐ CT   ☐ FS   ☐ D1   ☐ SL   ☐ D2   ☐ PR   ☐ CN   ☐ CO

Risk workshop   #1   ☐   ☐   ☐   ☐   ☐   ☐   ☐   ☐
              #2   ☐   ☐   ☐   ☐   ☐   ☐   ☐   ☐
              #3   ☐   ☐   ☐   ☐   ☐   ☐   ☐   ☐

Next workshop [_____] Date   [____] Start time   [_____] Venue

Workshop code _____ (e.g. FS#2)   _____ assigned facilitator

• Invited attendees (if required use back of form)

Name	Organisation/section

Signed _____ (project manager)   Date _____

Box 2

• Risk management plan

Comments

• WBS/RAM

| WBS | ☐ Available | ☐ Not available | Rev. # _____ | Issue date _____ |

| RAM | ☐ Available | ☐ Not available | Rev. # _____ | Issue date _____ |

Comments

Box 2 continued

- Risk qualification

State the system used in risk event classification (H, M or L) in each cell of the matrix below:

Risk consequence / Probability	Very low	Low	Medium	High	Very high
Very high					
High					
Medium					
Low					
Very low					

- Risk responses — explanation of approach

Risk response	Risk event type		
	High	Medium	Low
Avoidance			
Transference			
Mitigation			
Acceptance			

- Assigned responsibility for risk responses

Comments

- Risk response report

Report ref. # ________ Date of issue __________ Signed-off by __________________ (project manager)

Doc. #	*Circulated to*	*Organisation/section*

(1)	(2)	(3)	(4) Stakeholders										(5) Risk			(6) Response				(7) Actions	(8) Contingencies
Code	Level 2 element	Level 3 task	ACM	E&C	NWA	PM	DTA	MPP	BH	AR	AH	JPC	P	I	C	AV	TR	MI	AC	Actions	Contingencies
SWIMMING POOL																					
1.1	Freeze layout												0.1	VH	H						
-1		Owner/operator			A/M															Obtain acceptable fire certificate	
-2		Design team						A		A										Seek end user approvals	
-3		Contractor								A										Seek contractor agreement	
-4		Statutory bodies			M			R/M		A										Agree layout of plant room	
-5		Budget			M			A		R											
1.2	Site works												0.25	L	L						
-1		Exc. + disposal								M											
-2		Service trenches			R/M			R/M		M											
-3		Hardcore								M											
1.3	Foundations																				
-1		(to DPC)						M		M											
-2		Prepare foundations					M			M											
-3		Shutt'g/rebar/concrete						M		M											
1.4	Struct. steel																				
-1		Shop drawings					A														
-2		Approvals								M											
-3		Fabrication																				
-4		Erection					M			M											
1.5	Pool tank												0.75	VH	H					Ensure close supervision by RE + site team	
-1		Setting-out					A														
-2		Prepare formation								M											
-3		Services (1st fix)							R												
-4		Shutt'g/rebar/concrete					M			M											

RAM legend: S: Sign-off
M: Monitor
C: Certify
R: Responsible
A: Advising/recommend

Response legend: AV: avoid
TR: transfer
MI: mitigate
AC: accept

Scope procedures

This section contains six procedures that deal with certain aspects of project scope management. The procedures are:

SE-121   Study and project charter
SE-122   Conceptualising alternative options
SE-123   Evaluating and ranking options
SE-124   Project requirements and information document (PRID)
SE-125   Work breakdown structure (WBS)
SE-131   Delivering the operations manual

A brief overview of each procedure and what each procedure sets out to achieve is as follows.

SE-121: Study and project charter

A charter is a simple but important document that senior management uses to convey the purpose and requirements of a project to a project team. When developed in the concept or feasibility stages it is referred to as a 'study charter'; thereafter it is called a 'project charter'. A charter defines matters such as customer requirements, project scheduling, critical or constraining factors, the people resources including external entities needed to create the deliverables, and the authority and responsibility of a project's sponsor and manager. The project's sponsor and project's study (project) manager should sign the charter.

SE-122: Conceptualising alternative options

Whether an option is an element within a package of work, a package of work within a project, or one scheme versus other schemes, in order to determine which is the preferred option a means for arriving at a decision is required. This procedure offers a process for assisting in decision-making when comparing two or more options. It incorporates procedures from the knowledge areas of procurement, scope and value.

SE-123: Evaluating and ranking options

When comparing options, decisions are often taken by investigating such factors as technical, aesthetic, social, political, and so on. Costs of different options are usually based on a comparison of initial costs (i.e. the cost to purchase). Cost comparisons must always take account of the total life cycle costs, which include maintenance cost, replacement cost and operational cost, as well as the initial cost. This procedure provides a template for undertaking net present value (NPV) or net present cost (NPC) calculations on the total life cycle costs of options.

SE-124: Project requirements and information document (PRID)

A PRID is a (the) deliverable from the concept stage; it is also the primary input into the feasibility stage. A PRID describes the possible solutions (options) that could satisfy the social need or business need and provides an order-of-magnitude assessment of each one. Using an appropriate combination of cost, procurement, risk, scope and value procedures, the performing organisation reduces a possible long list of options to two or three possible schemes that would be the basis for a more rigorous feasibility examination.

SE-125: Work breakdown structure (WBS)

The WBS is perhaps the single most important element in the project management process. It is the basis for setting the framework and structure for deciding on issues such as time and cost planning, resource allocation, identifying risk items, and many more. The project's structure is subject to continuing change as the project develops and as the detail can be defined. The WBS is determined early in the development of a project and is dynamically linked to project change, as and when it is to happen or has happened. Any WBS should be a decomposition of the work of a project into work packages, activities and tasks; the lowest level being the basis for problem solving and decision-making.

SE-131: Delivering the operations manual

Many projects, but not all, have a commissioning stage. Commissioning applies when the owner, the performing organisation, developing a project is required to become the operator of the completed project. The normal outcome is an operations manual and the skills transfer from the contractor or the commissioning agent to the operator. This procedure provides a process overview that can be used for commissioning but it must be tailored for each project.

SE-121: Study and project charter

Policy

A charter document outlines the purpose and requirements of whatever is to be achieved for the project's owner and/or customer, and sets down the responsibility and authority of the manager of the undertaking and the sponsor of the performing organisation or department. A charter created in the concept or feasibility stages, where the deliverable is normally a document, is referred to as a *study charter*. A charter created in subsequent stages is referred to as a *project charter*. The use of the term *charter* can therefore mean either study charter or project charter.

Whatever is to be achieved is referred to as the deliverable(s). The deliverable may be a service, a product or a project. The sponsor is the named person who acts as liaison between the owner's management (performing organisation) and the team responsible for managing the associated work.

It is the responsibility of the sponsor to create the charter. In the event of non-compliance by the sponsor it is the responsibility of the study (project) manager to create the charter and have it approved by the sponsor.

Once a need to undertake a study or to carry out a project has been decided, it is a requirement to follow procedure CN-002. Associated aspects of this 'kick off' procedure are identifying a study (project) manager and obtaining delegated function for the manager. A study (project) manager needs to be identified who is assigned to manage the study (project) stages. A charter document needs to be produced and signed-off by the sponsor and study (project) manager; at that point the single source responsibility can perform and be supported by the sponsor, who is required to provide the manager with the resources that he or she needs.

Outcome

The outcome of this procedure is a *study charter* if the current activities are in the concept stage or the feasibility stage. Alternatively, the outcome of this procedure is a *project charter* if the deliverable is a service, product or project in any of the stages subsequent to the feasibility stage.

The charter document transfers responsibility from corporate management to a single source for running the study or project and provides the assigned manager and the sponsor with clear lines of demarcation for their study (project) roles. The charter should be unambiguous regarding the responsibilities and the authorities of both the manager and the sponsor.

Process

Reference to *project manager* can also mean *study manager* when the project is at the pre-investment phase. *Sponsor* means the appointed person from within the performing organisation who has been assigned by senior management to arrange for a project's delivery and report its on going status during its development tenure.

The following process should be used:

Person	Responsibility
Sponsor	Associated with responding to 'study or project registration' (see procedure CN-002), the sponsor is required to draft a study (project) charter. The charter document commences its development cycle with the sponsor completing box 1 on form SE-121/1. The original of the form is passed to the study (project) manager along with copies of associated documents or other information that would be useful.
	Drafts the charter document and sends to assigned manager of study (project).
Project manager	In the event that the sponsor is non-compliant the assigned manager creates the charter and sends it to the sponsor to ratify.
Sponsor	Finalises the charter document and signs it and passes to the study manager for signature.
Project manager	Completes box 2 on form SE-121/1 before sending copies of the form and charter to approved recipients.
	(See exhibit SE-121/2, which shows a typical example of a study charter used for a public sector study. A project charter would be similarly structured.)

STUDY AND PROJECT CHARTER

Box 1

Study/Project name _____	Job ref. # [_____]

Customer/Department _____ Sponsor _____

> *Reason for study/project*

> *Deliverables and deadlines*

Nominated study/project manager _____ Contacted ☐ Yes ☐ No

Signed _____ (sponsor) Date _____

Box 2

- Sponsor/manager responsibilities and authorities

> *Explain*

- Team resources

Name	Organisation/section	Team title

- Time period

Planned start date [_____] Planned finish date [_____]

- Study budget

Stakeholder/entity	Fee	Expenses	Total

- Charter drafted and signed

☐ Yes   ☐ No

> *Explain*

Signed _____ (study manager) Date _____

STUDY CHARTER
ZZZZ Study

Business need and introduction

If development within the YYYY region is not satisfactorily planned, then deleterious impacts from an overloaded drainage system are very likely to occur, causing flooding, and environmental and health hazards. XXXX has recognised that the capacity and extent of portions of the sewerage system within the metropolitan area of DDDD are inadequate and need to be upgraded to cater for development in the city and surrounding counties.

A comprehensive study of the drainage system is to be achieved by procuring an experienced service provider (SP) to complete the investigating requirements and report their findings in stages and make recommendations (see Section 3).

At the time of preparing this charter the joint venture of AAAA Consultants and BBBB is the preferred bidder; AAAA is the lead partner. The joint venture includes the organisations of CCCC.

XXXX has been identified as the contracting authority (CA) in the association of seven Authorities who are stakeholders in the study and the study outcomes. With XXXX in such a role, they will be responsible for closely managing the service provider and monitoring and controlling the service provider activities. It is paramount that the study requirements as set out in the Briefing Document, dated October 2000, and the document that contains the preferred bidder's final offer are used as the means for ensuring that 'what is provided is what is wanted'.

Goals

The following are the stated goals of the planned study:

- capture and analysis of all data;
- construction and verification of a model of existing system;
- defining of system loads;
- assessment of treatment capacities;
- recommendation of policies;
- examination of implementation options;
- effective management of the study.

The study is to be totally completed within 18 months from study commencement.

Development stages

Based upon the preferred bidders proposal and subsequent modifications agreed during the period from the beginning of January 2001 to mid-March 2001 the following are definable stages and end points in the planned study period:

Mobilisation period	5 weeks from study commencement
Data collection and review	10 weeks after study commencement
Initial planning	18 weeks after study commencement
Study of GC sewer	26 weeks after study commencement
Report on GIS recommendations	32 weeks after study commencement
Model build, milestones achieved and status of deliverables	50 weeks after study commencement

- Strategic policy recommendations 64 weeks after study commencement
- Proposals for future options 68 weeks after study commencement
- Final report 76 weeks after study commencement

Study team

The CA's study team will consist of the following roles/positions. The nominated person for each position is:

Role/position	Nominated person
Study manager	Δαν ΜχΕντιε
Drainage system specialist	Παδραιγ Ηεννελλψ
Computer model specialist	Βριαν Δοψλε
Land survey specialist	Δεσ Φινν
GIS specialist	Λαρρψ Βεψηαν
Study management specialist	Βερτ Ηαμιλτον
Principal co-owners and their representatives	
L	ϑον Βατεσ
M	Φεργυσ Γρινχη
N	Τιμ Ολεαρψ
O	Τομ Ολεαρψ
P	Μιχηαελ Μοψνε
Q	Σαμυελ Νειλλ

The sponsor for this project is Τιμ Βροχκ.

Responsibilities/authorities

The sponsor will be CA's principal liaison. The sponsor will be responsible for providing resources (personnel, equipment and materials) that will be required from time to time by the study team. The sponsor will be responsible for signing-off on the plan for the project and approving completion of the staged and final deliverables. The sponsor will be kept informed of events during the currency of the study. The responsibilities and authorities of the other team members are:

Study manager The study manager will be responsible for approving payments to the service provider in accordance with the terms of the contract, and ensuring that any requirement of the sponsor has been incorporated into the study activities. The study manager will be responsible for ensuring that the service provider achieves the study aims and the associated goals. The study manager will be the sole authority for the day-to-day management of the study.

Co-owner representatives Each co-owner will have a liaison person for the study whose responsibility will be to identify and support any and all enquiries raised by the members of the study team and/or project team. The representatives will identify and nominate other specialists within their organisations who will from time to time be needed to assist the study team/project team. These specialists will be provided with the opportunity to participate during the tenure of the study with the study team on all matters within their expertise.

Drainage specialist	The drainage system specialist will be responsible for liaising with the service provider and the co-owner representatives and other nominated specialists on all aspects of the physical infrastructure. This will include, but not be limited to, catchment data, asset data, event data (rainfall, dry weather flow, storm flow, diversion, etc.), calibration recommendations and installation, etc.
Computer specialist	The computer model specialist will be responsible for liaising with the service provider to ensure that the model and its verification are fully in accordance with the study requirements. The computer model specialist's responsibilities will include ensuring that the service provider examines and interprets possible risk and implementation scenarios.
Land survey specialist	The land survey specialist will be responsible for shadowing the service provider's personnel who have the responsibility for all surveying activities of the existing urban drainage system that will be required. These activities will include viewing of aerial photographs, examination of drawings of zonal infrastructure, physical measurement of coordinates and levels, assessing physical properties of watercourses, etc.
GIS specialist	The GIS specialist will be responsible for shadowing the service provider's personnel who have responsibility for developing the geographical information system for the YYYY. The responsibilities will include liaising with the modelling group in their investigation into gaps in the asset records and be involved in ratifying solutions that will be compatible with XXXX and the other co-owners requirements and determining the most appropriate GIS to be used in the study.
Management specialist	The specialist will report to the study manager. The study management specialist will be responsible for providing advice on all aspects relating to the project management process and providing special support to the study manager on any aspect of the study activities and the management of the study. The specialist will also be available for facilitating required study workshops.

Budget constraints

The estimated cost of the SP's proposal to undertake the study work is Euro 9,075,590. The estimated cost of XXXX's study team for the period of the study is Euro 1,046,065.

Agreed to

The above Charter content has been discussed and agreed between the study sponsor and the study manager as confirmed by their signatures:

....

Τιμ Βροχκ (sponsor)   Date

....

Δαν ΜχΕντιε (study manager)   Date

SE-122: Conceptualising alternative options

Policy

The procedure is applied as part of the process in identifying any best option from a range (i.e. two or more) of options. It is equally appropriate in the micro or macro situations. The micro application includes such matters as deciding on an appropriate element of a project. The macro application includes such issues as deciding on the preferred strategy for a project that when implemented satisfies a need.

Most projects are conceived as a response to addressing and satisfying social needs (public sector) or business needs (private sector). At the concept stage all alternative options should be appropriately investigated. Investigations are generally undertaken by a multidisciplinary internal team supplemented, if necessary, by external individual experts. The maximum representation of the project stakeholder community should be reflected in whole, or in part, in the conceptualisation process. Stakeholders include the end-users, residents associations, retail associations, the customer, senior management, the statutory agencies, the study team, special subject experts, and such like. The combined knowledge and experience of the stakeholders is applied as a continuous input to the process.

Conceptualisation is carried out using order-of-magnitude level investigations, and these should be robust enough to incorporate technical, economic, social, environmental and, if imposed, political factors. The level of detail must be sufficient to allow relative comparisons of each option and provide guidance on which are the best options to go forward with. At this initial stage of any project's development great care and constraint needs to be exercised in interpreting and using the investigation outputs of each option. Forecasts, such as those relating to deliverables, timing of implementation, probable out-turn cost, and other important objectives, can be provided as long as the forecasted value is associated with the numerical probability of being achieved.

In any economic analysis the range of evaluation techniques are used as appropriate. The range includes:

- payback period
- return on investment
- net present value
- internal rate of return.

Outcome

The procedure provides a means of converging from an initial range of identified options that could satisfy a need to a short-list of options, or a single option, that satisfies the need. In other words, the procedure provides a form of prequalification of options, one of which is likely to be the preferred option that can become the basis of the project requirements and information document (PRID). The PRID (see procedure SE-124) is the deliverable from the concept stage and is used as the primary input to kick off the feasibility stage.

The stakeholders, under the direction and management of a study manager and a cross-functional team of expertise, are essentially involved in conceiving the options. Should it be necessary to procure external assistance to support and work with the study team, such short-term, part-time requirements are specified and procured by the study manager using the purchasing procedure (see procedures PT-062 and PT-063).

The outcome of this human resource effort includes:

- an identification of all possible options
- a broad or strategic analysis of all socially (and politically) acceptable options
- an economic evaluation of all technically viable options
- the identification of what appears to be the preferred option.

To create the outcome requires the application of three other procedures, namely:

- PT-066: Evaluate external service proposals
- SE-123: Evaluating and ranking options
- VA-162: Value planning exercise

which are referred to in the flow diagram at the end of this procedure.

Process

Reference to *project manager* can also mean *study manager* when the project is at the pre-investment phase. *Stakeholder* means any party, or entity, within the performing organisation, and it can also mean any external entity that impacts on, or is impacted by, the project under consideration.

The following process should be used:

Person	Responsibility
Project manager	May initially have a team of experienced team members. The project manager initiates the process of conceptualising the alternative solutions by completing box 1 of form SE-122/1 and sends copy to the sponsor and the project support office (PSO).
Project support office	Assigns a facilitator to liaise with and support the study manager in any aspect of the initiating aspects of the process, such as identifying the right stakeholders and assembling appropriate documentation.
Stakeholders	Each organisation, division, department or unit assigns a knowledgeable and experienced person who can make decisions on behalf of the stakeholder. The name of each nominated representative is advised by e-mail/telephone to the project manager.
Project manager	Initiates a workshop (see procedure CN-003), communicates with the sponsor, stakeholders and PSO, and sends out any pre-workshop documentation.
Project support office	Provides a facilitator to direct and motivate the workshop attendees and achieve the workshop outcomes.
Project manager	Prepares a report of the workshop outcomes and sends a copy to each workshop attendee.
	Completes box 2 on form SE-122/1 and files the form in the project file.

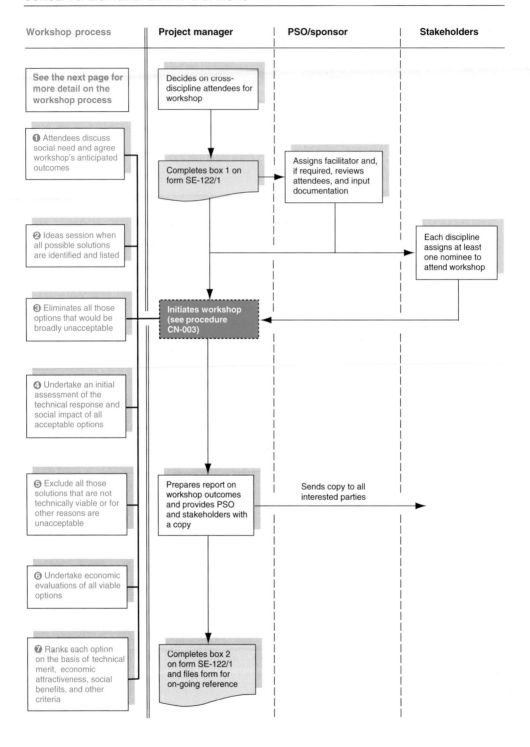

Workshop process	Project manager	PSO/sponsor	Stakeholders
See the next page for more detail on the workshop process	Decides on cross-discipline attendees for workshop		
❶ Attendees discuss social need and agree workshop's anticipated outcomes	Completes box 1 on form SE-122/1	Assigns facilitator and, if required, reviews attendees, and input documentation	
❷ Ideas session when all possible solutions are identified and listed			Each discipline assigns at least one nominee to attend workshop
❸ Eliminates all those options that would be broadly unacceptable	Initiates workshop (see procedure CN-003)		
❹ Undertake an initial assessment of the technical response and social impact of all acceptable options			
❺ Exclude all those solutions that are not technically viable or for other reasons are unacceptable	Prepares report on workshop outcomes and provides PSO and stakeholders with a copy	Sends copy to all interested parties	
❻ Undertake economic evaluations of all viable options			
❼ Ranks each option on the basis of technical merit, economic attractiveness, social benefits, and other criteria	Completes box 2 on form SE-122/1 and files form for on-going reference		

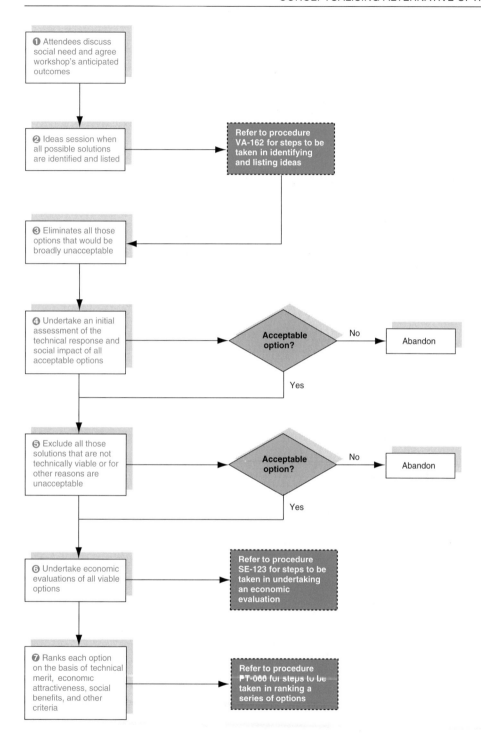

Box 1

Study/Project name _____ Job ref. # [_____]

Study/Project manager _____ Sponsor _____

Current project stage ☐ CT ☐ FS ☐ D1 ☐ SL ☐ D2 ☐ PR ☐ CN ☐ CO

☐ If at CT then workshop   ☐ If dealing with a project element

• Workshop

Date [_____]   Venue [_____]   Time [_____]

• Workshop attendees

Name	Organisation/section

• If ... project element

Work package	Element	WBS ref. #

Signed _____ (study manager)   Date _____

Box 2

• Alternative options outcome

Optioned examined	Ranked order	Options for FN

Report draft date [_____]   Issue date [_____]   Ref. # [_____]

Signed _____ (study manager)   Date _____

SE-123: Evaluating and ranking options

Policy

This procedure is used when comparing two or more options during any stage of a project's life cycle. An option may be a complete project, or a package within a project, or any element within a package. The term 'scheme' is applied to all alternative solutions that could satisfy the social or business need prior to identifying the preferred scheme, which then becomes known as the 'project'.

In any analysis of options an economic evaluation is carried out using the net present value (NPV) approach. To apply NPV it is necessary to develop the life cycle cost (LCC) for each option and to determine the appropriate discount rate. The LCC for any scheme or project or element should include all initial costs, design costs, implementation costs, maintenance costs, replacement costs, operational costs, etc. In other words, it is a requirement to create the whole life costs over an agreed period, which could be, say, 20 years. Discounting of future cash flows is assumed to be yearly and is applied at the end of each year.

When applied to options in which there is both a cost stream and an income stream, the option having the highest NPV is judged to be the preferred option, all other factors (technical, social, etc.) being the same. When applied to options in which there is only a cost stream, the option having the lowest NPV is judged to be the preferred option, all other factors being equal. The term NPV is used when there is both a cost stream and an income steam. The term net present cost (NPC) is used when there is only a cost stream.

NPV(C) is the current first choice economic technique to be used. However, there may from time to time be a need to use other measurement techniques, such as break-even analysis, return on investment (ROI) and internal rate of return (IRR). The project support office (PSO), when required, can provide guidance on the application and interpretation of these techniques on a scheme-by-scheme basis or project-by-project basis.

This procedure requires that each option be evaluated on all factors, not just economics, and that all factors scored be used to rank each option. The highest ranked option being the preferred option.

Outcome

The outcome of this procedure is the creation of a cash flow for each acceptable option identified under procedure SE-122 and a ranking of options within a range from 'most preferred' (or highest) to 'least preferred' (or lowest). To create the cash flows for a complete, or significant part of, an option the requirements set out in procedure CS-024 need to be followed. When investigating the cash flow of an element then the procedures that govern the approach are a combination of CS-023 and CS-024.

From the cash flows for each option the NPV(C) calculations are obtained. It may be necessary to run a series of NPV(C) calculations using a range of discount rates because the discount rate has been forecast as approaching a period of fluctuation coinciding with the calendar time of a cash flow.

Process

For the process, flow diagram and other related aspects of the associated procedure, see procedure SE 122.

To calculate the NPV(C) the following should be known:

- For the complete project or package:
  - (a) the cash flow for the design of each option (procurement–implementation–commissioning), including all internal and external costs and VAT
  - (b) the cash flow for all future projected maintenance and operations costs
  - (c) the cash flow for all projected replacement costs
  - (d) the discount rate
  - (e) the nominal period over which discounting should be performed.
- For an element:
  - (f) the initial cost of procurement, and (b) to (e) above.

SE-123/1 is a template that can be used for NPV(C) evaluations. The following table summarises what each column in the template represents:

Column	Explanation
First column (unnumbered)	
	State the scheme or element name
	State the period over which the discounting is to be calculated
	State the discount rate (if a range of discount rates is to be applied, take a new form for each discount rate)
Cost streams	
1 to 5 (odd Nos.)	Insert the budget cost for each option in the appropriate cell
2 to 6 (even Nos.)	From the cash flows calculate the NPV(C) using the discount rate and place the result against each option in the associated cell
2 to 6 (even Nos.)	Add the values in the cells for the total initial cost, replacement cost, maintenance cost and operational cost, and insert in the cell 'TOTAL PRESENT WORTH COSTS (C)' in row W
Income streams – if applicable	
1 to 5 (odd Nos.)	Insert the budget cost for each option in the appropriate cell
2 to 10 (even Nos.)	From the cash flows calculate the NPV using an agreed discount rate, and place the result against each option in the associated cell
Summary (rows X, Y and Z)	
2 to 6 (even Nos.)	Transfer the NPV that was calculated for each option's income stream and place in the associated cell in row X
2 to 6 (even Nos.)	From the C and I values calculate the total NPV (if income streams available) or NPC (if no income stream) and place in the associated cell in row Y
2 to 6 (even Nos.)	Rank the NPVs from highest to lowest or rank the NPCs from lowest to highest, and place in the appropriate cell on row Z

An example is presented of an NPC analysis of a project element (see exhibit SE-123/2), where there are three vendors to chose from when selecting a package element — an electric pump; the result is that option 1 is ranked first.

Item .... Life cycle period ...... years Interest/discount rate ...... %	1 Option 1 est. cost	2 Option 1 NPV(C)	3 Option 2 est. cost	4 Option 2 NPV(C)	5 Option 3 est. cost	6 Option 3 NPV(C)
COST						
Initial cost						
Option 1 Budget cost						
Option 2 Budget cost						
Option 3 Budget cost						
Replacement cost						
Replacement every ...... years						
Option 1 years ...... discount factor						
Option 2 years ...... discount factor						
Option 3 years ...... discount factor						
Maintenance cost						
Option 1 PWA factor						
Option 2 PWA factor						
Option 3 PWA factor						
Operational cost						
Option 1 PWA factor						
Option 2 PWA factor						
Option 3 PWA factor						
INCOME						
Option 1						
Option 2						
Option 3						
(W) TOTAL PRESENT WORTH COSTS (C)						
(X) TOTAL PRESENT WORTH INCOME (I)						
(Y) TOTAL NPV/NPC = I − C						
(Z) HIGHEST/LOWEST						

EXHIBIT

Item: electrically operated pump Life cycle period 30 years DCC discount rate 6%	1 Option 1 est. cost	2 Option 1 NPC	3 Option 2 est. cost	4 Option 2 NPC	5 Option 3 est. cost	6 Option 3 NPC
COST						
Initial cost						
Option 1 Budget cost	10,000	10,000				
Option 2 Budget cost			8,000	8,000		
Option 3 Budget cost					6,000	6,000
Replacement cost						
Replacement every (see below) years						
Option 1 Every 20 years discount factor 0.3118		3,118				
Option 2 Every 15 years discount factor 0.4173				3,338		
Option 3 Every 10 years discount factor 0.8702						5,221
Maintenance cost						
Option 1 1,000/year PWA factor 13.7648		13,765				
Option 2 1,400/year PWA factor 13.7648				19,271		
Option 3 1,650/year PWA factor 13.7648						22,712
Operational cost						
Option 1 1600/year PWA factor 13.7648		22,024				
Option 2 1860/year PWA factor 13.7648				25,603		
Option 3 1750/year PWA factor 13.7648						24,088
INCOME						
Option 1		Nil				
Option 2				Nil		
Option 3						Nil
(W) TOTAL PRESENT WORTH COSTS (C)		48,907		56,212		58,021
(X) TOTAL PRESENT WORTH INCOME (I)		Nil		Nil		Nil
(Y) TOTAL NPV/NPC = I – C		-48,907		-56,212		-58,021
(Z) HIGHEST/LOWEST		1		2		3

SE-124: Project requirements and information document (PRID)

Policy

Two procedural prerequisites to this procedure are procedures SE-122 and SE-123.

All projects are required to have a project requirements and information document (PRID) available by the end of the concept stage. A PRID is developed once all alternative potential options have been evaluated and the preferred option selected, providing there is one, as the potential basis for going forward with a more detailed analysis of their viability.

A PRID draws together all the technical, economic, social and political factors during the concept stage. The performing organisation undertakes the actions needed to examine and analyse the range of possible options. A study team led by a study manager, whose appointment is documented under procedure SE-121, undertakes the examination and analyses. As many options as possible should be identified during the concept stage and a standard approach used by the study team to compare them. Only if necessary is the study team permitted to procure external expertise to assist in these analyses and for a duration not to exceed the concept stage duration.

A PRID is a publication that offers documented information on the social need, the justification for taking action, the anticipated deliverables, and the quantifiable criteria that is used as the means of measuring successful outcomes. A PRID will be the document that determines if there are viable technical and economic solutions to meet the social or business need. The PRID is normally signed-off by the study manager and approved by the sponsor before the document and its contents are used as input into the commencement of the next stage.

Where possible the most up-to-date information and most detailed data are used in creating a comparison of options that could satisfy the need for the PRID to be a strategic and formal assessment of alternative solutions. It is anticipated that the PRID should provide relational comparisons of the anticipated performance (benefits), estimated time period and order-of-magnitude cost of each option. In other words, absolute and discrete values would not be appropriate, but ranges would be expected along with likelihood of a value being exceeded.

A study team is likely to expend considerable effort during the concept stage creating the PRID. The PRID is a document that can be referred to in the request for proposal (RFP) if a service provider (SP) is to be procured, or it can be used to create the content of the RFP. Should the preferred option recommendation be 'not to proceed', the document can then be used to communicate such a recommendation to senior management and/or the sponsor.

Outcome

Assuming that the outcome of the work undertaken during the conception stage is to proceed with the next stage, the feasibility stage, in determining the viability of the various solutions to satisfy the social need, a PRID is a mandatory requirement. A PRID contains, but is not limited to, the following elements:

- a justification of the social or business need and for taking action
- the anticipated deliverables
- the quantifiable criteria that are used as the means of measuring successful outcomes

- the identification of the range of solution options that are likely to satisfy the need
- the detailed technical and economic data for each solution option (see procedures SE-122 and SE-123)
- the technical guidelines and standards to be used
- the cost breakdown structure to be used for each option (see procedure CS-023)
- the procurement strategy (see procedure PT-061)
- the quality strategy (see procedure QY-081)
- the risk strategy (see procedure RK-101)
- the time planning and scheduling of each option (see procedure TE-141)
- the value strategy for each option (see procedure VA-161).

Process

Prerequisite scope procedures to this process are:

- SE-122: Conceptualising alternative options
- SE-123: Evaluating and ranking options

The following will be the process to be used:

Person	Responsibility
Sponsor	Identifies and assigns the responsibility for undertaking the conceptualisation work by creating a study charter (see procedure SE-121).
Study manager	Signs and agrees to the charter conditions. Assesses the overall resource needs, including the anticipated human resources (see procedure SE-121).
Sponsor	Signs charter and supports the study manager to obtain the human resources needed to undertake the study work (see procedure SE-121).
Study team	Led by the study manager, gathers and analyses all information pertaining to concept solutions for the options that will satisfy the social need (see procedures SE-122 and SE-123).
Study manager	The study manager arranges as many workshops as are considered necessary (see procedure CN-003).
Stakeholders	Represented at all concept workshops. Makes appropriate contribution as required by circumstances and as requested by the study manager. Also contributes to the creation of the PRID.
Study manager	With the study team, drafts the structure and the content for the PRID and, when drafted, signs-off its production. The PRID is sent for approval to the sponsor and, if appropriate, to senior management.
	Completes box 1 of SE-124/1 and places the form in the study file.

Box 1

Project/Study name _____ Job ref. # [_____]

Project/Study manager _____ Sponsor _____

Study start date [_____]   Study finish date [_____]   Period [_____]

Budget for study team [_____]   Budget for external team [_____]

- Inputs to concept process

Re.: SE-122 procedure

Re.: SE-123 procedure

Inputs to PRID

PRID section title	Contributing author(s): name(s)	Dates	
		Target submission	Actual

Document drafted (issue date) [_____]   Document ref. # [_____]

Copy sent to (date sent)

Signed-off _____ (project manager)   Date _____

Approved _____ (sponsor)   Date _____

SE-125: Work breakdown structure (WBS)

Policy

All projects, irrespective of size or complexity, need a work breakdown structure (WBS) created as early in their life cycle as possible. A WBS becomes the framework for assembling project work elements, allocating resources, time and cost allocation and performance monitoring, and many other matters that impact on the planning, execution and control of a project.

A WBS divides a project into product-related and discipline-related packages of work. The packages of work are then defined in greater and greater levels of detail until the individual tasks have been identified. A WBS should define the scope of work envisaged to be within the project, including all temporary work, and it is required to encompass all stages of the project from concept to commission and handover. During each stage and at the end of each stage a WBS should be revised to include the most up-to-date scope of the project.

A WBS is best developed through utilising the knowledge and experience of a project's stakeholders. The collective effort that is needed is generally achieved through the workshop process (see procedure CN-003). One-day workshops normally provide enough time to identify the scope of work and create the WBS, but occasionally it may be necessary to extend a workshop beyond 1-day modules.

Where an owner's requirement is solved by bringing together a number of related projects, these projects are referred to as a *programme*. A programme would have a WBS that is an amalgam of each individual project's WBS.

Outcome

The outcome of this procedure is the creation of a structure that reflects the total scope of work of a project at the time when it is developed and at any other subsequent time when it is revised and updated.

A WBS should be capable of being displayed as an inverted-tree structure and it is recommended that the upper levels of the WBS should be published in that format as a means of describing the structure of a project. It is recommended that the inverted-tree presentation be used from which the detailed WBS can be developed. A detailed WBS is best created as a vertical alignment of packages, activities and tasks (for an example see columns 1–3 in exhibit RK-104/2). The vertical alignment provides a convenient basis for establishing spreadsheet usage and manipulation of data. Such formats can easily add rows for additional work tasks and columns that can accommodate other criteria related to the work scope, such as code number and responsible stakeholder, and additional criteria that relate to other knowledge areas, such as risk.

An inadequately conceived WBS is often found to be the cause of later project difficulties and the missing of project targets and outcomes. The development of the WBS should be undertaken with great care and attention.

Process

Reference to *project manager* can also mean *study manager* when the project is at the pre-investment phase. *Stakeholder* means any party, or entity, within the performing organisation, and it can also mean any external entity that impacts on, or is impacted by, the project under consideration.

The following process should be used:

Person	Responsibility
Project manager	Initiates the development of a project's WBS and completes box 1 on form SE-125/1.
	In the event of any revision and update of an existing WBS, tracks all updates by completing box 2 on form SE-125/1. Concurrent with either creating the original WBS or updating an existing WBS a workshop is initiated by complying with procedure CN-003.
Stakeholders	Attend and contribute to the development, or revision, of a project's WBS.
	A typical upper level WBS, showing work packages, is presented as exhibit SE-125/2. Normally a WBS to this level would initially be developed before decomposing each work package to create the detailed WBS.

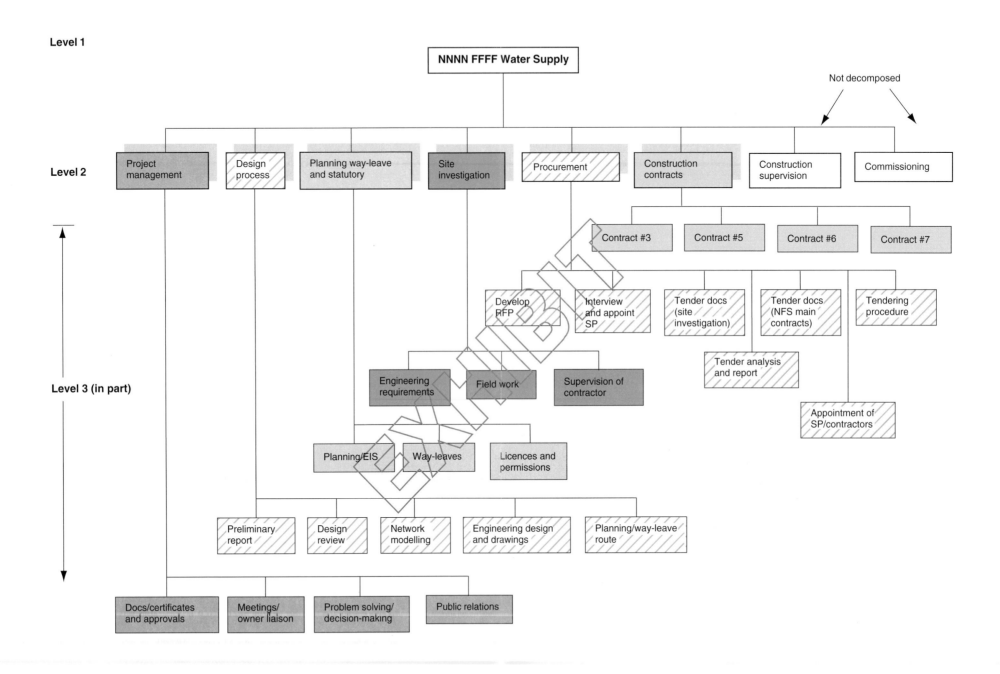

Box 1

Project/Study name _____   Job ref. # [_____]

Project/Study manager _____   Sponsor_____

Current project stage   ☐ CT ☐ FS ☐ D1 ☐ SL ☐ D2 ☐ PR ☐ CN   ☐ CO

• Initial workshop held   ☐ Yes   [_____] Date   ☐ No

• Scope management plan available   ☐ Yes   ☐ No

Explanation/reason

• Project stakeholder group

Ref. #	Name	Organisation/section	Project job title
1			
2			
3			
4			
5			
6			
7			
?			
?			

Signed _____ (project manager)   Date _____

Box 2

• Workshops and WBS

Rev. 1 _____ (date)   Attended by 1 2 3 4 5 6 7 8 9 10   Updated WBS issued _____ (date)

Rev. 2 _____ (date)   Attended by 1 2 3 4 5 6 7 8 9 10   Updated WBS issued _____ (date)

Rev. 3 _____ (date)   Attended by 1 2 3 4 5 6 7 8 9 10   Updated WBS issued _____ (date)

Rev. 4 _____ (date)   Attended by 1 2 3 4 5 6 7 8 9 10   Updated WBS issued _____ (date)

Rev. 5 _____ (date)   Attended by 1 2 3 4 5 6 7 8 9 10   Updated WBS issued _____ (date)

Rev. 6_ _____ (date)   Attended by 1 2 3 4 5 6 7 8 9 10   Updated WBS issued _____ (date)

Rev. 7 _____ (date)   Attended by 1 2 3 4 5 6 7 8 9 10   Updated WBS issued _____ (date)

Other comments

Signed-off _____ (project manager)   Date _____

SE-131: Delivering the operations manual

Policy

The last stage of a project's development provides for its commissioning and the deliverable at the end of that stage is the operations manual, a document that offers guidance to the owner or whoever shall be the project's operators. The commissioning stage includes inspection, testing, acceptance, facility turnover and initial operation. The commissioning process needs to be planned, resourced, executed and controlled in the same way as the other project stages.

Although the commissioning stage is shown as the final stage in a project's development, the sequence of commissioning steps is likely to commence much earlier, say, either during the feasibility or outline design stages.

For a project that requires a significant commissioning effort because of project type, the sequence of steps, and the terms to be used, are:

- pre-commissioning
- core commissioning
- initial operations.

Pre-commissioning relates to all activities that must be completed before the commissioning proper is started, i.e. checking the availability of utilities, pipe cleaning, etc. *Core commissioning* refers to introducing checking and evaluating the wet-running of the project. *Initial operations* refer to the final adjustment of the project to ensure it operates as intended.

In almost all projects an external provider carries out the commissioning stage work, with the project management continuing to be undertaken by the owner's project team.

Outcome

The outcome of this procedure is an operations manual that describes and provides everything necessary for the owner to operate the facility. The operations manual should be a complete document containing all record drawings (as-built), all instructions, and data sheets relating to all the control and operating equipment.

Process

As the processes to be used during commissioning of a project vary greatly, from relatively little to a full programme of work, it is difficult to be prescriptive on a process within this Handbook that could be meaningful. Likewise, it is not possible to offer standard forms that would be meaningful, as the standard forms are reflective of the process to be used. Accordingly, a flow diagram is provided that gives an indication of the sort of process that would be needed to address the core commissioning step.

The commissioning process is largely a contractor function, with the owner's project team maintaining a watching brief and managing the commissioning process as part of the overall project. The owner, the likely operator, of the facility should be involved with the commissioning through knowledge and skills transfer obtained from the contractor. There needs to be close liaison between these two parties during all commissioning steps.

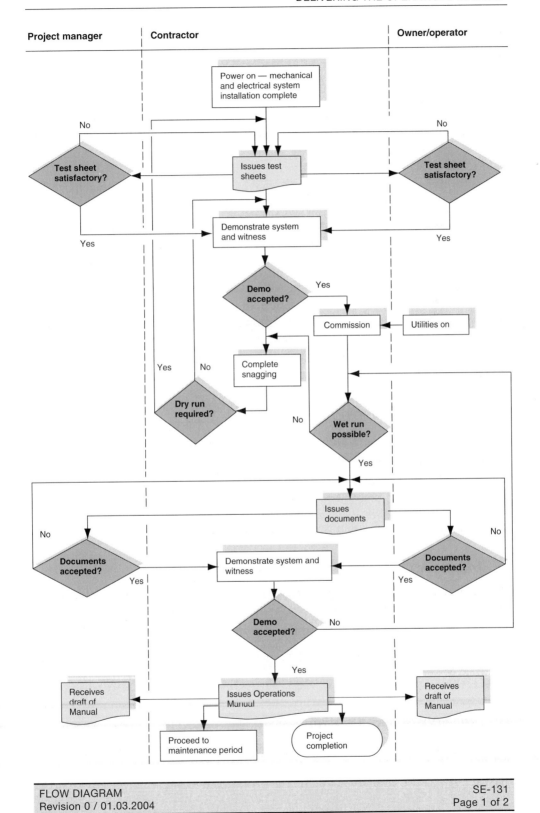

Project manager	Contractor	Owner/operator

Time procedures

This section contains four procedures that deal with certain aspects of project time management. The procedures are:

TE-141   Time schedule management plan
TE-142   Project planning
TE-143   Estimating activity duration
TE-144   Scheduling the plan

A brief overview of each procedure and what each procedure sets out to achieve is as follows.

TE-141: Time schedule management plan

The time schedule management plan procedure provides the discipline of stating what and how planning and scheduling will be undertaken for a project stage or for a project's full life cycle. The management plan is the result of the project team with appropriate stakeholders determining the methodology to be used for planning and scheduling a project. It also includes identifying, if possible, the major milestones and target dates, the frequency of re-planning and re-scheduling, and how plans and schedules are to be communicated to those that need to be informed.

TE-142: Project planning

Planning a project is something that should happen numerous times during a project's development. Planning relates to placing activities and tasks that are listed in a work breakdown structure (WBS) into a relational sequence. Planning does not require activities and tasks to be linked to a calendar time frame. This procedure documents the numerous plans created during a project's life, who was involved in their creation, and tracks plan revisions.

TE-143: Estimating activity duration

After creating a project plan, the next step is to determine the duration of each work breakdown structure (WBS) activity. Activity duration can be either a single value, because how long it is likely to take is known with a high degree of certainty, or it can have a range of durations. This procedure uses short cut formulae from probability theory to determine the expected duration of an activity, the standard deviation (the range) and the variance (another way of measuring range) of an activity.

TE-144: Scheduling the plan

This procedure uses the sequence of activities and tasks developed using procedure TE-142 and the activity/task duration from applying TE-143 to create a logic diagram that can be analysed to obtain the overall time period for a package of work or for a complete project. This procedure offers management a means of identifying those work items that must be done on certain dates and those work items that are less critical. The scheduled plan becomes the basis for monitoring and controlling work and making project management decisions.

TE-141: Time schedule management plan

Policy

Time-related plans, more commonly called 'schedules', should be created as early in the life of a project as is feasibly possible. This could possibly be at the concept stage, but should be no later than outline design (D1) stage.

The accuracy and completeness of a time schedule is directly proportional to the time elapsed since the project's kick off. In other words, time schedules prepared in the early stages are likely to be less accurate and less definitive than the same time schedule model at later stages in a project's life cycle.

The time schedule management plan is a prerequisite to the first time schedule produced for a project. It is also the basis for initiating and determining the content of a project's first time schedule that with the time schedule management plan is the reference standard for all subsequent revisions.

The time schedule management plan normally states the planning and scheduling elements that must be undertaken from the commencement of project planning to the completion of the project or settling the final account, whichever comes later. The elements would normally consist of:

- inputs to the planning process
- the planning process
- the scheduling process
- the forecasting to completion process
- the reactive process of tracking project activity actual expended time against activity planned time
- how to deal with changes to the project's time-based plans.

The project manager would normally create the time schedule management plan. Any subsequent changes affecting the content of the plan are required to be fed back into the plan and the plan revised to show its currency.

Outcome

The outcome of this procedure is a time schedule management plan that contains the following:

- primary structure of the project
- major milestones and target dates for each milestone
- methodology to be used in planning and scheduling
- frequency and process to be used in revising time schedules
- related stakeholder communication plan.

The primary structure of the project is influenced by what is documented in the work breakdown structure (WBS) (see procedure SE-125). In most cases the work package level or lower levels of detail define a project's structure. Another influencing factor could be the procurement management plan (see procedure PT-061).

The target date for each significant milestone is, in most cases, the result of a robust planning and scheduling analysis (see procedures TE-142 and TE-144), but there can be situations where certain milestones are predetermined. Such predetermination can be the result of owner requirements and be part of the project requirements and information document (PRID) (see procedure SE-124), which is the deliverable from the investigative and analysis work undertaken during the concept stage.

The methodology used for planning a project is invariably through a workshop of stakeholders who contribute, using their expertise, to developing a logic diagram (type of flow diagram) of project activities. From time to time it may be necessary to procure the services of an external specialist or expert to contribute to a discipline or sector which the project stakeholders would not have expertise in. However, if such assistance is required it is documented in procedure TE-142.

A change process is required to ensure that a project's schedule is current and as relevant as possible; the time schedule management plan provides general guidance on how this is to be achieved.

The last element of the plan is related to the communication management plan for any project and states who receives what, and when, etc.

Process

Reference to *project manager* can also mean *study manager* when the project is at the pre-investment phase. *Stakeholder* means any party, or entity, within the performing organisation and it can also mean any external entity that impacts on, or is impacted by, the project under consideration.

The following process should be used:

Person	Responsibility
Project manager	Normally prepares the time schedule management plan. However, for the larger project the project manager is likely to arrange a workshop (see procedure CN-003) to be attended by all project stakeholders to determine the inputs and outputs required to create a time schedule management plan.
Stakeholder(s)	Attends workshop and contributes to determining the content of the time schedule management plan.
Project manager	Uses form TE-141/1 as a tracking device and completes boxes 1–4 inclusive as agreement is reached on the related issues. The project manager, or nominated other, is assigned the role of ensuring that the time schedule management plan is adhered to and has been revised and updated, and that the assigned individual has been compliant in communicating with all the associated stakeholders.

Box 1

Study/Project name _____ Job ref. # [_____]

Project/Study manager _____ Sponsor _____

Current project stage ☐ CT ☐ FS ☐ D1 ☐ SL ☐ D2 ☐ PR ☐ CN ☐ CO

• Input documents to initiate the time schedule management plan

Documents	Availability		Explanation (if 'No')
	Yes	No	
• WBS	☐	☐	_____
• OBS	☐	☐	_____
• RAM	☐	☐	_____
• Milestones and milestone target dates	☐	☐	_____
• _____	☐	☐	_____
• _____	☐	☐	_____

Signed _____ (project manager)   Date _____

Box 2

• Planning process

☐ Stakeholder workshop   ☐ Other _____ (explain)

• Scheduling process

☐ By hand   ☐ Computer model   State name/maker _____

Explanation

Box 3

• Register of planning actions

☐ Attaching the progressive register template from procedure tracking form TE-142
☐ Refer to tracking form TE-142

• Register of scheduling actions

☐ Attaching the progressive register template from procedure tracking form TE-144
☐ Refer to tracking form TE-144

Box 4

• Communications plan

☐ List of recipients attached showing intended receipt of all plans/schedules including revisions
☐ Refer to tracking forms TE-142 and TE-144

Comments

Signed _____ (project manager)   Date _____

TE-142: Project planning

Policy

Planning is the process of determining the sequence in which activities and tasks should be carried out. Scheduling is the process of converting the sequence of activities and tasks into a calendar-related time frame. Planning and scheduling a project should happen at least once in every stage of the life cycle: there are eight stages in the model capital works project. Completeness and accuracy of the planning process increases as a project progresses through its life stages and more and more information becomes available, or existing data can be ratified as germane to that stage.

It is corporate policy for the planning process to be carried out by hand using collaborating project stakeholders operating within a workshop environment. Should the in-house expertise be insufficient to cover all aspects of what has to be planned consideration should be given to procuring the services of an external expert(s) for those missing aspects. Examples of expertise that might be needed include:

- the development of private finance initiative (PFI) contracts
- specialised areas of engineering
- technical methodologies
- specialist implementation processes.

A project plan consists of work tasks identified at the lower levels of a work breakdown structure (WBS) that are linked together to create a logic diagram of dependent activities. WBS activities at too high a level do not provide a basis for an acceptable decomposition template. An acceptable WBS is one that decomposes the project into tasks that together form packages of work. The activities and tasks are those required for all project stages from the time at which the project plan is developed. For example, the project plan developed at the outline design stage (D1) should include all tasks from D1 through the subsequent stages to, if possible, the commissioning stage (CO). In other words, the activities of the performing organisation, the project team and all external entities (e.g. designers, contractors, subcontractors, vendors, specialists) shall be the basis of a project's WBS.

In linking activities and tasks the dependencies between activities and tasks are either:

- mandatory (due to the natural relationship between two or more activities)
- discretionary (a relationship between two or more activities due to a preferred way of doing the work).

In most cases the normal dependency is finish-to-start (FS) and lags (delays) or leads (overlaps) between activities and tasks are used where appropriate.

Outcome

The outcome of this procedure is an integrated logic diagram of linked project tasks that describes the totality, known at the time of the plan's development, of the work to be undertaken. Integration is the joining together of each stage's logic diagram where, at that time, such information is available.

A logic diagram cannot be developed until a WBS, at a suitable level of decomposition, is available. It is possible in certain circumstances to develop the WBS and the logic diagram in parallel; however, this should only be attempted if there is insufficient time to treat these actions in series.

When the project plan is created, or when revisions of the initial project plan have been developed, the information should be captured electronically for ease of accommodating future changes and for communicating to project stakeholders.

A project plan does not have any time associated with it. Therefore a project plan does not require either activity or task duration to be assessed or the overall project time calendar to be established. Applying time to activities and tasks, and setting the total plan against a calendar time frame, are features of the time scheduling process in procedures TE-143 and TE-144.

Process

Reference to *project manager* can also mean *study manager* when the project is at the pre-investment phase. *Stakeholder* means any party, or entity, within the performing organisation, and it can also mean any external entity that impacts on, or is impacted by, the project under consideration.

The following process should be used:

Person	Responsibility
Project manager	Arranges a workshop (see procedure CN-003) to be attended by all project stakeholders to work as a total group, or if appropriate in subgroups, to determine the most appropriate sequence of activities and tasks that reflects the work scope of the project.
	Decides if out-of-house expertise is needed to supplement the stakeholder knowledge. If so required, secures the services of an individual, or individuals, under procedure PT-063 to assist the in-house team and other stakeholders to create the plan.
Stakeholders	Attendees to the workshop, including if necessary external experts, contribute to developing: • a project's work activities and tasks, including the performing organisation, a service provider(s) and all other stakeholders • the dependencies and sequencing between activities • a logic diagram of all work needed to undertake and complete a project.
Project manager	Uses form TE-142/1 as a tracking device and completes box 1 as information is obtained or planning achievements reached. The project manager, or a designated other, is assigned the role of ensuring that the plan is satisfactorily developed and, when needed, revised to reflect current thinking for the way ahead.

Box 1

Study/Project name _____	Job ref. # [_____]
Project/Study manager _____	Sponsor _____
Initial project plan initiated _____ (date)	Document ref. # _____

- Current status of project plan

Project stage	Date revised	Document revision #	Plan ref. #	Checked by	Approved by
Concept Feasibility Outline design S & L Detail design Procurement Construction Completion					

- Project plan created

By hand   ☐ Yes   ☐ No

Inputted using software model   ☐ Yes   ☐ No

Name and explanation

- Outside expertise used   ☐ No   ☐ Yes (see below)

Name	Organisation	Expertise	Contact details

- Stakeholders engaged in creating plan

Name	Section/organisation	Workshop attendance	Communications copied	Checked by

TE-143: Estimating activity duration

Policy

Once a project's logic diagram has been developed the next step is to determine each activity's duration. It is recommended that the duration estimated for an activity is presented as a range of duration. A duration range is used because of the uncertainty associated with most methods of estimating. Where there is significant certainty of how long an activity is likely to take then a discrete (single) value duration can be used.

In deriving the duration for any single activity the experts of the work relating to that activity should examine and determine responses to the following three questions:

- Under the best possible circumstances, what will the activity's duration be?
- Under the worst possible circumstances, what will the activity's duration be?
- Under the most likely circumstances, what will the activity's duration be?

Utilising certain assumptions from probabilistic theory the responses to these questions can be used to analyse a project's logic diagram. The theory provides values for the expected duration, the standard deviation and the variance. These values are used as input data to the mathematical analysis of the logic diagram (see procedure TE-144). The analysis is the next step in the time planning and scheduling process.

The estimation of duration range for each work item within a work breakdown structure (WBS) would normally be carried out by relevant experts with the knowledge and, if possible, data to ensure that the estimates are fully reflective of past experience of works of a similar nature. Where there are project activities that are unfamiliar then the project manager must decide if procuring such external expertise is required.

The primary unit to be used in measuring activity duration is the working day, but for the smaller project working hours would be acceptable and can be used if more appropriate.

Outcome

The outcome of this procedure is a spreadsheet of project activity and task estimates that are used as input data to the mathematical analysis of a project's logic diagram (project plan). By taking account of uncertainty in developing estimates this procedure provides a range of estimates for each activity from the 'best possible duration' to the 'worst possible duration'.

The template, shown as exhibit TE-143/1, can be established as an Excel spreadsheet to provide a table of 'activity duration data'. Columns 1 and 2 are input data obtained from the development of a project's WBS (see procedure SE-125). The following is a summary for columns 3–8 of what each column heading means and how to calculate the relevant value.

- Column 3: the value that is placed in this column is the *optimistic* estimate (denoted by *a*) of how long an activity is likely to take as assessed by the expert or the team engaged in compiling the duration. Quite simply, it should be the response to the question 'Under the best possible circumstances, how long is it likely to take to complete the activity?'. If working from historical data it is likely to be the 'best time ever' for the activity under consideration.

- Column 4: the value that is placed in this column is the *most likely* estimate (denoted by *b*), as assessed by the experts, of an activity's or task's duration. 'Most likely' means the duration that is found to happen most often, either through analysis of project records or through analysing expert opinion.
- Column 5: the value that is placed in this column is the *pessimistic* estimate (denoted by *c*) of how long it is likely to take to complete the activity or task under consideration. The pessimistic duration is the value that is the response to the question 'Under the worst possible circumstances, how long will it take to complete the activity?'.
- Column 6: the *expected duration* of each task or activity is obtained by taking 1/6 of the sum of the optimistic and pessimistic durations and 4 times the most likely duration:

$$t_e = (a + 4b + c)/6$$

  The value in column 6 is used as input data for the mathematical analysis of a project's logic diagram.
- Column 7: the value that is placed in this column is 1/6 of the difference between column 5 and 3, i.e. $(c - a)/6$. This gives the standard deviation (σ), and is used as input data for the mathematical analysis of a project's logic diagram.
- Column 8: the value that is placed in this column is the square of the value in column 7, i.e. σ^2. This gives the variance, and this value is used as input data for the analysing a project's logic diagram.

The total outcome from this procedure is a file containing completed form TE-143/1, the content of which is essential input data for creating, or updating, a project's schedule.

Process

Reference to *project manager* can also mean *study manager* when the project is at the pre-investment phase. *Stakeholder* means any party, or entity, within the performing organisation, and it can also mean any external entity that impacts on, or is impacted by, the project under consideration.

The following process should be used:

Person	Responsibility
Project manager	Arranges a workshop (see procedure CN-003) to be attended by all project stakeholders, to work as a total group, or if appropriate, in subgroups, to determine the most appropriate duration for a project's WBS activities and tasks.
	Decides if out-of-house expertise is needed to supplement the stakeholder knowledge. If so required, the project manager secures the services of an individual, or individuals, under procedure PT-063 to assist the in-house team and other stakeholders to create the duration data.
Stakeholders	Attend the workshop, including if necessary external experts, and contribute to determining the values in columns 3–5 of TE-143/1.

Project manager

Checks and sanctions each TE-143/1 sheet. The checking action should confirm that the data are complete and that each sheet has been prepared acceptably.

1	2	3	4	5 4	6	7	8
WBS code No.	Project name .... Sheet ... of ... WBS activities and tasks Package number	Best duration a	Most likely duration b	Worst duration b	Expected duration t_e	Standard deviation $\sigma = (c - a)/6$	Variance σ^2

(watermark: EXAMPLE)

TE-144: Scheduling the plan

Policy

A scheduled plan should contain all the envisaged project-related activities and tasks, including those by the performing organisation, external service provider, vendor, contractor, etc. It is to be used by project teams, and other interested stakeholders, for forward planning and for project control.

A scheduled plan should be developed as early as possible in the life of a project and in conjunction with the creation of the work breakdown structure (WBS), the logic diagram, and the activity duration data. Having been developed, and refined, prior to the commencement of a project's implementation, it should be continually updated to reflect the implementation period when, in general, the greatest project effort is expended.

This procedure is primarily a mathematical analysis of a project's logic diagram, using activity and task duration to determine the project's *critical path*, and the *float* that exists in activities that are not critical. The mathematical analysis takes account of any milestones (constraints) that must be met, as set out in the time management plan. The mathematical analysis provides the early start (ES), early finish (EF), late start (LS) and late finish (LF) for each activity and task that has been included in the logic diagram. Once resource allocation and the related use of the float have been determined, the resulting balanced schedule plan is used to create the cost breakdown structure (CBS) (see procedure CS-023).

What is normally required by this procedure is a hand calculation method for most mathematical analyses. However, a computer method of analysis or the use of a computer time scheduling model is acceptable, providing that the method used produces the output data demanded by this procedure.

The mathematical analysis and its interpretation is the responsibility of the project team and is carried out under the guidance of the project manager. The project manager is required to check and sign each sheet of form TE-144/1. When a computer model or other electronic means of computation produces the same data set, the project manager is responsible for checking the results.

Outcome

The outcome of this procedure should be a spreadsheet showing recorded input data obtained form other procedures and the results of a mathematical analysis of a project's plan. It is this procedure which converts a project's plan into a project's scheduled plan (i.e. a project's WBS activities and tasks, sequenced in a logic diagram, are established against a calendar time frame).

The information, obtained from other procedures, that is used as input into this procedure are:

- Columns 1 and 2: procedure SE-125
- Columns 3 to 8 inclusive: procedure TE-143
- Column 9 and 10: procedure TE-142.

Columns 11–17 are used for output data as a result of the mathematical analysis of the information contained in columns 1–10. An explanation of columns 1 and 2 and 3–8 are to be found within their respective procedures. An explanation of columns 9–17 is as follows:

- Column 9: all activities that immediately precede (come before) the activity under consideration are recorded in this column. To find these activities is a matter of studying the logic diagram.
- Column 10: all activities that immediately succeed (come after) the activity under consideration are recorded in this column. Again, it is a matter of studying the logic diagram.
- Column 11: commencing with the first activity (or activities) in any logic diagram, all activities are given the ES value of 0. The convention being that all start activities commence at *midnight* on day 0, which means that day 0 does not exist. This convention is used to simplify the mathematical analysis.
- Column 12: the EF is obtained by adding the duration of the activity under consideration to the ES of that same activity. Thus, for any activity x:

$$EF_x = ES_x + duration_x$$

  Where the activity under consideration is preceded by a number of other activities (see column 9), then it is the latest (largest) EF that determines the ES of the activity under consideration.
- Column 13: the LS is obtained by subtracting the duration of the activity under consideration from it's LF. Thus, for any activity x:

$$LS_x = LF_x - duration_x$$

  Where the activity under consideration is succeeded by a number of other activities (see column 10), it is the earliest (smallest) LS that determines the LF of the activity under consideration.
- Column 14: the starting point is the latest (or largest) EF within the logic diagram. This value becomes the LF for each and every activity that has a value coinciding with the latest EF.
- Column 15: a critical activity is one in which the ES and LS have the same value (or the EF and LF have the same value). It is these critical activities that determine the critical path within the logic diagram.
- Column 16: the total float (TF) is calculated by subtracting the ES from the LS (or the EF from the LF) on all activities that are not critical. Thus, for any activity x:

$$TF_x = LS_x - ES_x$$

- Column 17: the free float (FF) is calculated by subtracting the EF of a preceding activity from the ES of a succeeding activity on the same chain. Thus, for any preceding activity:

$$FF = ES_s - EF_p \text{ (where s and p are succeeding and preceding).}$$

A simple worked example is presented in exhibit TE-144/2. The critical activities (those with zero TF) and the non-critical activities (those with TF values) are clearly shown. By using the central limit theorem (CLT) on the critical path the following is a summary of a range of project duration and associated probability:

Duration	Probability
58	21%
60	50%
62	78%
64	94%

Process

Reference to *project manager* can also mean *study manager* when the project is in at pre-investment phase.

The following process should be used:

Person	Responsibility
Project manager	Undertakes the mathematical analysis of a project's logic diagram (see the example in exhibit TE-144/2).
	The hand calculation method described in this procedure may be carried out by computer or time scheduling software model. In such circumstances the information to be recorded must be the same as required by this procedure.
	The project manager is required to check all calculations to confirm acceptance of each scheduling analysis by signing-off on the mathematical analysis data sheets TE-144/1.
	The data are used as inputs to other processes. Once the information has been disseminated to other procedures and processes, the data sheets are placed in the project files.

1	2	3	4	5	6	7	8	9	10	11	12	13	14	15	16	17
WBS code No.	Project: .... Sheet ... of ... Revision # ...... Date .... WBS activities and tasks	Best duration a	Most likely duration b	Worst duration c	Expected duration t_e	Standard deviation $\sigma = (c - a)/6$	Variance σ^2	IPA immediately preceding activities	ISA immediately succeeding activities	ES	EF	LS	LF	Critical activity	TF	FF
	Package No.															

Prepared by _____ Date _____ Checked by _____ Date _____

1	2	3	4	5	6	7	8	9	10	11	12	13	14	15	16	17
WBS code No.	Project; .... Sheet ... of ... Date ..... Revision # ...... Date WBS activities and tasks	Best duration a	Most likely duration b	Worst duration c	Expected duration t_e	Standard deviation $\sigma = (c-a)/6$	Variance σ^2	IPA immediately preceding activities	ISA immediately succeeding activities	ES	EF	LS	LF	Critical activity	TF	FF
	Package No.															
	A	6	10	13	9.83	1.17	1.37	None	B,C	0	9.83	0	9.83	Critical	0	0
	B	5	6	8	6.17	0.50	0.25	A	E,F	9.83	16.00	9.83	16.00	Critical	0	0
	C	13	18	21	17.66	1.33	1.77	A	H	9.83	27.49	19.17	36.83		9.34	9.18
	D	6	8	9	7.83	0.50	0.25	E,F	G,I	36.67	44.50	39.17	47.00		2.50	2.34
	E	14	17	20	17.00	1.00	1.00	B	D	16.00	33.00	19.67	36.67		3.67	3.67
	F	14	21	26	20.67	2.00	4.00	B	D, H	16.00	36.67	16.00	36.67	Critical	0	0
	G	10	11	14	11.33	0.67	0.45	D	K	44.50	55.83	44.50	55.83	Critical	0	19.16
	H	8	10	13	10.17	0.83	0.69	C,F	I, J	36.67	46.84	36.83	47.00		0.16	0
	I	5	6	7	6.00	0.33	0.11	D,H	K	46.84	52.84	49.83	55.83		2.99	0
	J	6	9	11	8.83	0.83	0.69	H	K	46.84	55.67	47.00	55.83		0.16	0.16
	K	3	4	6	4.17	0.50	0.25	G, I, J	None	55.83	60.00	55.83	60.00	Critical	0	0

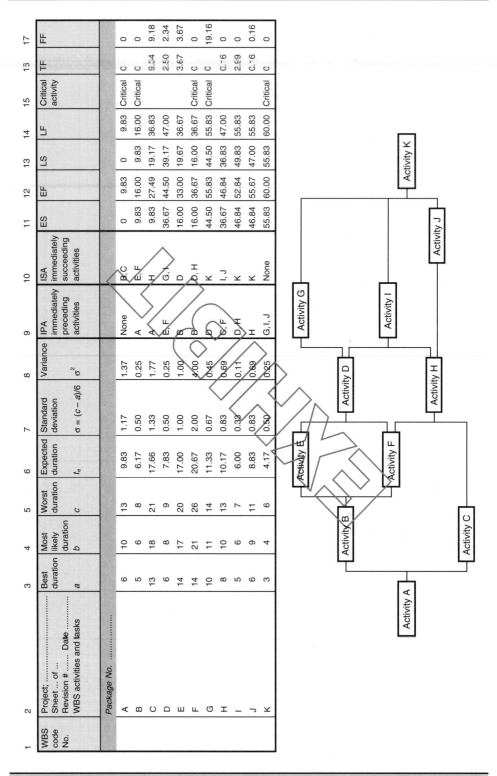

Value procedures

This section contains four procedures that deal with certain aspects of project value management. The procedures are:

VA-161   Value management plan
VA-162   Value planning exercise
VA-163   Value engineering exercise
VA-164   Value review

A brief overview of each procedure and what each procedure sets out to achieve is as follows.

VA-161: Value management plan

The outcome of this procedure forms the focus for the value exercises and value processes that a project team and its stakeholders would use in creating value in a project. The procedure requires that the overall value strategy for a project should be specified along with the strategies for value planning, value engineering and value review.

VA-162: Value planning exercise

In the early stages of a project's development, concept and feasibility, it is essential that the value process is used to ratify an owner's overriding purpose in potentially initiating a project and before committing to establishing a capital budget for implementation and commissioning. Value planning helps to establish the macro level hierarchy of goals, objectives and value criteria that support the owner's overriding purpose. From the value criteria the various options that could satisfy the requirements are evaluated to help to determine the preferred option.

VA-163: Value engineering exercise

Having identified the preferred option and assigned a capital budget for design and implementation there is a need to continue with the value process but at a micro level. Value engineering exercises decompose a project into its elements and at elemental level or higher value engineering investigates function, worth, cost, etc., and attempts to remove redundant function, increase functionality and reduce the associated life cycle costs. Value engineering uses a series of analytical techniques. Some of these techniques can be suitably applied to other knowledge areas, such as project procurement.

VA-164: Value review

Value planning and value engineering are proactive processes and value review is a reactive exercise. This procedure examines the completeness and the effectiveness of previous value exercises, either value planning or value engineering, and determines what action, if any, needs to be taken to improve the achievement of value to a project. The review is documented, and whatever actions are agreed to be taken are checked periodically to ensure closure has taken place.

VA-161: Value management plan

Policy

The value process is a structured approach to expose and eradicate redundant costs and to reinforce project functionality through the analysis of project alternatives to produce a functional solution satisfying or exceeding the owner's requirements. The demonstration of removing redundant costs and enhancing functionality is undertaken not just on project alternatives but on project elements, in other words, at the lowest level of project decomposition, i.e. structural elements, pumps, guard rails and so on.

In the course of the life cycle of a project it is anticipated that a series of value management exercises are performed. A different noun is used in association with the word 'value' depending when in the life cycle a value exercise is carried out. The terms used are:

- value planning
- value engineering
- value review.

The term 'value planning' is used for value exercises carried out during the feasibility stage. The term 'value engineering' is used for value exercises carried out during the definition phase, i.e. the design stages. The term 'value review' is used for value exercises carried out during the implementation and close out stages. Although the terms used are dependent upon when in the cycle the value process is applied, the tools and techniques used within each of the value processes are similar. The value management plan should contain all the elements that are considered necessary to manage the creation and continuance of value within a project.

The project support office (PSO) is responsible for advising project managers on the design, content and facilitation of a workshop(s) that could be of benefit to a particular project. The PSO should appoint a facilitator for all value workshops.

Outcome

This procedure initiates the process for producing a document known as the value management plan (VMP) that describes how project value is to be created and maintained during the life of the project under consideration. The content of a project's VMP is directly related to the size and complexity of the project and any special extenuating circumstances associated with the owner's view on value.

The VMP is a document that is the deliverable from a value management workshop. The VMP is likely to include:

- the requirements for satisfying project value
- how value is to be measured
- the number of value workshops, relative to the project's life cycle when they are to be held, the attendees, and the goals and objectives of each workshop
- who is responsible for a project's value management
- the means to be used in documenting and communicating the actions that emanate from all workshops.

The inputs for a value planning workshop, a value engineering workshop and a value review workshop are likely to be quite different. For instance, as value planning workshops are undertaken at the beginning of any project's life cycle, then very little information other than the potential project's name, the anticipated outcome(s), and some of the constraints such as completion date and anticipated budget are likely to be known. On the other hand, value engineering workshops, held when the project's design is being undertaken, have considerably more detailed input information available than would be the case for a value planning workshop.

Process

Reference to *project manager* can also mean *study manager* when the project is at the pre-investment phase. *Stakeholder* means any party, or entity, within the performing organisation and it can also mean any external entity that impacts on, or is impacted by, the project under consideration.

The following process should be used:

Person	Responsibility
Project manager	Is required to arrange a workshop of all appropriate stakeholders to examine the approach that should be adopted for determining the content of the value management plan. In this regard the project manager is required to use procedure CN-003.
Stakeholders	Invited to attend a value workshop, and nominate the attendee to represent them and inform the project manager accordingly. Each attendee is required to make a positive contribution to the outcomes and goals of the pre-arranged workshop.
Project manager	Upon initiation of the value workshop the project manager completes box 1 and box 2 of form VA-161/1.
	As a direct result of the workshop outcomes and/or through independent actions, the project manager completes the content within box 3. The project manager is responsible for signing-off to the content of form VA-161/1, which along with any other associated and detailed information forms the basis of a project's VMP.
	The project manager is responsible for circulating a copy of the completed VMP — overview form to the appropriate and associated stakeholders.

Box 1

Project and workshop data

Project/Study name _____   Job ref. # [_____]

Previous value workshop record   ☐ Never had a previous workshop

                               ☐ Last workshop ref. _____   ☐ Workshop date _____

Preferred date for workshop   [_____] Start date   [_____] Finish date

Workshop code ref. #   _____   Assigned facilitator _____

• Invited attendees (if required use back of form)

Name	Organisation/section

Signed _____ (project manager)   Date _____

Box 2

• Input documents to the value workshop

Documents

                                        Availability

                                          Yes   No   Why?

_____   ☐   ☐   _____

_____   ☐   ☐   _____

_____   ☐   ☐   _____

_____   ☐   ☐   _____

_____   ☐   ☐   _____

• Pre-workshop document

☐ Drafted   ☐ Signed-off by _____   Date _____

☐ Sent out   ☐ Signed-off by _____   Date _____

☐ Checked   ☐ Signed-off by _____   Date _____

Document content

Signed _____ (project manager)   Date _____

Box 3

- Overall value strategy

  Explanation of approach

- Quality management plan

  ☐ Available   Ref. # [_____]   Date [_____]   ☐ Not available

  Comments (if any)

- Value planning strategy

  Explain

- Value engineering strategy

  Explain

- Value review strategy

  Explain

Signed _____ (project manager)   Date _____

VA-162: Value planning exercise

Policy

Value planning (VP) should be used on all projects during the initial concept stage and/or the feasibility stage of their development cycle; under certain circumstances it may be acceptable for a project to by-pass the concept stage. The concept stage work should be carried out by the performing organisation. Feasibility stage work can be carried out either by the performing organisation or by an external service provider. The former would be the preferred route unless there is good reason to have it otherwise.

During the concept stage it is not possible to carry out a detailed value analysis (value engineering) because the preferred project option that would satisfy the business need or social need has yet to be identified. VP is therefore used as part of the process for identifying project objectives and project value criteria. The aims of value planning are:

- review what has been presented as the owner's (customer's) requirements
- determine the attributes that are needed to satisfy to these requirements and place them in a ranked order
- identify the alternative options that could satisfy the requirements and score them against the ranked attributes.

One or more VP workshops should be held for each project. The simple, less complex, project may require only one workshop; the larger more complex project may require more than one workshop.

The project support office (PSO) is responsible for advising project managers on the design, content and facilitation of workshop(s) that could be of benefit to a particular project. The PSO is required to appoint a PSO resource to facilitate all value workshops.

Outcome

It is important to ensure that the steps taken and the associated actions are in accordance with the demonstrated process and the process is adequately documented. The outcome of this procedure is to:

- develop a shared stakeholder view of the over-riding purpose, goals and objectives of the project
- establish an agreed set of attributes that could achieve the over-riding purpose
- identify the range of potential options that could satisfy the over-riding purpose
- assess each option, or potential solution, against the agreed attributes and identify the best option for satisfying the over-riding purpose
- document the results of each workshop and provide feedback to each stakeholder that offers a framework for monitoring the agreed action plan(s).

The outcome of each value planning workshop should be a report document which sets out the workshop outcomes, the action plan, the responsible entity for each item within the action plan, and the deadline by which the actions need to be started/completed.

Process

Reference to *project manager* can also mean *study manager* when the project is at the pre-investment phase. *Stakeholder* means any party, or entity, within the performing organisation and it can also mean any external entity that impacts on, or is impacted by, the project under consideration.

The following process should be used:

Person	Responsibility
Study manager	Initiates the value planning workshop process by completing form VA-162/1. A copy of the form is sent to the PSO.
PSO	Meets with the study manager to agree the terms of reference for the workshop.
	An information pack on the planned structure and processes to be used is prepared by the appointed PSO facilitator and sent to the study manager.
Study manager	Is required to prepare a technical overview document of the project, which should be sent to each stakeholder in the week preceding the planned workshop date.
Stakeholders	The attendees nominated to the workshop are required to be positive in their approach to the workshop and proactive in their contribution. They should bring to the workshop whatever information, data or other supporting documentation that they may have that would be relevant or have a bearing on the workshop outcomes.
PSO	The facilitator presents the planned workshop programme and proceeds to motivate, direct and encourage the attendees to produce the outcomes in accordance with the processes as set out in the information pack supplied by the PSO.
PSO	During the week succeeding the workshop the facilitator prepares and sends to the study manager a workshop outcome report.
Study manager	Completes box 3 of form VA-162/1 and approves the final draft report.
	A copy of the form is sent to the PSO.
	A copy of the approved report is sent to each workshop stakeholder.

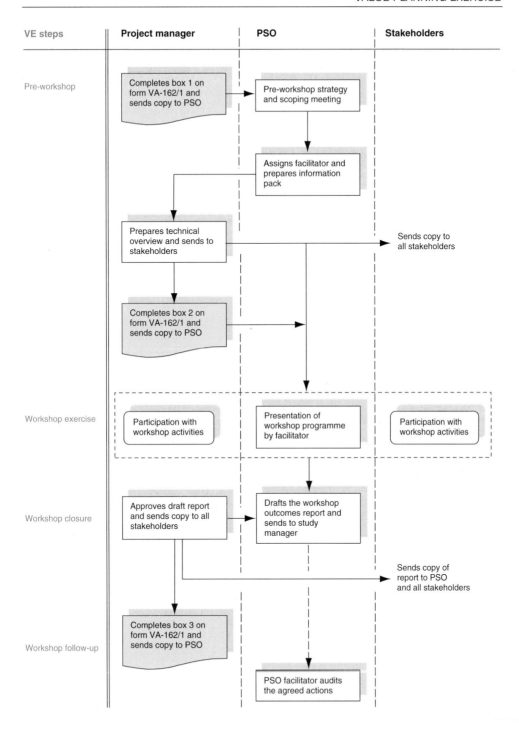

VE steps	Project manager	PSO	Stakeholders
Pre-workshop	Completes box 1 on form VA-162/1 and sends copy to PSO	Pre-workshop strategy and scoping meeting	
		Assigns facilitator and prepares information pack	
	Prepares technical overview and sends to stakeholders		Sends copy to all stakeholders
	Completes box 2 on form VA-162/1 and sends copy to PSO		
Workshop exercise	Participation with workshop activities	Presentation of workshop programme by facilitator	Participation with workshop activities
Workshop closure	Approves draft report and sends copy to all stakeholders	Drafts the workshop outcomes report and sends to study manager	Sends copy of report to PSO and all stakeholders
Workshop follow-up	Completes box 3 on form VA-162/1 and sends copy to PSO	PSO facilitator audits the agreed actions	

Box 1

Project and workshop data

Project/Study name _____ Job ref. # [_____]

Current project stage   ☐ CT   ☐ FS

Previous value workshop record   ☐ Never had a previous workshop

                             ☐ Last workshop ref. _____   ☐ Last workshop date _____

Preferred date for workshop   [_____] Start date   [_____] Finish date

Workshop code ref. #   _____   Assigned facilitator _____

- Invited attendees (if required use back of form)

Name	Organisation/section

Signed _____ (project manager)   Date _____

Box 2

- Input documents to the value workshop

Documents   *Availability*
                                      Yes   No   Explanation (if 'No')

_____ ☐   ☐   _____
_____ ☐   ☐   _____
_____ ☐   ☐   _____
_____ ☐   ☐   _____
_____ ☐   ☐   _____

- Pre-workshop document

☐ Drafted   ☐ Signed-off by   _____   Date _____
☐ Sent out   ☐ Signed-off by   _____   Date _____
☐ Checked   ☐ Signed-off by   _____   Date _____

Document content

Signed _____ (project manager)   Date _____

Box 3

- Value strategy

Explanation of approach

Technique:

- ☐ Cost modelling
- ☐ Cost ranking
- ☐ FAST diagramming
- ☐ Basic/secondary functions
- ☐ Life cycle costing
- ☐ Criteria ranking (SMART)
- ☐ Evaluation matrix
- ☐ Other (specify)

Comments

- Responsibility for value actions

Value item	Responsible stakeholder	Action date

- Documenting and communicating value actions

Explanation of approach

- Draft clause for inclusion within RFP

Signed _____ (project manager) Date _____

VA-163: Value engineering exercise

policy

Value planning (VP), see procedure VA-162, focuses on establishing an opportunity's over-riding purpose (i.e. the response to a need), the goals, the objectives, and the measurable criteria against which many future decisions can be taken; VP seeks to define 'the bigger picture' at the start of a project. On the other hand, value engineering (VE) seeks to examine the detail of the defined solution to the need, that which is now called the project, and such examinations are carried out on sections, subsections and elements that together constitute the whole project.

The process of VE is to be used during the definition phase (design and procurement stages) of a project. The VE exercises are to be held under the auspices and direction of a project team but facilitated by the project support office (PSO). The utilisation of the PSO facilitator's neutrality and skills can be dispensed with if a project team believe that they can effectively, and without bias, lead the VE exercise(s).

VP would normally be recommended as a prerequisite to undertaking VE exercises on the same project. If a project has not been exposed to VP, for whatever reason, it should be subject to at least one VE exercise, preferably two exercises — but as many as four exercises may be carried out. VE exercises should normally be undertaken at about 30% design completion and, again, at about 70% design completion. If only one exercise is to be provided, then it should be at about 30% design completion. If there is a requirement to hold third and fourth exercises, they can be linked to some exceptional design consideration or design milestone. The VE exercises for any project are to be referenced and referred to in sequence as VE1, VE2, etc.

Each VE exercise should take the form of a stakeholder workshop attended by all knowledgeable individuals engaged in a project and whose project involvement places them in a position to deal with, and know about, the detail of the evolving project. The objectives of each VE exercise include:

- examine all, or certain, aspects of design
- brainstorm the options for value improvement
- make recommendations for improving value
- provide the project team with an opportunity to review the cost estimate
- engender a high level of motivation and cooperation within the project team.

Normally each VE exercise follows a five-step process defined as follows:

- step 1: information gathering
- step 2: function analysis
- step 3: speculation
- step 4: evaluation
- step 5: proposals and final report.

The aim of *step 1* is to obtain a thorough understanding of a project by discussing the owner's requirements and value criteria, listing the essential functions of the project, and have available for reference during subsequent steps of the exercise all scheme drawings and specifications, and pertinent reports.

During *step 2* the aim is to define the function and value of the project elements using such tools as FAST diagramming, cost histograms, cost–worth assessments, and value trees.

Having defined function and value at elemental level within a project the aim of *step 3* is to examine high-cost and/or low-value elements, and attempt to generate alternative solutions and ways to better perform the elemental functions.

The aim of *step 4* is to evaluate the solutions identified under step 3, and using such tools as cost models, life cycle costing, etc., determine cost and schedule implications, compare solutions using evaluation matrices, and confirm that each solution is/is not practical and that it can/cannot deliver value improvement.

In *step 5* the solutions are listed, offering potential cost and time–schedule implications, value enhancements and risk impacts. From this listing, a short-list of recommendations is agreed that become the proposals for value changes. The workshop is normally concluded with concurrence on proposals and an action plan for completing a post-exercise report that is submitted to the owner for accepting/rejecting the proposals. The project team is responsible for managing the implementation of the accepted value change proposals.

A VE exercise can be aimed at the design of the whole project or certain selected parts of a project; this depends on the size of the project and/or the range of specialisation required to address a complete project.

Outcome

It is important to ensure that the steps taken and the associated actions are in accordance with the stated process and the process is adequately documented. The outcome of this procedure is to:

- provide a systematic review of a project at the time of the VE exercise workshop
- detail the pre-workshop design and the basis for the changes as set out in the value proposals emanating from the workshop
- list the advantages and disadvantages of each value proposal
- predict the potential capital cost and other costs (redesign, etc.) of each recommended value proposal
- summarise the impact on the project's time schedule, the impact of project risk, and all other impacts that could affect the owner's decision-making.

The outcome of each VE workshop should be a report that documents the workshop outcomes, the action plan, the responsible entity for each item within the action plan, and the deadline by which the actions need to be started/completed.

Process

Reference to *project manager* can also mean *study manager* when the project is at the pre-investment phase. *Stakeholder* means any party, or entity, within the performing organisation and it can also mean any external entity that impacts on, or is impacted by, the project under consideration. *PSO* means the office within the performing organisation's (owner's) structure that is assigned to support project teams and/or audit the use of project management procedures.

The following process should be used:

Person	Responsibility
Project manager	Initiates the value engineering workshop process by completing box 1 on the form VA 163/1. A copy of the completed form is sent to the PSO.
PSO	Meets with the project manager to discuss the terms of reference for the workshop.
	An information document on the planned structure and processes to be used is prepared by the appointed PSO facilitator and sent to the project manager.
Project manager	Is required to prepare, or arrange to have prepared, a technical overview document of the project, which should be sent, along with the information document prepared by the PSO, to each stakeholder in the week preceding the planned workshop date.
Stakeholders	The attendees nominated to the workshop are required to be positive in their approach to the forthcoming workshop and proactive in their contribution. They should bring to the workshop whatever information, data or other supporting documentation that they may have that would be relevant to, or have a bearing on, the workshop outcomes.
PSO	The facilitator presents the planned workshop programme and continues to motivate, direct and encourage the attendees to produce the outcomes in accordance with the predetermined processes. Some of the tools to be used include:
	• cost model (see exhibit VA-163/2)
	• cost ranking (see exhibit VA-163/3)
	• FAST diagramming: see exhibit VA-163/4)
	• cost–worth analysis (see exhibit VA-163/5)
	• life cycle costs and analysis (see exhibit VA-163/6)
	• criteria ranking (see exhibit VA-163/7)
	• evaluation matrix (see exhibit VA-163/8)
	During the week following the workshop, the facilitator prepares and sends to the project manager a workshop outcome report.
Project manager	The project manager completes box 3 of form VA-163/1 and approves the final draft report.
	A copy of the form is sent to the PSO.
	A copy of the approved report is sent to each workshop stakeholder.

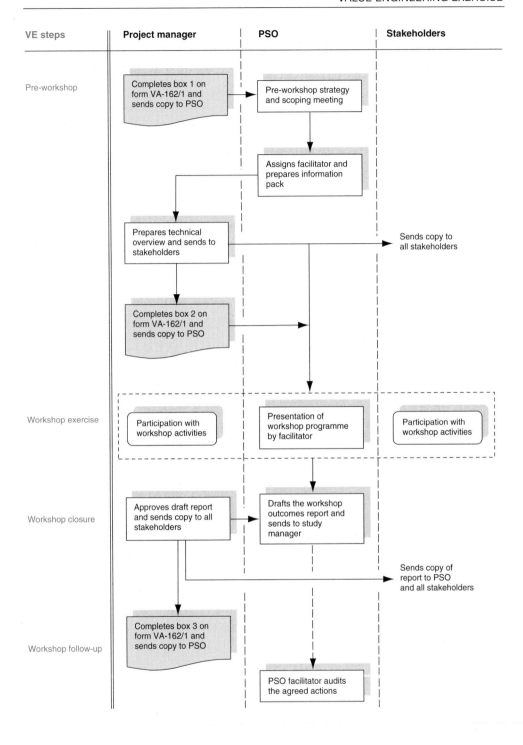

VE steps	Project manager	PSO	Stakeholders
Pre-workshop	Completes box 1 on form VA-162/1 and sends copy to PSO →	Pre-workshop strategy and scoping meeting	
		Assigns facilitator and prepares information pack	
	Prepares technical overview and sends to stakeholders		Sends copy to all stakeholders
	Completes box 2 on form VA-162/1 and sends copy to PSO		
Workshop exercise	Participation with workshop activities	Presentation of workshop programme by facilitator	Participation with workshop activities
Workshop closure	Approves draft report and sends copy to all stakeholders	Drafts the workshop outcomes report and sends to study manager	
			Sends copy of report to PSO and all stakeholders
Workshop follow-up	Completes box 3 on form VA-162/1 and sends copy to PSO		
		PSO facilitator audits the agreed actions	

Box 1

<table>
<tr><td colspan="2">Project and workshop data</td></tr>
</table>

Project/Study name _____   Job ref. # [_____]

Current project stage   ☐ D1   ☐ SL   ☐ D2

Previous value workshop record   ☐ Never had a previous workshop

                               ☐ Last workshop ref. _____   ☐ Last workshop date _____

Preferred date for workshop   [_____] Start date   [_____] Finish date

Workshop code ref. # _____   Assigned facilitator _____

- Invited attendees (if required use back of form)

Name	Organisation/section

Signed _____ (project manager)   Date _____

Box 2

- Input documents to the value workshop

Documents	Availability		Explanation (if 'No')
	Yes	No	
_____	☐	☐	_____
_____	☐	☐	_____
_____	☐	☐	_____
_____	☐	☐	_____
_____	☐	☐	_____

- Pre-workshop document

☐ Drafted   ☐ Signed-off by _____   Date _____
☐ Sent out   ☐ Signed-off by _____   Date _____
☐ Checked   ☐ Signed-off by _____   Date _____

Document content

Signed _____ (project manager)   Date _____

Box 3

- Value engineering workshop strategy

Explanation of approach

- Assessing value (techniques to be used)

Technique:

- [ ] Cost modelling
- [ ] Cost ranking
- [ ] FAST diagramming
- [ ] Basic/secondary functions
- [ ] Life cycle costing
- [ ] Criteria ranking (SMART)
- [ ] Evaluation matrix
- [ ] Other (specify)

Comments

- Responsibility for value actions

Value item	Responsible stakeholder	Action date

- Documenting and communicating value actions

Explanation of approach

- Draft clause for inclusion within RFT

Signed _____ (project manager)   Date _____

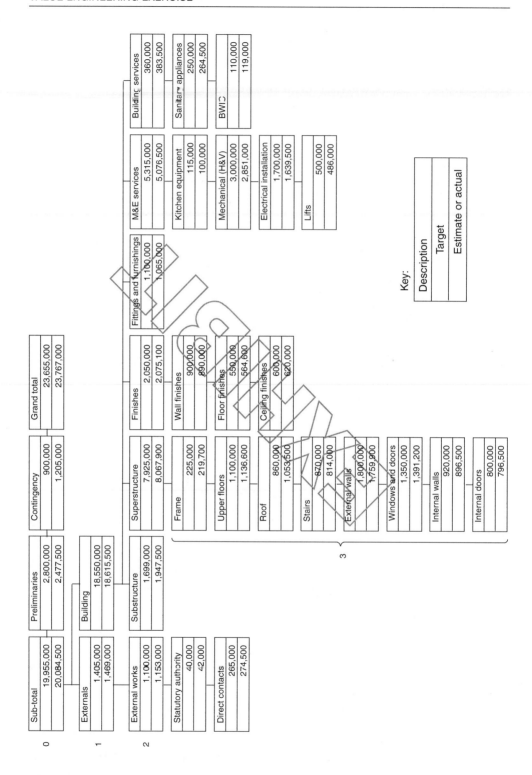

Key:

Description
Target
Estimate or actual

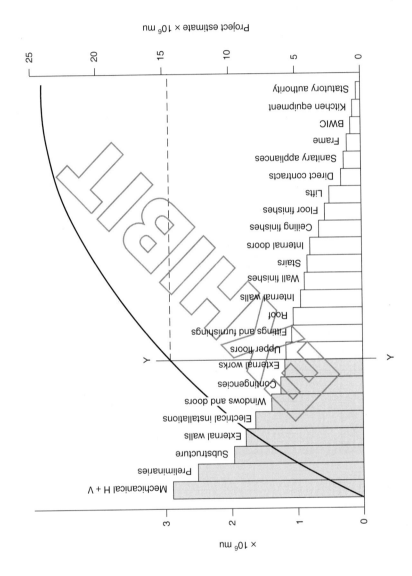

Project estimate × 10⁶ mu

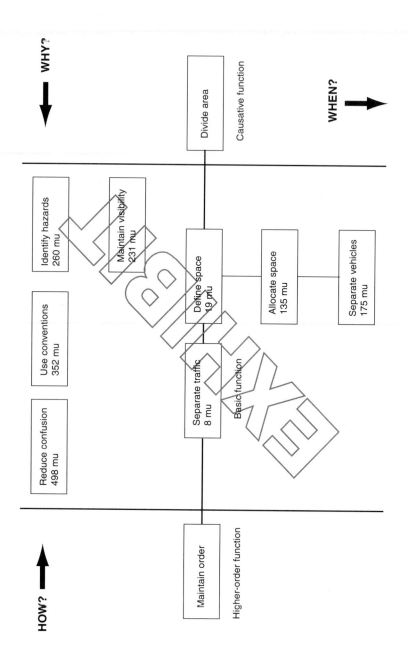

Project .... Item .... Basic function ....
Date ....

Quantity	Unit	Component or element	Verb	Function noun	Type	Original cost	Worth	Cost/worth ratio
10	No.	Warehouse door	Provide	Access	B	2500	400	
			Exclude	Elements	B		800	
			Provide	Security RS	S		600	
			Enhance	Appearance	S		–	
		Ironmongery	Control	Door	B	1000	450	
			Enhance	Appearance	S		–	
		Painting	Protect	Material B		500	350	
			Enhance	Appearance	S		–	
Totals Cost/worth ratio						4000	2600	1.54

Worth = the cost of the basic function + required secondary function

Project: γπηγυψφμφλνδφτ ηγεδ   Item: fan coil unit   Life cycle period: 20 years   Discount rate: 10%   Date: DD/MM/YY

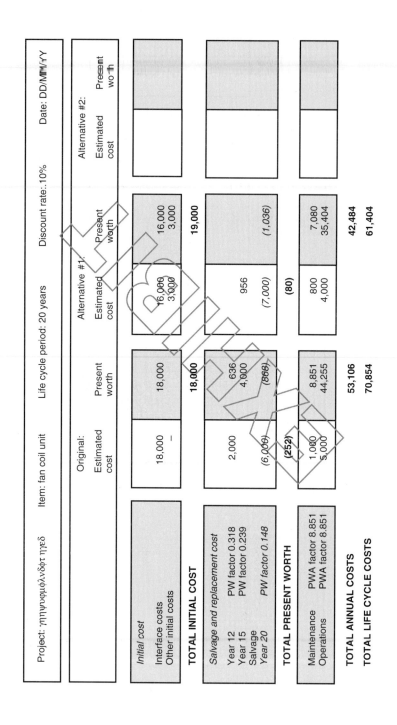

	Original: Estimated cost	Original: Present worth	Alternative #1: Estimated cost	Alternative #1: Present worth	Alternative #2: Estimated cost	Alternative #2: Present worth
Initial cost						
Interface costs	18,000	18,000	16,000	16,000		
Other initial costs	–		3,000	3,000		
TOTAL INITIAL COST		**18,000**		**19,000**		
Salvage and replacement cost						
Year 12 PW factor 0.318	2,000	636				
Year 15 PW factor 0.239		4,000	956			
Salvage	(6,000)		(7,000)			
Year 20 PW factor 0.148		(868)		(1,036)		
TOTAL PRESENT WORTH	**(252)**		**(80)**			
Maintenance PWA factor 8.851	1,000	8,851	800	7,080		
Operations PWA factor 8.851	5,000	44,255	4,000	35,404		
TOTAL ANNUAL COSTS		**53,106**		**42,484**		
TOTAL LIFE CYCLE COSTS		**70,854**		**61,404**		

	B	C	D	E	F	G	Raw score	Weight	Rank
A — Segregated areas	A-2	A-2	D-4	A-3	F-2	A-3	10	0.208	1
B — Low ratio of unscheduled to scheduled areas		B-C	B-2	B-E	B-F	B-4	9	0.188	2
C — Low running costs			C-2	C-3	C-F	C-G	7	0.146	= 4
D — Low noise propagation				D-2	D-F	D-G	8	0.167	3
E — Effective working space arrangement					E-2	E-G	4	0.083	5
F — Effective structural arrangement						F-2	7	0.146	= 4
G — Visual aesthetics							3	0.062	6

4: Major
3: Medium
2: Minor
1: No preference (e.g. B-C)

Alternative	Weight	A Segregated areas (0.250)	B Low ratio of unscheduled to scheduled areas (0.125)	C Low running cost (0.175)	D Low noise propagation (0.200)	E Effective working space arrangement (0.075)	F Effective structural arrangement (0.125)	G Visual aesthetics (0.050)	Total
1		7 / 1.750	3 / 0.375	6 / 1.050	4 / 0.800	2 / 0.150	1 / 0.125	2 / 0.100	4.35
2		9 / 2.250	8 / 1.000	6 / 1.050	7 / 1.400	6 / 0.450	2 / 0.250	8 / 0.400	6.80
3		5 / 1.250	4 / 0.500	4 / 0.700	1 / 0.200	4 / 0.300	5 / 0.625	5 / 0.250	3.83

Excellent = 10; Good = 7; Neutral = 5; Fair = 3; Poor = 1

VA-164: Value review

Policy

A value review (VR) exercise may be carried out at any time after the initiation of the value planning (VP) process and/or the value engineering (VE) process. VR provides the owner with the opportunity to momentarily stop the value processes and evaluate or re-evaluate the benefits being achieved. Such evaluations either confirm the effectiveness of the processes in achieving value or identify particular shortfalls and the appropriate corrective actions. Such corrective actions can be fed forward into later value exercises.

In the course of any VR exercise it is a requirement that the following be investigated:

- stakeholder involvement
- effectiveness of the value processes
- achievement of value
- management of the processes and implementing the changes.

It is essential for any VR exercise that all preceding VP and/or VE exercise documentation is made available to the reviewer of the VR exercise. A VR exercise is normally undertaken through a workshop. All, or as many as possible, of a project's stakeholders involved in previous value exercises should be in attendance at a VR workshop. If the VR exercise is being held during a current VP or VE period of investigation and/or application of VP/VE recommendations, then all stakeholders should be in attendance at the VR workshop.

Where VP and VE are proactive processes to create value, VR is a reactive process that determines the effectiveness of the preceding value processes.

Outcome

The result of any VR exercise is to determine the efficacy of the preceding VP/VE exercises. This determination should include identifying actions that need to be taken in the event of some inadequacy in creating value for the project under consideration or in the use of the processes being used to create value. Such actions might include:

- change of personnel
- change of strategy
- change of tactics
- re-running a previous exercise or exercises.

The VR exercise findings need to be documented in a report that becomes part of that project's file record.

Process

Reference to *project manager* can also mean *study manager* when the project is at the pre-investment phase. *Stakeholder* means any party, or entity, within the performing organisation, and can also mean any external entity that impacts on, or is impacted by, the project under consideration. Reference to *value manager* means the independent entity appointed to undertake the VR, probably a project support office (PSO) facilitator.

The following process should be used:

Person	Responsibility
Project manager or value manager	Arranges a workshop of all appropriate stakeholders to examine a previous VP/VE exercise(s). In this regard the project manager or value manager is required to use procedure CN-003.
Stakeholders	Each person invited to attend a VR workshop is required to make a positive contribution to the outcomes and goals of the pre-arranged workshop.
Project manager	Upon initiation of the VR workshop the project manager completes box 1 and box 2 of form VA-164/1.
	As a direct result of the workshop outcomes and/or through independent actions, the project manager completes the main content in box 3. The project manager is responsible for sign-off to the content of form VA-164/1.
Value manager	Within 30 days from the date of the VR workshop, undertakes the first check of the project team and stakeholders to ensure that the outcomes from the workshop are being/have been actioned. If there are shortfalls in planned achievement versus actual achievement, the value manager repeats the checks as often as necessary.
	The value manager is required to complete the bottom of box 3 in relation to the checks he or she carries out including referenced memos to the project's manager.

Box 1

Project and workshop data

Project/Study name _____   Job ref. # [_____]

Previous VR workshop record   ☐ Never had a previous VR workshop

☐ Last workshop ref. _____   ☐ Workshop date _____

Preferred date for workshop   [_____] Start date   [_____] Finish date

Next workshop code ref. # _____   Assigned facilitator _____

• Invited attendees (if required use back of form)

Name	Organisation/section

Signed _____ (project manager)   Date _____

Box 2

• Input documents to the value workshop

Documents

Availability
Yes   No   Why?

_____   ☐   ☐   _____
_____   ☐   ☐   _____
_____   ☐   ☐   _____
_____   ☐   ☐   _____
_____   ☐   ☐   _____

Other comments

Signed _____ (project manager)   Date _____

Box 3

- Outcome of VR workshop

Change of personnel

Change of strategy

Change of tactics

Rerun a previous exercise

- VR report

☐ Drafted and signed-off by _____ Date _____

☐ Approved by project manager _____ Date _____

Value manager checks   Reference memo

☐ 1st check   Date _____   Signed _____ (value manager)   [_____]

☐ 2nd check   Date _____   Signed _____ (value manager)   [_____]

☐ 3rd check   Date _____   Signed _____ (value manager)   [_____]

Signed _____ (project manager)   Date _____

Part 4

Route maps

A. Project life cycle: capital works project
B. Procedures sequence: concept stage
C. Procedures sequence: feasibility stage
D. Procedures sequence: outline design stage
E. Procedures sequence: statutory and legal stage
F. Procedures sequence: detail design stage
G. Procedures sequence: procurement stage
H. Procedures sequence: construction stage
J. Procedures sequence: commissioning stage

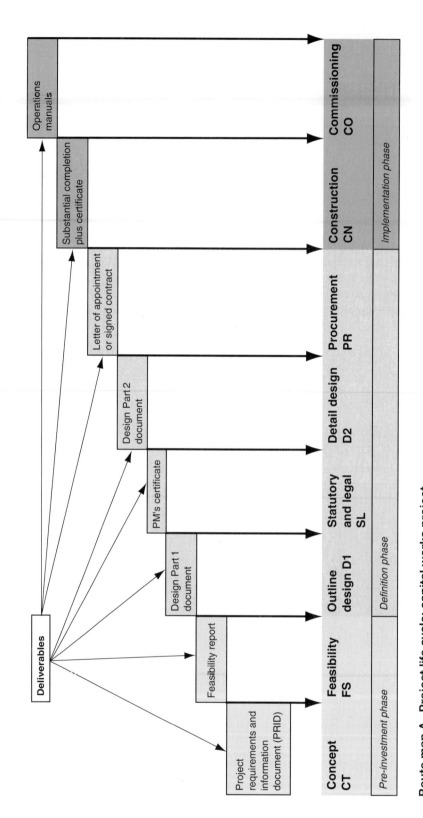

Route map A. Project life cycle: capital works project

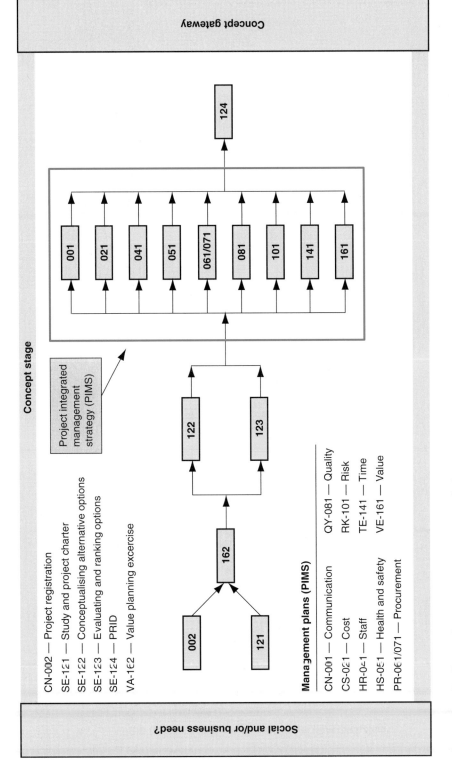

Route map B. Procedures sequence: concept stage

Concept gateway

Concept stage

Social and/or business need?

Project integrated management strategy (PIMS)

124

001
021
041
051
061/071
081
101
141
161

122
123

162

002
121

CN-002 — Project registration

SE-121 — Study and project charter

SE-122 — Conceptualising alternative options

SE-123 — Evaluating and ranking options

SE-124 — PRID

VA-162 — Value planning excercise

Management plans (PIMS)

CN-001 — Communication

CS-021 — Cost

HR-041 — Staff

HS-051 — Health and safety

PR-061/071 — Procurement

QY-081 — Quality

RK-101 — Risk

TE-141 — Time

VE-161 — Value

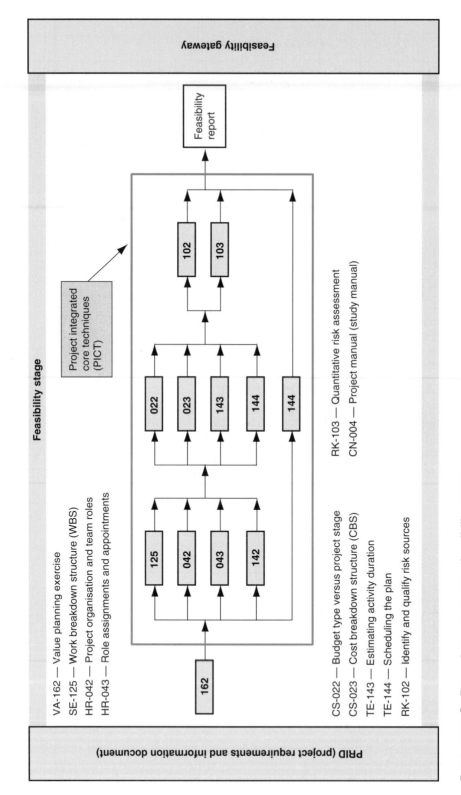

Feasibility stage

Feasibility gateway

Feasibility report

Project integrated core techniques (PICT)

162

125	022	102
042	023	103
043	143
142	144
	144

PRID (project requirements and information document)

VA-162 — Value planning exercise

SE-125 — Work breakdown structure (WBS)

HR-042 — Project organisation and team roles

HR-043 — Role assignments and appointments

CS-022 — Budget type versus project stage

CS-023 — Cost breakdown structure (CBS)

TE-143 — Estimating activity duration

TE-144 — Scheduling the plan

RK-102 — Identify and qualify risk sources

RK-103 — Quantitative risk assessment

CN-004 — Project manual (study manual)

Route map C. Procedures sequence: feasibility stage

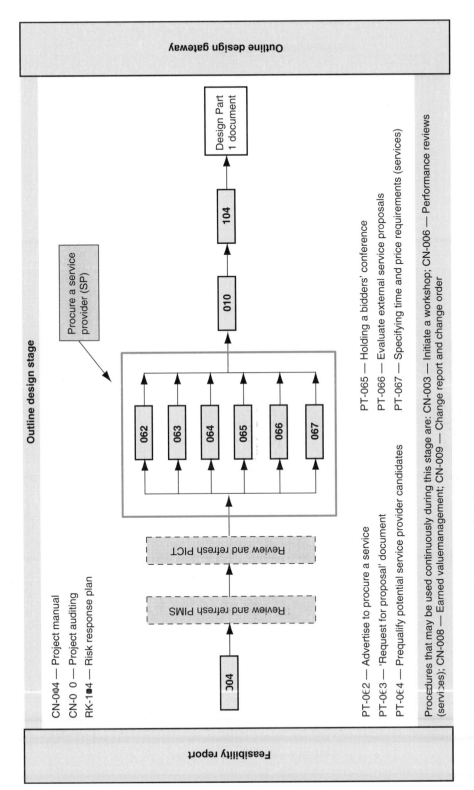

Outline design stage

Outline design gateway

Feasibility report

CN-004 — Project manual
CN-005 — Project auditing
RK-104 — Risk response plan

004

Review and refresh PIMS

Review and refresh PICT

Procure a service provider (SP)

| 062 |
| 063 |
| 064 |
| 065 |
| 066 |
| 067 |

010

104

Design Part 1 document

PT-062 — Advertise to procure a service
PT-063 — 'Request for proposal' document
PT-064 — Prequalify potential service provider candidates

PT-065 — Holding a bidders' conference
PT-066 — Evaluate external service proposals
PT-067 — Specifying time and price requirements (services)

Procedures that may be used continuously during this stage are: CN-003 — Initiate a workshop; CN-006 — Performance reviews (services); CN-008 — Earned valuemanagement; CN-009 — Change report and change order

Route map D. Procedures sequence: outline design stage

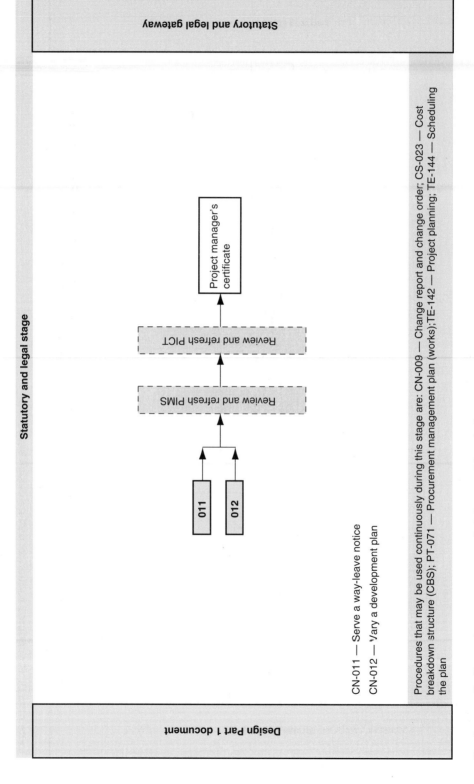

Statutory and legal stage

Statutory and legal gateway

Project manager's certificate

Review and refresh PICT

Review and refresh PIMS

011

012

CN-011 — Serve a way-leave notice

CN-012 — Vary a development plan

Procedures that may be used continuously during this stage are: CN-009 — Change report and change order; CS-023 — Cost breakdown structure (CBS); PT-071 — Procurement management plan (works);TE-142 — Project planning; TE-144 — Scheduling the plan

Design Part 1 document

Route map E. Procedures sequence: statutory and legal stage

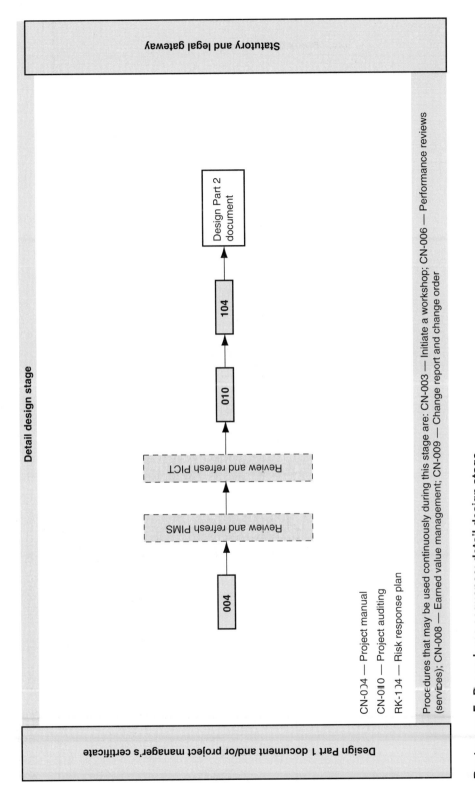

Statutory and legal gateway

Detail design stage

004

Review and refresh PIMS

Review and refresh PICT

010

104

Design Part 2
document

CN-004 — Project manual
CN-010 — Project auditing
RK-104 — Risk response plan

Procedures that may be used continuously during this stage are: CN-003 — Initiate a workshop; CN-006 — Performance reviews (services); CN-008 — Earned value management; CN-009 — Change report and change order

Design Part 1 document and/or project manager's certificate

Route map F. Procedures sequence: detail design stage

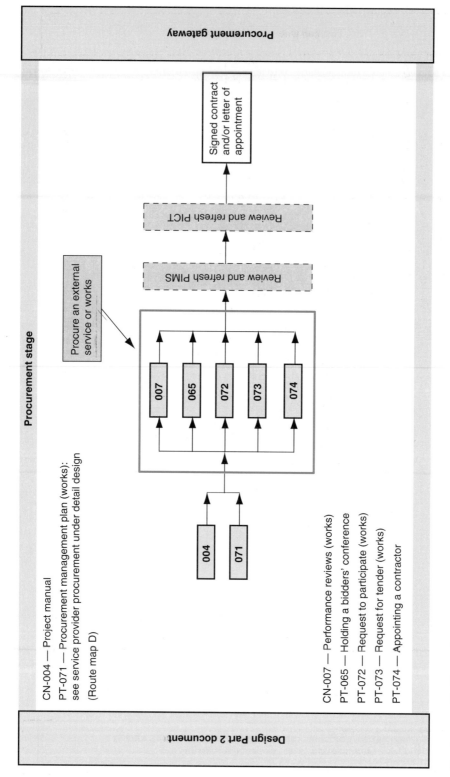

Procurement gateway

Signed contract and/or letter of appointment

Review and refresh PICT

Review and refresh PIMS

Procure an external service or works

| 007 |
| 065 |
| 072 |
| 073 |
| 074 |

| 004 |
| 071 |

Procurement stage

CN-004 — Project manual

PT-071 — Procurement management plan (works): see service provider procurement under detail design (Route map D)

CN-007 — Performance reviews (works)
PT-065 — Holding a bidders' conference
PT-072 — Request to participate (works)
PT-073 — Request for tender (works)
PT-074 — Appointing a contractor

Design Part 2 document

Route map G. Procedures sequence: procurement stage

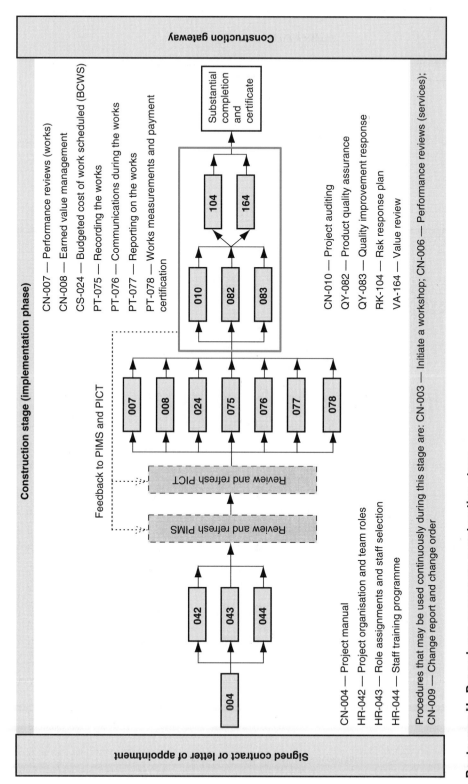

Route map H. Procedures sequence: construction stage

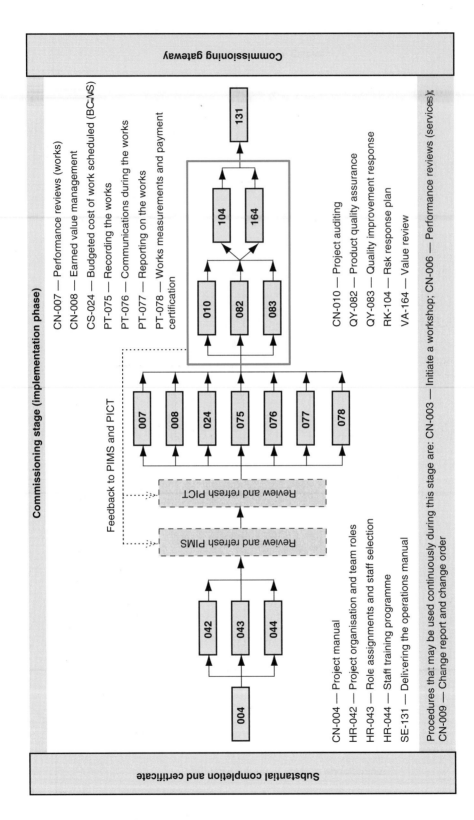

Route map J. Procedures sequence: commissioning stage

Commissioning gateway

Commissioning stage (implementation phase)

CN-007 — Performance reviews (works)
CN-008 — Earned value management
CS-024 — Budgeted cost of work scheduled (BCWS)
PT-075 — Recording the works
PT-076 — Communications during the works
PT-077 — Reporting on the works
PT-078 — Works measurements and payment certification

CN-010 — Project auditing
QY-082 — Product quality assurance
QY-083 — Quality improvement response
RK-104 — Risk response plan
VA-164 — Value review

Feedback to PIMS and PICT

Review and refresh PICT

Review and refresh PIMS

CN-004 — Project manual
HR-042 — Project organisation and team roles
HR-043 — Role assignments and staff selection
HR-044 — Staff training programme
SE-131 — Delivering the operations manual

Procedures that may be used continuously during this stage are: CN-003 — Initiate a workshop; CN-006 — Performance reviews (services);
CN-009 — Change report and change order

Substantial completion and certificate